APOLLO
AND THE UNIVERSE

*Selected Lectures on the U.S. Manned Space Flight
Program and selected fields of modern
physics and cosmology*

EDITED BY

S. T. BUTLER, M.SC., PH.D., D.SC.
Professor of Theoretical Physics, University of Sydney

AND

H. MESSEL, B.A., B.SC., PH.D.
Professor of Physics and Head of the School of Physics, University of Sydney

PERGAMON PRESS
OXFORD · LONDON · EDINBURGH · NEW YORK
TORONTO · SYDNEY · PARIS · BRAUNSCHWEIG

Pergamon Press Ltd., Headington Hill Hall, Oxford
4 & 5 Fitzroy Square, London W.1

Pergamon Press (Scotland) Ltd., 2 & 3 Teviot Place, Edinburgh 1

Pergamon Press Inc., 44–01 21st Street, Long Island City, New York 11101

Pergamon of Canada Ltd., 207 Queen's Quay West, Toronto 1

Pergamon Press (Aust.) Pty. Ltd., Rushcutters Bay,
Sydney, New South Wales

Pergamon Press S.A.R.L., 24 rue des Écoles, Paris 5ᵉ

Vieweg & Sohn GmbH, Burgplatz 1, Braunschweig

Printed in Great Britain by A. Wheaton & Co., Exeter

08 103560 8 (flexicover)
08 203560 1 (hard cover)

PREFACE

The Science Foundation For Physics within the University of Sydney (formerly the Nuclear Research Foundation) is honoured to present such a distinguished group of lecturers at its 10th Anniversary Summer Science School for High School Students.

On behalf of the Foundation we wish to take this opportunity of thanking Dr. Seaborg, Dr. Mueller and Professors Bondi, Gold, Miller and Salpeter for having given so generously of their time and effort.

We have chosen the general heading "Apollo and the Universe" for the 1967 Summer Science School because its lecture topics range from America's Manned Space Flights Programme (now entering the Project Apollo stage) to modern atomic physics and cosmology.

In each of the fields discussed the lecturers are specialists of world renown and the material presented has been specially prepared, written and edited for fourth-year high school students. We therefore feel that the lectures will be of interest not only to the students but to the widest sections of the public. We feel that the material presented will be generally appreciated by the increasingly more science-conscious layman in this scientific age, and also, in fields other than his own, by the specialised scientist.

The book also contains a series of Essays on great scientists written by well-known Professor Julius Miller who, through his ingenious demonstrations of physical phenomena, has done so much to enthuse people the world over in the cause of science.

The Foundation's 1967 Summer Science School and, indeed, this book, are intended to stimulate and develop science-consciousness in Australia generally, and particularly in the 162 outstanding high school students who have won Foundation scholarships to attend the Summer School. Ten of these were chosen from the leading high school students in the United States under a special scheme endorsed by the U.S. President who has kindly consented to the American students being designated Lyndon B. Johnson Australian Science Scholars.

The Foundation wishes to applaud and reward the ability and diligence of these young people.

S. T. BUTLER and H. MESSEL

Sydney, January, 1967.

CONTRIBUTORS OF LECTURES

H. BONDI

Professor of Applied Mathematics,
King's College, University of London.

T. GOLD

Professor of Astronomy,
Cornell University, Ithaca, N.Y., and
Director of the Cornell University Center for
Radiophysics and Space Research.

J. S. MILLER

Professor of Physics,
El Camino College, University of California.

G. E. MUELLER

Associate Administrator for Manned Space Flights,
National Aeronautics and Space Administration,
Washington, D.C.

E. E. SALPETER

Professor of Theoretical Physics,
Cornell University, Ithaca, N.Y.

G. T. SEABORG

Chairman, U.S. Atomic Energy Commission,
Washington, D.C.

CONTENTS

THE SPONSORS

The Science Foundation for Physics within the University of Sydney (formerly the Nuclear Research Foundation) gratefully acknowledges the generous financial assistance given by the following group of individual philanthropists and companies, without whose help the 1967 Summer Science School for fourth-year High School students and the production of this book would not have been possible.

Ampol Petroleum Limited

The Sydney County Council

W. D. & H. O. Wills (Aust.) Limited

and

A. Boden, Esq.

M. W. A. Cullen, Esq.

The late Dr. S. Goldberg

Philips Industries Pty. Limited

Wolf Electric Tools (Aust.) Pty. Limited

Space Rocketry

And

A Man On The Moon

(Four Chapters)

by

DR. GEORGE MUELLER

Dr. George E. Mueller

Associate Administrator for Manned Space Flights, National Aeronautics and Space Administration, Washington, D.C.

CHAPTER 1

The U.S. Space Effort

The exciting era of space flight began on October 4, 1957, with the launch of the first man-made satellite by the Soviet Union. The earth orbital flight of Sputnik I dramatized the potential of space exploration and its impact added urgency and impetus to all U.S. efforts toward unmanned and manned space flight.

The advances of the U.S. manned programs in less than a decade since the first Sputnik will be discussed in this lecture series. Lectures will be devoted to the manned flights of the U.S. Mercury and Gemini programs already completed, and to the role of the Apollo program in furthering the development of manned space flight capability to be demonstrated in the Apollo lunar mission. Finally, the values and worth of present and future space exploration will be placed in perspective.

Unmanned Programs

No such perspective of space exploration is possible, however, without recounting the remarkable accomplishments achieved in space thus far through the use of unmanned satellites and space-craft, beginning with the limited exploratory probes begun more than 20 years ago.

One of the interesting early experiments conducted in the U.S. took place in 1946, when a captured V-2 rocket was launched from White Sands, New Mexico, to an altitude of 55 miles, and obtained the first spectrum of the sun in the far ultra-violet. Radiation in the ultra-violet and a number of other regions of the spectrum is largely absorbed by the earth's atmosphere.

Rockets have been launched at increasing rates since 1946 on suborbital flights to explore the upper atmosphere, to make weather observations, to explore the region of space near the earth, and to make astronomical observations.

9

Since 1957, man has been able to employ rockets to launch satellites about the earth and, since 1959, he has been able to use them to overcome the earth's gravity and send instrumented spacecraft out into inter-planetary space.

Near-earth exploration

The first major scientific advance resulting from this ability was the discovery of the radiation belts surrounding the earth. The first United States satellite, Explorer I, launched January 31, 1958, detected radiation of such intensity that it swamped the instruments that were intended to measure the cosmic rays. Another satellite, Explorer III, was launched less than two months later with instruments calibrated differently. Dr. James A. Van Allen, of the State University of Iowa, announced the discovery of the radiation belts before the National Academy of Sciences on May 1, 1958.

Another interesting early finding is related to the shape of the earth. We are all taught that the earth is an oblate spheroid—generally round but with a somewhat greater diameter at the equator than at the poles. It was believed until a decade ago that the ratio of the oblateness was 1/197. However, careful study of the orbit of the Vanguard I satellite, launched in 1958, showed that the fraction is 1/298.2. Further analysis showed also that the southern hemisphere is a little more oblate than the northern hemisphere. The difference is about 100 feet. The sea level in the Arctic Ocean is 50 feet higher than expected, and 50 feet lower around Antarctica. In other words, the earth is just a bit pear-shaped.

Exploration beyond earth

Much of the emphasis of our unmanned satellite programs in succeeding years has been to learn in detail about the earth and its relationship to the sun, and to explore the moon, Venus and Mars, and interplanetary space, and to provide practical applications. We should keep in mind, however, that it has been necessary to employ military rockets adapted for the purpose. It is only now that launch vehicles designed from the beginning for space flight are coming into use.

Study of the earth focuses on the atmosphere, the ionosphere and the magnetosphere. To learn about the sun, instruments are

Figure 1.1. Picture of the moon's surface taken from Ranger IX spacecraft as it made its lunar approach.

pointed to observe the corona, the chromosphere and the disc itself, with particular attention to flares, solar storms and sunspots.

Lunar exploration

Another area of special interest is the exploration of the moon. In 1964 and 1965, three Ranger spacecraft were launched to impact the moon, taking pictures continually during the final minutes of flight (*Figure 1.1*). Altogether more than 20,000 pictures were obtained, indicating that a significant percentage of the moon's surface is acceptable for landing sites insofar as topography is concerned. The Ranger IX transmissions were seen live on television here on earth.

Next in our unmanned lunar program was Surveyor. In 1966, the first Surveyor accomplished a successful soft landing on the

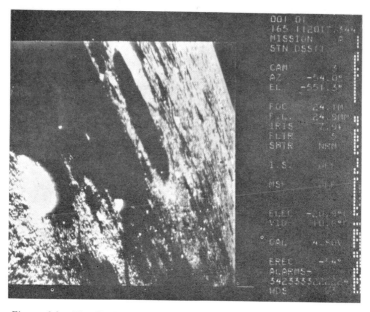

Figure 1.2. The NASA's Surveyor I took this photograph of the moon surface and transmitted it to earth. The rimmed crater in the centre of the photograph is approximately 11 metres from the spacecraft and is three metres wide.

moon and returned more than 10,000 photographs indicating that this particular spot is suitable for a landing (*Figure 1.2*).

The third program, which also began in 1966, is the Lunar Orbiter, designed to gain additional photographic information on potential landing sites *(Figure 1.3)*. The Lunar Orbiter flights are scheduled to continue through 1967.

Planetary exploration

In the exploration of the solar system we have conducted flights past the two nearest planets, Venus and Mars, as well as several through interplanetary space. In 1962, Mariner II passed 21,500 miles from Venus after a journey of 109 days and transmitted information about the planet across a distance of 36 million miles. The most important finding was that the atmosphere of Venus

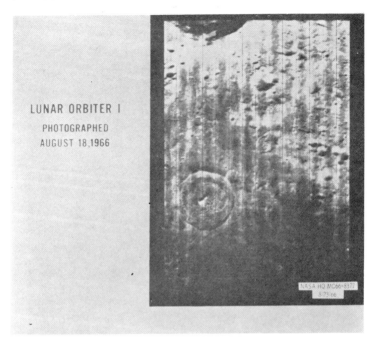

LUNAR ORBITER I
PHOTOGRAPHED
AUGUST 18,1966

*Figure 1.3. A picture of the moon's surface transmitted from
Lunar Orbiter I.*

is hotter than previously believed.   Temperature reading of 600
degrees Fahrenheit was obtained.

In 1965, Mariner IV travelled 228 days and passed within
7400 miles of the planet.   Over a distance of 134 million miles,
Mariner IV transmitted to earth 21 clear photographs, which
indicated that the surface is cratered like that of the moon (*Figure
1.4*).   Radio signals sent when Mariner passed behind Mars showed
that the planet's atmosphere is thinner than expected.   Data
transmitted failed to supply evidence of a dust belt, a magnetic
field or radiation belts.

Spacecraft in the Pioneer series have measured particles and
fields in interplanetary space up to distances of more than 50
million miles.

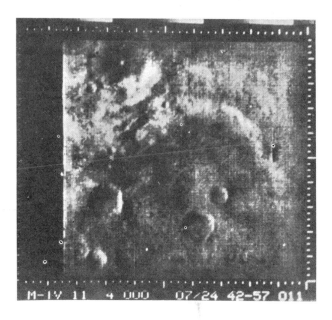

Figure 1.4. In 1965, Mariner IV took this and twenty other pictures of the planet Venus, showing that the planet's surface is cratered like that of the moon.

Applications of space technology

In earth orbit, unmanned spacecraft have been employed with great success to develop, demonstrate and begin operation of practical applications of space technology. The most advanced of these applications are in weather, communications and navigation.

In meteorology, there have been two unmanned spacecraft programs, TIROS and NIMBUS. The TIROS series consisted of 10 successful satellites orbited between 1960 and 1965, photographing cloud cover, obtaining infra-red measurements and transmitting the results to earth. As I feel sure is well understood here in

Australia, the weather originates to a large extent in the five-sixths of the earth's surface covered with water, where weather stations on the surface are few and far between. Consequently, photographs of a developing storm system or typhoon from a satellite provide timely warnings that can prevent losses of life and property. In addition, the infra-red readings enable us to understand the earth's energy balance. Beginning this year, the U.S. Department of Commerce has had an operational system of weather satellites similar to those in the TIROS series.

One of the limitations of TIROS is that its orientation is constant with respect to space. Thus it points to the earth only during half of earth orbit. In addition, the orbits have been inclined, so that the satellites do not pass over the polar regions where some of the most interesting weather is found. To overcome these limitations, we are now flying the NIMBUS satellites, which are larger, constantly pointed toward the earth, and are launched from California into near-polar orbits.

As many of you may know, a station has been constructed at the University of Melbourne to receive TIROS and NIMBUS photographs, which should make a very real contribution to the advance of meteorology here in Australia. Two other stations are being constructed at Darwin and Perth, also.

In communications, a number of experiments have been carried out successfully, beginning in 1960 with the Echo balloon satellite and later with Telstar, Relay and Syncom. In principle, a communications satellite acts as a tall antenna tower, which enables us to transmit beyond the horizon as seen from the surface. The Syncom satellite demonstrated that it is possible to station a transmitting antenna at an altitude of 22,000 miles. At this altitude, the spacecraft maintains its position above a fixed point on the Equator, since its period of rotation is 24 hours.

This orbit is also used by the Early Bird satellites of the Communications Satellite Corporation, the first commercial venture in space, which is now supplying telephone and television communications between the United States and Europe.

A third application now operational is navigation by satellite. The U.S. Navy Transit satellites now supply all-weather navigation services to units of the fleet.

Relationship between unmanned and manned programs

It should be emphasized that an intimate interrelationship exists between the NASA unmanned and manned programs. While our attention will be focused on manned flights, we should be aware of the complementary role of the unmanned missions. The unmanned scientific investigations of the earth, moon, sun, planets, stars, galaxies and outer space invariably support advances in the manned programs. Some of these, such as the recent Surveyor mission, are essential forerunners of specific manned flights. The experiments of manned flights, in turn help to increase the body of knowledge concerning the phenomena of space and our quest for earthly applications of this knowledge.

The manned programs, concurrently, have made possible and in a sense, have demanded the successive advances in manned space capability achieved continuously from the first Mercury missions. The tasks that man can perform are expanding with this increased capability, which can be measured almost from flight to flight. Considered with the incredible growth of human knowledge on all fronts, the ultimate role of man, working in the extraterrestrial environment, is virtually beyond prediction.

THE SPACE ENVIRONMENT

In building its programs of space flight and exploration, NASA has assigned a key role to man. He is not merely a passenger on a space vehicle, but an important element in the man-machine complex. He is a point of decision and command, an experimenter, and a source of intelligent reporting and interpretation of things seen and done. He is a sensor, a manipulator, an evaluator, and an investigator.

The conditions of his flight into space therefore must be such that he not only survives but maintains the efficiency level needed to participate in many essential activities.

Man's survival in space depends upon achieving two basic conditions — a habitable environment and protection against the physiological stresses and incidental hazards of space flight and the space environment.

Life support requirement

On earth, man functions in a gaseous environment consisting of about 20 per cent oxygen and 80 per cent nitrogen at a total pressure of 14.7 pounds per square inch at sea level. He is, however, quite an adaptable mechanism and he can function in other atmospheres, although his range of adaptability does not accommodate survival in the vacuum of space. It is, therefore, necessary for him to take his environment with him into space.

Stresses of space flight

Sustaining life in the space environment is not alone a matter of providing a habitable atmosphere and taking care of the metabolic needs of man. In addition, he must be protected from the physiological effects of environmental factors incidental to space flight. These factors include noise, vibration, acceleration, and impact, weightlessness, isolation, confinement and altered diurnal cycles.

Weightlessness

Prior to the Mercury and Gemini flights, very little was known concerning the effects of prolonged weightlessness on man. This was because, except for very brief periods, there were no methods by which this condition could be realistically simulated on earth. Our lack of ability to simulate weightlessness and the consequent lack of information available concerning its effects, led to its being regarded as one of the critical potential problems limiting man in space travel. The Gemini flights demonstrated that it was not nearly the problem it had been anticipated for flights of this type.

THE ROLE OF MAN IN SPACE

Despite the hostility of space to man, the feasibility of his role in this alien environment already has been convincingly demonstrated. As I have noted, the means of providing a habitable environment has been established for the requirements of flights presently being undertaken, and the capability for attenuation of foreseeable hazards and potential hazards continues to develop.

Motivation for manned Exploration

The nature of man to explore the far reaches of his earthly environment has been amply documented by his successive accomplishments throughout history. Space exploration is but a new level of achievement in probing and exploiting the unknown. The thrust of mankind to master the barriers of mountains, then oceans, and finally the atmosphere, has proceeded to the ocean of space. The curiosity, courage and adventurous determination which has characterized all of man's previous advances in the mastery of his environment are now being brought into play in the scientific, technological and operational gains of the U.S. space effort.

Early rocket technology

Man's conquest of space is based upon the utilization of rocket thrust. Prominent in the background of the U.S. space program is the early rocket technology which served as a forerunner to the development of the launch vehicles which are essential to all space endeavors.

The U.S. manned space flight program incorporates a broad range of technology which emerged from previous programs dating back to early rocket research. Among these contributing national efforts were aircraft programs, ballistic missile development programs, aerospace medicine research, and the development of rocket technology in general, which is the basis of all space flight.

The pioneers of the scientific exploration of space were aware of the practical application of rocket propulsion for space flight. Men such as Konstantin E. Tsiolkovsky of Russia, Robert H. Goddard of the U.S. and Herman Oberth of Rumania and Germany, had published works early in the twentieth century contributing to space technology.

Goddard's work

The foundation in rocketry laid by Dr. Robert H. Goddard is now widely recognized. As early as 1914, he was granted two patents which developed his ideas of a multi-stage rocket and liquid propellants. During this period, by static laboratory test, he proved his theory that a rocket would perform in a vacuum and was therefore capable of operating in space.

His experimentation in rocketry continued unceasingly from 1917 until his death in 1945. During 1920 he began his pioneering experimentation with liquid-fuel propulsion, considering an idea for a hydrogen and oxygen fuel supply he had conceived as early as 1909. He accomplished the first liquid-fuel rocket flight in history in March, 1926.

During the 1930s he performed numerous rocket flight tests in New Mexico, as he continued to develop the science of rocketry. With his lifetime of effort in this field, Dr. Goddard demonstrated all of the fundamentals for successful rocket flight, covered by more than 200 patents. They range from fuels, multi-stage design, guidance and control, to payloads.

V-2 missiles

Goddard's work went virtually unnoticed in the United States, even into World War II. In Germany, however, liquid-fuelled rocket study had proceeded during the 1930s and by 1944 the German V-2 ballistic rockets were being launched from Germany against Britain. In basic design, the supersonic V-2 with its 200-mile range was almost identical to Dr. Goddard's much smaller liquid-fuel rocket.

Postwar Development

Interest in rocket technology gradually developed in the United States following World War II, largely because of the impact of the German V-2 rocket on American military and scientific observers. The full realization of Dr. Goddard's contribution was to follow after a growing awareness of his experiments.

U.S. ROCKET RESEARCH

The potential of large rockets demonstrated by the V-2 missiles gave increased impetus to plans for exploring the realm of space with instrumented, and eventually manned, rocket vehicles. The U.S. armed services pursued several rocket projects in the postwar period, using V-2 components and adaptations of the V-2 engines, as well as other engine developments. By 1949, the Navy had developed a more powerful rocket, the Viking, for high altitude atmospheric probes. By 1952 the National Advisory Committee for Aeronautics (NACA) was devoting a modest amount of effort to studies looking forward to manned space flight. The X-15 rocket research airplane project carried out jointly by the NACA and the Air Force began in 1952. The U.S. inter-continental ballistic missile program was begun in 1954, leading to the development of a new generation of rocket systems with the great thrust needed for military payloads.

PROJECT VANGUARD

The first United States earth satellite program was project Vanguard, initiated in 1955 under the management of the Naval Research Laboratory. Its purpose was to develop a satellite-launching vehicle and tracking system, and to place at least one satellite in orbit with an experiment payload during the International Geophysical Year beginning July 1, 1957.

Impact of Sputnik launch

On October 4, 1957, the Soviet Union Sputnik was launched, while flight tests of the Vanguard rocket stages were in progress. The impact of Sputnik was amplified further by the launch of Sputnik II a month later. The Army Ballistic Missile Agency's satellite proposal was revived and activated as a back-up to Vanguard and the Advanced Research Projects Agency was formed to take charge of all Department of Defense space programs.

Vanguard and Explorer satellites

The launch of the first Vanguard rocket with potential orbit capabilities was attempted on December 6, 1957. The launch failed when the first stage engine lost thrust two seconds after ignition, and the vehicle burned up on the pad. The launch of the first U.S. satellite, Explorer I, was accomplished by the Army Ballistic Missile Agency on January 31, 1958. After a second unsuccessful Vanguard launch attempt in February of 1958, the first Vanguard satellite was launched into orbit on March 17, 1958.

ESTABLISHMENT OF NATIONAL SPACE AGENCY

Following the success of the Soviet Union in orbiting Sputnik, the President and the Congress of the United States began a careful and detailed review of the national competence and potential in the interdependent areas of missile and space development.

Early in 1958, the President's Advisory Committee on Government Organization recommended that a civilian space agency be established, patterned after the successful National Advisory Committee for Aeronautics. The President's Science Advisory Committee soon after urged national action to develop space technology.

National Aeronautics and Space Administration

In March, 1958, the President approved his advisory committee's recommendation that a civilian space agency should be created upon the structure of the existing National Advisory Committee for Aeronautics, and that this agency should have responsibility for all non-military space activities in an integrated program. A space agency bill reflecting these recommendations was proposed by the President and sent to the Congress. The House and Senate special committees immediately considered the proposed bill in their hearings.

The result of these deliberations was a national decision involving the President, the Congress, and the American public. The decision was embodied in the National Aeronautics and Space Act of 1958, signed by the President on July 29, 1958. The agency created by the Act to carry out a mandate for a national civilian space effort was the National Aeronautics and Space Administration (NASA).

National objectives in space

In addition to creating a national space agency, the legislation provided the objectives which were to be the guide for all national space efforts in the future (*Figure 1.5*). The objectives in brief were (1) the expansion of human knowledge; (2) improvement of aeronautical and space vehicles; (3) development and operation of space vehicles; (4) long-range studies for peaceful and scientific use of aeronautics and space; (5) international co-operation; and (6) effective utilization of resources.

U.S. NATIONAL AERONAUTICS AND SPACE ACT OF 1958

- PEACEFUL PURPOSES
- ESTABLISHMENT OF NASA
- NATIONAL OBJECTIVES

    - EXPANSION OF KNOWLEDGE
    - DEVELOPMENT AND OPERATION OF VEHICLES
    - IMPROVEMENT OF VEHICLES
    - STUDIES OF POTENTIAL BENEFITS
    - INTERNATIONAL CO-OPERATION
    - EFFECTIVE UTILIZATION OF RESOURCES

NASA HQ. MC 66-8367

Figure 1.5. The objectives which are set down as the guide for all future space efforts.

CONSOLIDATION OF SPACE EFFORT

NACA nucleus of new agency

The new space agency was formed by using the National Advisory Committee for Aeronautics as the nucleus. Eight thousand NACA personnel, including scientists, engineers, and technicians were transferred to NASA. Facilities of NACA absorbed by NASA included the Langley, Ames, Lewis, and Edwards Research Centres, with their 40-year legacy of NACA aeronautical, rocket propulsion and missile research.

Transfer of non-military space projects

Army, Air Force, Navy and Department of Defence non-military space projects also were transferred to NASA. Integrated with this move were the space probes, satellites, and rocket engine programs of the services. Among the projects and personnel acquired were the Project Vanguard scientific satellite program and 200 highly qualified scientific and technical personnel from the Naval Research Laboratory.

By the end of 1958, the Jet Propulsion Laboratory of the California Institute of Technology, previously under contract to the Army, was brought under NASA direction. At the same time, the Army Ballistic Missile Agency at Huntsville, Alabama, was made responsive to NASA requirements. The large liquid-fuelled Saturn rocket program at Huntsville, initiated in 1958 under Department of Defence auspices, also became responsive to NASA direction.

In mid-1960, this group of rocket experts of the Army Ballistic Missile Agency's Development Operations Division, and their facilities, were transferred to NASA. With the transfer, the George C. Marshall Space Flight Centre was established.

The NASA Launch Operations Centre at Cape Canaveral also was established in 1960 and became an independent NASA Centre in July, 1962. It was renamed the John F. Kennedy Space Centre in November, 1963, in honour of the late President, concurrent with the redesignation of Cape Canaveral as Cape Kennedy.

Manned space flight capability

Specific capabilities for manned space flight were created by this organizational alignment of the U.S. space exploration projects. Efforts which had been fragmented came together under the new space agency, each contributing to the total national program.

Key personnel from several laboratories of the National Advisory Committee for Aeronautics were transferred to the Langley Research Laboratory. They later became the nucleus for the Project Mercury team which eventually expanded to become the Manned Spacecraft Centre at Houston, Texas.

The Project Vanguard team formed the nucleus of the new Goddard Space Flight Centre at Greenbelt, Maryland, concentrating on unmanned satellites and spacecraft, and creating the basis for the world-wide Goddard tracking and communications network. This network was later expanded and refined to support both unmanned and manned space flight and, in addition, supplied expert personnel for other NASA activity.

The rocket development team from the Army came to provide the large booster support for advanced manned flight. The efforts of the military services were drawn upon heavily to provide the early rocket boosters, as well as launch facilities and crews, and recovery support for manned space flight.

With the capability created through consolidation of people and projects in NASA, the new agency was able to proceed without delay on the programs for U.S. manned space flight, beginning with Project Mercury.

MANNED SPACE FLIGHT PROGRAMS

Project Mercury had its origins in study effort accomplished by and for the Air Force and the National Advisory Committee for Aeronautics. Its specific origin was the recommendation of a committee formed in September 1958, composed of representatives from the Department of Defence and the National Advisory Committee for Aeronautics, immediately prior to the official birth of NASA. The national manned satellite program which it recommended, named Project Mercury by the end of 1958, was approved by the NASA Administrator on October 7, 1958, and the project was immediately set in motion.

During Project Mercury, NASA's planning for the future pointed to manned exploration of the moon and the nearby planets as a goal of the indefinite future beyond 1970. In July, 1960, following a Congressional committee recommendation for a high priority manned lunar landing program, NASA announced that the successor to Project Mercury would be Project Apollo. Its goal, however, was to carry three astronauts in sustained earth orbital or circumlunar flight. Plans for an eventual manned lunar landing were to be studied.

In May, 1961, President Kennedy recommended to Congress an expanded national space program with the major accelerated goal of "landing a man on the moon and returning him safely to earth, during this decade". Congress subsequently endorsed the plan for expanding and accelerating Apollo including the development of spacecraft, large rocket boosters, and unmanned explorations which would support the Apollo objectives.

Meanwhile, in December, 1961, the decision was taken to extend the manned space flight effort beyond Mercury providing an interim program before the flights of Apollo hardware could begin. This

MAJOR MSF MILESTONES

GEMINI   1964 - 1ST GEMINI FLIGHT

1965 - 1ST GEMINI MANNED FLIGHT

1966 - 1ST GEMINI RENDEZVOUS FLIGHT

1967 - GEMINI OPERATIONS

APOLLO   1966 - 1ST APOLLO SATURN IB UNMANNED FLIGHT

1967 - 1ST APOLLO SATURN IB MANNED FLIGHT

1967 - 1ST APOLLO SATURN V UNMANNED FLIGHT

1968 - 1ST APOLLO SATURN V MANNED FLIGHT

1969 - APOLLO OPERATIONS

NASA MC65-5185
1/26/65

Figure 1.6. Major MSF milestones.

program, utilizing a two-man spacecraft, was officially named Gemini, after the third constellation of the zodiac with twin stars Castor and Pollux, in January, 1962.

Major milestones for the Gemini and Apollo programs later were established, from the first Gemini flight scheduled for 1964 to Apollo operations scheduled for 1969 (*Figure 1.6*).

In my next lecture of this series, I will discuss the program philosophy of the first U.S. manned space flight program— Project Mercury — and will measure the accomplishments of Gemini against its program objectives. In so doing, I hope to provide an insight of some of the lessons we have learned concerning man in space.

CHAPTER 2

Mercury and Gemini Programs

MERCURY

Project Mercury had its origins in study effort accomplished by and for the Air Force and the National Advisory Committee for Aeronautics. Its specific origin was the recommendation of a committee formed in September, 1958, with representatives from the Department of Defence and the National Advisory Committee for Aeronautics, immediately prior to the official birth of NASA. The national manned satellite program which it recommended, named Project Mercury by the end of 1958, was approved by the NASA Administrator on October 7, 1958, and the project was immediately set in motion.

Unprecedented relationships between government agencies, contractors, and the scientific community were necessary to produce timely results in this very complex program. Working teams were formed of appropriate people from various government agencies, as well as private industry, to accomplish the basic objectives of Project Mercury: place a man in earth orbital flight, observe his physical and mental reactions in the space environment, and recover the man and spacecraft.

Beginning late in 1958, aeromedical personnel were assigned to the Space Task Group by the Army, Navy and Air Force to work with NASA personnel and a special committee on life sciences. This group established an astronaut selection procedure, set up qualifications and requirements, and selected a group of 110 potential astronauts.

Astronaut selection

By April, 1959, seven men had been chosen for the project and reported to begin their two-year group training program

27

Figure 2.1. The Project Mercury astronauts. Front row (l. to r.): Walter H. Shirra Jr., Donald K. Slayton, John H. Glenn Jr., and M. Scott Carpenter. Back row (l. to r.): Alan B. Shepard Jr., Virgil I. ("Gus") Grissom and L. Gordon Cooper Jr.

(Figure 2.1). All seven were experienced jet aircraft pilots and graduates of test-pilot training. Their group training consisted of astronautical science instruction, systems training, spacecraft control training, environmental familiarization, and egress and survival training. In addition they maintained their flying proficiency and trained for the activities of specific missions.

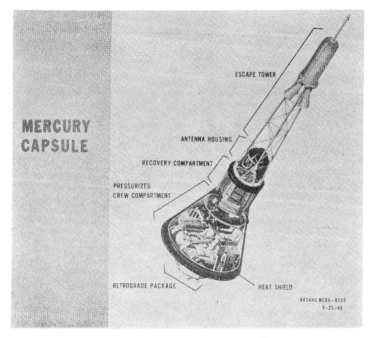

ESCAPE TOWER

MERCURY CAPSULE

ANTENNA HOUSING

RECOVERY COMPARTMENT

PRESSURIZED CREW COMPARTMENT

RETROGRADE PACKAGE

HEAT SHIELD

NASAHQ MC65-8355
8-23-66

Figure 2.2. The Mercury capsule.

Mercury design

Four basic-design guide-lines were established at the beginning of Project Mercury. These guide-lines were (1) that existing technology and equipment would be used wherever possible; (2) the simplest and most reliable approach to system design would be followed; (3) an existing rocket launch vehicle would be used for the orbital mission; and (4) a progressive and logical test program would be conducted. Automatic operation of all critical systems of the Mercury spacecraft was provided, since man's capabilities in the space environment were unknown. Redundant systems were included to give maximum reliability for safety and assurance of mission success.

The familiar bell-shaped spacecraft was protected from re-entry heating by a heat shield covering the curved surface of the blunt end (*Figure 2.2*). The tapered portion was of double construction. The outer wall comprised overlapping shingles of a thin refractory metal, corrugated for strength. The inner cabin walls comprised two layers of thin gauge titanium. A solid-propellant rocket was mounted on top of the escape tower to lift the spacecraft clear of danger in case of a launch vehicle failure on the pad. In a normal mission, the escape tower was jettisoned after the booster stage had shut down.

Interior design of the Mercury spacecraft provided a form-fitting contour couch designed to distribute high acceleration loads. At all critical phases of the mission the spacecraft was oriented so that the direction of acceleration forces were the same, from back to front. Thus, the spacecraft was pointed nose up at launch and heat shield forward on re-entry.

The life support system inside the pressurized crew compartment supplied breathing oxygen, purified the air by removing carbon dioxide and other foreign matter, and controlled the temperature and air flow inside the astronaut's full-pressure space suit. These provisions protected the pilot from the hard vacuum of space as well as the extreme temperature variations associated with the orbital flight profile. This system also included provision for food and drinking water, as well as waste management within the weightless environment of space.

Development program

Both development and production of the flight systems for the Mercury program, from man-rating the rocket boosters to creation of the spacecraft sub-systems, were characterized by extensive ground testing of each component, then of assembled components. A plan was followed which called for concurrent development and testing of all major aspects of the project. Thus, the astronauts were selected and trained, the world-wide tracking network planned and built, and research and development of the flight hardware accomplished on parallel and closely co-ordinated schedules. Although early schedules proved to be optimistic, elapsed time between project initiation and the first manned orbital flight was only three years and four months and the entire program of six manned flights was completed in four years, seven months.

The flight program as actually accomplished consisted of 25 major launches between August, 1959, and May, 1963. Six of these flights were manned; two were suborbital ballistic profiles and four were earth orbital missions. Although launch failures and test anomalies were experienced in the course of the program, no injuries to passengers were sustained.

Redstone-boosted flights

The first launches in the Mercury program used the Redstone missile which had been developed by the Army's Ballistic Missile Agency. The Redstone's thrust was adequate to place the Mercury spacecraft into a trajectory with a high point about equal to the planned orbital altitude, producing weightlessness for one-third of the flight. This was particularly important because the biological effects of weightlessness upon man were unknown save for the very limited data acquired through experiments in aircraft where zero-g conditions did not exceed a few seconds.

Three Mercury-Redstone flights were accomplished as tests of the spacecraft booster combination: a systems test with an empty spacecraft; a second test with a chimpanzee as passenger; and a third flight to check on changes made to improve the accuracy of the booster. The fourth flight, on May 5, 1961, was the first United States manned space flight (*Figure 2.3*). In this 15-minute flight over a ballistic trajectory through space, Alan Shepard experienced about five minutes of weightlessness and reached a maximum altitude of 116 statute miles. A slightly modified spacecraft, with an added window and modified instrument panel, piloted by Virgil Grissom, was launched on a similar flight in July, 1961.

Atlas-boosted flights

The launch vehicle used for Project Mercury orbital flights was the Atlas intercontinental ballistic missile, developed and modified for manned flights by the Air Force. When the program began in 1958, the Atlas was the only rocket in existence or development in the United States which had the potential of achieving an early manned orbital launch. The primary consideration in the "man-

Figure 2.3. The launching of America's first man in space on the Mercury Redstone III from Cape Canaveral (now Cape Kennedy) launch site on May 5, 1961.

rating" process was pilot safety during countdown and launch. By April, 1959, an abort system had been designed which used measurements of critical engine chamber pressures, rates of change in vehicle attitude, electrical power status, and various tank pressures to determine when a dangerous condition developed. If sufficient variations occurred, the system would shut down the engines and initiate spacecraft escape.

A total of ten Mercury-Atlas launches were accomplished in the program from September, 1959, to the last Mercury flight in May, 1963. Six unmanned flights tested the performance of booster and spacecraft before the first manned orbital flight.

The original primary objective of Project Mercury was attained on February 20, 1962, when astronaut John Glenn, Jr., piloted the first U.S. manned orbital flight to a safe conclusion. The planned three-orbit mission was completed, the astronaut's performance was excellent, and no adverse effects from weightlessness were noted. Glenn controlled the attitude of the spacecraft manually for a large part of the mission and performed well under stress.

Attainment of the basic Mercury program objectives on the first orbital mission made it possible to extend the aims of the program and conduct expanded space exploration and experimentation in subsequent missions. A second three-orbit flight was completed in May, 1962, with Scott Carpenter as the pilot, followed by a flight of six orbital passes in October, piloted by Walter Schirra, Jr. The Schirra flight provided information on extended exposure to the space environment, additional operational experience, and an opportunity to conduct a series of experiments and measurements in space.

The last Mercury flight was the 22 orbit, 34 hour and 20 minute mission of astronaut Gordon Cooper, Jr., in May, 1963 (*Figure 2.4*). Evaluation of extended weightlessness effects was the major objective of this mission. Cooper, who slept for seven and one half hours during the flight, was in excellent condition upon recovery in the Pacific Ocean, although he had lost seven pounds of weight due to temporary dehydration. Several scientific experiments were conducted during this last Mercury mission, including aeromedical studies, radiation measurements, photographic studies, and visibility and communications tests.

B

Figure 2.5. The gains from Project Mercury — thus far.

Mercury summary

Program objectives were gradually expanded from the original goal to simply place a man in orbit, recover him safely and evaluate the data acquired to encompass a 34 hour mission. As the program progressed, the data base was expanded many-fold and additional objectives introduced, resulting in a much more comprehensive program of pioneering space exploration.

Figure 2.4 (Page 34). Mercury Atlas 9 ("Faith 7") leaves the launching pad at Cape Canaveral on May 15, 1962, with astronaut Gordon Cooper aboard for what was, to that time, the longest U.S.-manned orbital flight.

Gains from Project Mercury were many (*Figure 2·5*).   We learned to design, build and test manned spacecraft; to prepare launch vehicles for safe and reliable manned flight; to operate a world-wide network of radio and radar tracking and communicating with the spacecraft and pilot; to recover the spacecraft and pilot; to select and train astronauts; and to develop and operate life support and biomedical instrumentation systems.   In addition, valuable experience in large-scale management and systems engineering was acquired, important scientific knowledge about the space environment was gained, and technological advances necessary for further progress in space exploration were made.   The ability of a well-trained man to contribute substantially to the exploration of space was demonstrated, lending confidence to further plans for manned space exploration.

GEMINI PROGRAM ORIGINS

In December, 1961, the decision to extend manned space flight effort beyond Mercury, providing experience in space operations which would support the lunar landing program, was made.   This program, named Gemini, was based on a series of primary objectives.   It was to be a logical follow-on program after Mercury, minimizing time and expense, designed to subject two men and necessary supporting equipment to long duration flights, accumulating the experience and knowledge necessary for trips to the moon or beyond.   Another specific objective was to achieve rendezvous and docking with another orbiting vehicle and manoeuvre the combined spacecraft, using the propulsion system of the "target" vehicle.   Rendezvous and docking comprise a key element of the Lunar Orbit Rendezvous approach to lunar landing in Project Apollo.   Experience with this technique and equipment would be necessary not only for Apollo, but for many advanced missions.

In addition, experiments with astronauts leaving the spacecraft in orbit to determine their ability to perform mechanical and other tasks, were planned.   This extravehicular activity was another technique projected for more advanced missions, assembling structures and repairing equipment in space, as well as operations outside

Figure 2.6. The Mercury (left) and the Gemini (right) spacecrafts are shown side by side to compare the relative sizes of the one-man and the two-man spacecrafts. Project Gemini followed Project Mercury.

the Apollo spacecraft on the lunar surface. Another objective of the program was to perfect methods of controlled re-entry and landing at pre-selected sites. This would be necessary for return from the lunar landing mission of Apollo. A major overall objective was accumulation of information and experience with the effects of weightlessness and physiological reactions of crew members during long duration missions, compiling the medical data necessary for planning missions in Apollo and later programs.

The Gemini spacecraft was planned to be, in many ways, a two-man orbiting laboratory by means of which knowledge of and experience in the space environment would be increased by several orders of magnitude. Time in space, and room within the spacecraft, would be provided for conducting a variety of experiments and observations during the course of the program.

Spacecraft design

Major changes from the Mercury spacecraft were incorporated into the Gemini design, placing increased emphasis on man (*Figure 2.6*). Where Mercury was designed to provide completely automatic control from the ground with redundant capability for pilot control, Gemini was designed from the beginning to be controlled by the astronauts, with ground control as the back-up. A dramatic example of this change in design philosophy is that in Mercury an impending launch vehicle failure was automatically sensed and the escape system activated. A launch vehicle malfunction in the Gemini system activates lights and gauges on the instrument panel and the astronauts then exercise judgment and make the decision on the seriousness of the situation and the necessity to abort.

Another major advancement in the Gemini design is the difference in the type and placement of sub-systems and components. In the Mercury spacecraft, almost all systems were in the pilot's cabin, where space limitations caused them to be stacked in layers. Thus, when troubles were encountered with one system, it was often necessary to disturb a number of other systems to get at the problem area. In Gemini many of the systems are outside the cabin area, making access much easier. Further, the systems were designed in modular packages, arranged so that any system can be removed without disturbing another. Also, spare packages can be completely checked out and kept in reserve for replacement purposes.

The complete Gemini spacecraft comprises two major units (*Figure 2.7*). These are (1) the adapter module, consisting of the retrograde section and the equipment section; and (2) the re-entry module, consisting of the rendezvous and recovery section, the re-entry control system, and the cabin section. The heat shield is attached to the cabin section, in the manner of the Mercury capsule. The re-entry module is the only portion of the spacecraft recovered from orbit.

Provisions for crew safety in the event of a mission abort are significantly different for Gemini as compared to Mercury and Apollo. Mercury had a tower atop the spacecraft with a tractor rocket to pull the entire spacecraft away from the danger area if

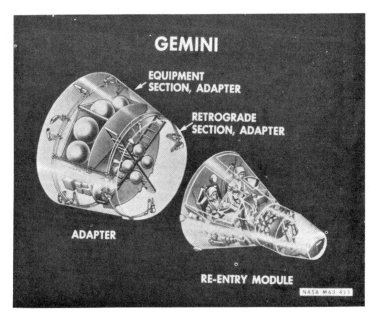

Figure 2.7. A sectionalised diagram of the Gemini spacecraft.

needed. Apollo's design is similar. Gemini, however, is designed to provide the crew with ejection seats similar to those used in high performance aircraft, and personnel parachutes for descent to earth. The use of ejection seats is possible because the fuel used by the Gemini launch vehicle burns on contact with the oxidizer, minimizing the explosion hazard which was present in the Mercury launch sequence. An additional benefit of the ejection seat method is that it can be used during the re-entry phase, at low altitudes, in the event of trouble during the terminal portion of the mission.

Gemini launch vehicle

The Gemini launch vehicle is 90 feet tall and 10 feet in diameter with a first stage engine developing 430,000 pounds of thrust and a second stage engine producing 100,000 pounds at the ignition altitude of approximately 200,000 feet (*Figure 2.8*). As noted

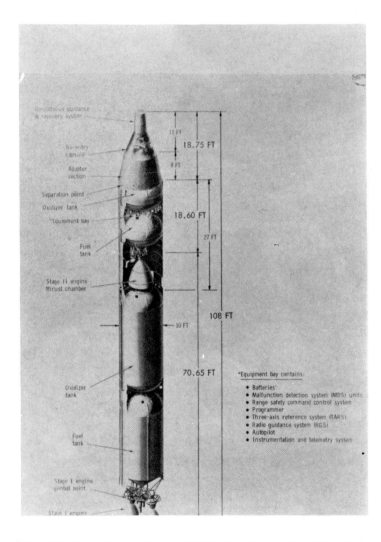

Figure 2.8. An artist's drawing of NASA's Titan II launch vehicle and the Gemini spacecraft.

earlier, the Titan II uses storable propellants which ignite on contact. This design feature added feasibility to the precise launches necessary for Gemini rendezvous and docking missions.

A series of modifications to the basic missile were made to attain required reliability and safety for manned launches. Redundant hydraulic systems and additional instrumentation were installed, and a malfunction detection system, sensing any critical problems in the rocket and transmitting this information to the crew, was added.

Target Vehicles

The target vehicle designed for Gemini rendezvous and docking missions is a specially modified Air Force Agena, with a docking collar and instruments peculiar to these missions (*Figure 2.9*). An Atlas launch vehicle is used to boost the Agena to near orbital speed where the Agena propulsion system takes over to place the vehicle in orbit. Development and modification of the Gemini launch vehicle and the Atlas-Agena combination, are the responsibility of the Air Force in response to National Aeronautics and Space Administration requirements.

Achievement of program objectives

Beginning with Gemini III in March, 1965, eight manned missions were flown in less than 16 months. As the Gemini program nears completion it is possible to evaluate how well the program objectives have been reached.

Long-duration flight

First, the program objective of investigating long duration flight has been achieved with complete success, in three missions of 4, 8 and 14 days' duration. These were the flights of Gemini IV, Gemini V and Gemini VII in June, August and December, 1965, respectively. The second of these, the Gemini V mission in August, established a new Manned Space Flight record of 190 hours, 55 minutes, surpassing the previously-held Russian record. Medical evaluation of the crews after these flights revealed no adverse effects from their lengthy exposure to weightlessness, and a definite pattern

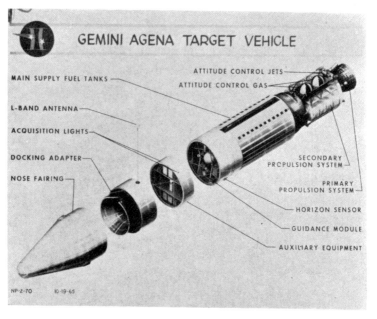

Figure 2.9. The Gemini Agena Target vehicle.

of adaptation to weightlessness was detected as blood pressure and heart rates showed a levelling trend after the first several days (*Figure 2.10*). This information is of great significance, since eight days is the approximate length of the first lunar landing mission planned in Apollo, while other flights—both lunar and earth-orbital—will last for periods of 14 days and more.

Extravehicular activity

In the first long-duration mission Gemini IV, pilot Edward White also demonstrated the feasibility of conducting activity outside the spacecraft (*Figure 2.11*). In this first U.S. extravehicular activity, White stayed outside the spacecraft for 23 minutes, manoeuvring himself about the spacecraft, taking pictures and making observations of equipment. During the early portion of the manoeuvre, he used a hand-held manoeuvring unit which provided propulsion by emitting jets of oxygen.

CONTRIBUTION OF GEMINI MEDICAL INFORMATION (THRU GEMINI VII) TO PRE-GEMINI MEDICAL PROBLEM AREAS

CARDIOVASCULAR .... DECONDITIONING TREND DEMONSTRATED
                                     NO DISABILITY- 14 DAYS

WATER BALANCE........................ DEHYDRATION TREND DEMONSTRATED
                                     NO DISABILITY-14 DAYS

SKELETAL................................... EARLY ATROPHY SUGGESTED NO DISABILITY- 14 DAYS

MUSCULAR .... EARLY ATROPHY NOTED; SYMPTOMS VERY MILD -14 DAYS

BEHAVIORAL................................ NO DEGRADATION

VESTIBULAR................................ NO CHANGE

METABOLIC AND DIGESTIVE .. NO DYSFUNCTION NOTED

RESPIRATORY............................. NO DYSFUNCTION NOTED

CELLULAR.................................... (APOLLO)

SLEEP AND DIURNAL .... SLEEP PATTERNS ALTERED - THEN NORMALIZED
RHYTHMS   IMPORTANCE OF W-R-S CYCLE STRESSED

VISUAL .... ACUITY UNCHANGED — VISIBILITY EXCELLENT
                                       FROM EARTH ORBIT

NASA MG5-10.101

Figure 2.10. The Gemini Medical Information chart.

Astronaut White was restrained by a 25-foot tether, to which was attached an umbilical hose system to supply breathing oxygen. Additional life support was provided by a chest pack which maintained his suit pressure and contained an emergency supply of oxygen. White wore a special protective suit and a special protective helmet visor for the mission.

An expanded extravehicular mission was included in the Gemini IX flight in June, 1966, during which astronaut Eugene Cernan worked outside the spacecraft for over two hours. A more ambitious demonstration of extravehicular mobility, using an Astronaut Manoeuvring Unit, was cancelled when a moisture overload inside Cernan's suit caused his visor to fog. This activity has been rescheduled for the final Gemini flight, Gemini XII.

Figure 2.11. Astronaut Edward H. White outside his spacecraft during the third orbit of the Gemini-Titan IV flight. The astronaut was secured to the Gemini IV spacecraft by a 25-foot umbilical line. White was the first American astronaut to "walk in space", remaining outside for 21 minutes. He is holding a Hand-held Self-manoeuvring Unit which enabled him to move about in his weightless environment. The spacecraft was under the command of astronaut James A. McDivitt.

On the Gemini X flight in July 1966, pilot Michael Collins performed two extravehicular assignments. During his first exposure to space outside the cabin, Collins stood up in the open hatch of the spacecraft for nearly 45 minutes and performed picture-taking and other assignments. Later in the flight, during rendezvous with the Agena used in the Gemini VIII mission, he egressed from the cabin and manoeuvred in space for 55 minutes with a hand-held manoeuvring unit. Using a 50-foot tether and umbilical, Collins manoeuvred to the Agena and retrieved a micrometeoroid collection experiment.

Figure 2.12. A photograph of the Gemini VII spacecraft, taken through the hatch window of Gemini VI during a rendezvous in space, altitude 160 miles, on December 16, 1965.

Rendezvous and docking

The in-flight manoeuvring capability necessary for spacecraft rendezvous and docking was demonstrated during the first manned flight, Gemini III, with changes in orbital attitude and orbital phase.

The Gemini VI mission in December 1965 accomplished the first successful space rendezvous, and also demonstrated the high degree of launch and preflight operational capability necessary to carry out the rendezvous. The lift-off of the Gemini VI space vehicle

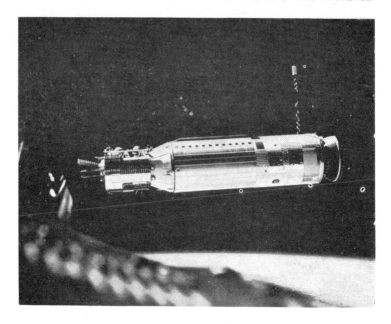

Figure 2.13. The Agena Target Docking Vehicle seen from the Gemini VIII spacecraft during the latter's approach for rendezvous and station keeping. Astronaut David Scott took this picture from an approximate distance of 45 feet.

occurred within 11 days of the Gemini VII launch from the same pad, and within one-tenth of a second of the scheduled lift-off time. Four orbits later, command pilot Walter Schirra manoeuvred the spacecraft to within 120 feet of the Gemini VII spacecraft to accomplish rendezvous of the two manned spacecraft. Later the Gemini VI spacecraft was manoeuvred to less than one foot of Gemini VII following station-keeping and fly-around manoeuvres (*Figure 2.12*).

Rendezvous and docking with an Agena Target Vehicle was accomplished with the Gemini VIII flight in March 1966. The docking manoeuvre, achieved for the first time, was completely successful. The mission was terminated shortly after the docking, however, because of a spacecraft malfunction. *Figure 2.13* shows the Agena Target Vehicle as seen from the spacecraft during the latter's approach.

Three other types of rendezvous manoeuvres were performed during the Gemini IX flight. An "augmented target docking adapter" was used as the target for this flight in place of the Agena Target Vehicle. Docking could not be performed, however, because the target vehicle shroud had failed to jettison.

One of the most significant rendezvous manoeuvres carried out on this mission was a simulation of a rendezvous of a Lunar Module with an Apollo spacecraft in lunar orbit. The manoeuvre successfully performed by Gemini IX would be required during an Apollo lunar mission if a decision were made not to continue with a lunar landing after the Lunar Module had descended to the 50,000 foot level.

Post-docking manoeuvres

The third portion of the rendezvous and docking objective, manoeuvring while docked by using the Agena's primary propulsion system, was accomplished on the Gemini X flight. During this dual rendezvous mission, rendezvous was first made with the Agena X Target Vehicle launched one orbit earlier. After docking with Agena X, the combined Gemini/Agena vehicle was manoeuvred to a higher orbit, with an apogee of 476 miles, the highest man had yet ventured in space.

This orbital change was the first of a series of orbital manoeuvres using the Agena X propulsion system, in preparation for rendezvous with another orbiting target. The second rendezvous target was the Agena vehicle remaining in orbit since the Gemini VIII mission four months earlier. Terminal rendezvous of Gemini X with Agena VIII was successfully accomplished after the spacecraft had separated from Agena X.

Re-entry control

Guided re-entry of the spacecraft to a particular target was included in all of the Gemini flights. By use of an on-board computer, the pilots have been able to use the aerodynamic lift of the spacecraft as it re-enters the atmosphere to guide the spacecraft toward a preselected area. The most accurate demonstrations of this capability were provided by Gemini IX and Gemini X both of which "splashed-down" within three miles of the intended target point.

Space experiments

Advances in operational techniques and equipment in the Gemini program have made it possible to conduct a large number of scientific and technological experiments in the course of Gemini flights. A total of 49 separate experiments have been scheduled in the program, many of them repeated on several flights. These experiments range from specific physiological measurements of the crew to technological developments proving out new equipment and techniques.

One particularly interesting experiment concerns synoptic terrain photography, that is, successive pictures of geographic and geological points of interest from orbital altitude. For example, *Figure 2.14* shows a portion of the Queensland coastline as seen from the Gemini V spacecraft. Geologists, geographers, and oceanographers have obtained valuable new information from these colour photographs. For instance, new geological knowledge was gained as a result of photographs taken during Gemini IV, which revealed new characteristics of a volcanic field in Mexico and a previously unknown fault in the Lower California peninsula. The advantage of cloud-free conditions is obtained, since the pictures are taken by men rather than pre-programmed equipment.

Similarly, synoptic weather photography has produced colour photographs of storm patterns and cloud cover from relatively low orbital altitudes. These pictures have been very helpful as additional data to assist in interpreting unmanned meteorological satellite results.

Another example of new knowledge gained from the Gemini experiments program may be found in the zodiacal light photography experiments conducted for Professor E. P. Ney of the University of Minnesota. Begun on Gordon Cooper's 34-hour Mercury flight in 1963, and continued into the Gemini program, these experiments comprised photographs of the zodiacal light in the night sky, the visible manifestation of dust grains in orbit about the sun. Taken from orbital altitudes according to directions provided by the experimenter, the photographs taken by Cooper confirmed theories about the zodiacal light which had not been subject to proof through earlier means.

Figure 2.14. A Gemini earth-sky view. The land mass (left) is Capricorn Island, Keppel Bay, Queensland, Aust., and was taken from Gemini V during its eight-day space mission.

On the Gemini V flight, in August 1965, photographs of the gegenschein phenomenon were obtained. This first photographic evidence indicates that the gegenschein, a glow in a direction opposite the sun from the earth, is probably produced by back scattering of sunlight through dust. Further astronomical advances are anticipated in the future through orbital photography and observations with telescopes in orbit.

Summary

Achievements in the Mercury and Gemini programs can be summarized under three interrelated categories. We have acquired a significant body of knowledge concerning both men and machines in relation to and interaction with the space environment, we have gained invaluable experience in space operations, and we have demonstrated the value of manned spacecraft as vehicles for scientific experimentation and observation.

Great advances have been made since the early days of Project Mercury when highly respected medical opinion warned against the unknown effects of weightlessness and rapid heart rates. We now know that trained astronauts can function well for at least 14 days in space, supported by environmental control systems based on contemporary technology. We know that these trained crewmen can also withstand the stresses of launch operations and re-entry into the earth's atmosphere. We have learned that the radiation hazard in near earth orbit is acceptably small. We have developed and utilized biosensors to relay critical physiological data from spacecraft to earth stations by means of telemetry. We have demonstrated that a crewman can leave his spacecraft to perform useful work in space. We have gained experience in producing large rocket boosters with sufficient reliability of performance to be "man-rated". A world-wide tracking and communications network, tied into an advanced Mission Control Centre, enables us to execute positive mission control in real time. Crewmen have performed as experimenters, conducting a wide variety of scientific and technological investigations.

During the short history of manned space flight, less than six years since the first manned venture into this new medium, we have accumulated hundreds of man-hours of operating experience. Valuable knowledge gained includes how to select and train crew members for space flight and how to control and recover men and machines through missions of increasing length and complexity. Since our first hesitant steps into space in 1961, we have gradually increased the time during which crewmen experience weightlessness from five minutes to two weeks and the complexity of their tasks until they are now full-time pilots and navigators. We have developed and exercised techniques for manoeuvring in space and controlling re-entry flight paths to accurate landings in planned recovery areas on the earth's surface. Our operations have progressed from flight over a ballistic trajectory to dual and triple rendezvous manoeuvres with other spacecraft, manned and unmanned. We have joined spacecraft and used the rocket propulsion unit already "stored" in orbit to propel the linked configuration through new manoeuvres, opening the door to future assembly, crew transfer, and re-supply operations in space.

Man's exploration of the space environment is accelerating at a rapid rate. The size and complexity of the spacecraft and launch vehicles have increased with each major program and the missions to be accomplished become ever more complex. Mercury and Gemini have established the basic knowledge of the space environment in combination with men and machines, and the operational techniques necessary for the next steps in this great new age of exploration.

CHAPTER 3

Apollo Program

The Apollo program is the third step in NASA's manned space flight program. Its goals are to build a broadbased capability for Manned Space Flight, and to demonstrate this capability by landing men on the moon, and returning them safely to earth within this decade.

As previously noted, Project Mercury paved the way by developing one-man space vehicles and techniques for their use. Gemini's two-man spacecraft has provided the capability for longer orbital missions and for developing the technique of orbital rendezvous and docking, during which two space vehicles are manoeuvred close together and joined or "docked".

The technique of orbital rendezvous — in orbit around the moon — will be a key manoeuvre in achieving the Apollo lunar landings.

Major elements in the Apollo program include (*Figure 3.1*):

• Design and construction of a three-man spacecraft, composed of three separate units, or modules.

• Development of powerful new launch vehicles, including the up-rated Saturn I and Saturn V. The 7.5 million pound thrust of the Saturn V is equal to that of 21 Atlas boosters (Atlas was the launch vehicle used for the Mercury manned orbital flights).

• Development of operational proficiency and facilities.

• Creation of the government-industrial team and the logistics base.

• Design and construction of test and launch facilities on an unprecedented scale.

The Apollo/Saturn launch vehicles, spacecraft, and instrumentation are under development and test today. The first unmanned flight of the Apollo spacecraft and the uprated Saturn I launch vehicle took place on February 26, 1966. This was a major milestone in the Apollo program. Apollo astronauts are in training

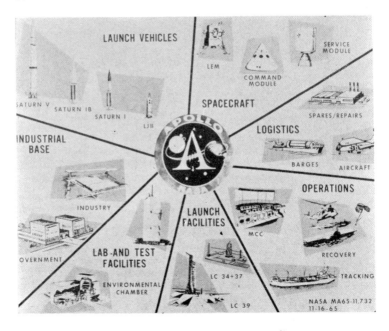

Figure 3.1. The major elements of the Apollo program.

for the manned earth orbital flights scheduled to be launched by the uprated Saturn I in 1967 and the Saturn V in 1968, leading to the manned lunar landing mission.

Barring unforeseen setbacks, the Apollo Program will fulfil the timetable that the late President Kennedy set in his message to Congress in May 1961, and meet the goal he gave America — to place men on the moon and return them safely to earth "within this decade".

Organization

The Apollo Program Office at NASA Headquarters, Washington, D.C., is responsible for the overall direction of the Apollo design, development and manufacturing effort in which all three Manned Space Flight Centres participate. The Marshall Space Flight Centre in Huntsville, Alabama, is responsible for development of the Saturn series of launch vehicles and engines, as well as associated ground support equipment and flight operations support. The Manned Spacecraft Centre at Houston, Texas, is responsible for development of the Apollo spacecraft and ground support equipment, space flight crew training, and support of manned space flight missions. Kennedy Space Centre at Merritt Island, Florida, is responsible for Apollo launch operations, facilities and common ground support equipment.

Support for the Apollo program is also received from various other NASA centres and offices. In addition, a number of major contractors are involved in the Apollo Program. The Apollo team today adds up to more than a quarter of a million people throughout government, industry and the academic community.

Design and development

The basic Saturn I, first of the Saturn series of launch vehicles, was first flown in October 1961. Since then, nine more basic Saturn I vehicles were launched. All ten flights were successful. Evolutionary design changes continued throughout the series, although the final four flights were considered operational flights. The sixth and seventh launches lifted a test Apollo "boilerplate" spacecraft into earth orbit demonstrating physical compatibility of the launch vehicle and spacecraft as well as testing a number of sub-systems. The eighth, ninth and tenth flights each boosted a Pegasus meteoroid detection satellite into long-duration earth orbital flights, to measure the intensity of micrometeoroids in space in order to assure adequate safeguards for the Apollo spacecraft.

The design of the second vehicle in the Saturn series, the uprated Saturn I launch vehicle, was completed in 1964, using the basic Saturn I technology. Design of the first Apollo spacecraft for the preliminary earth orbital flights was also completed in 1964. As noted earlier, the combined Apollo/Uprated Saturn I space vehicle had its first flight in February 1966. Within the next six months, two additional flights of this vehicle were successfully accomplished.

Design of the Saturn V launch vehicle and the Block II Apollo spacecraft, to be used for the actual lunar missions, was completed in 1965.

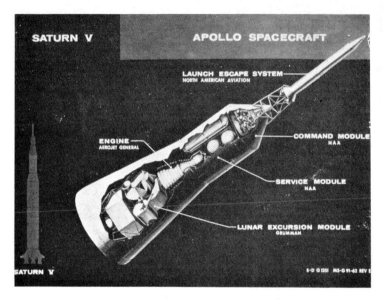

Figure 3.2. The Apollo spacecraft.

The design of the Apollo/Saturn space vehicles is sufficiently conservative to provide for contingencies arising from information obtained from early development flights. This conservatism is shown in the margins of the design itself. Flexibility has been retained to allow changes in such subsystems as the Lunar Module landing gear and the Service Module outer shell.

Apollo spacecraft

The Apollo spacecraft is 82 feet tall and weighs about 47 tons (*Figure 3.2*). It is divided into three separable units, or modules, and a launch escape system.

Launch escape tower

On the top is a launch escape system tower with rocket engines, much like that of Mercury. The Apollo launch escape tower is 34 feet tall and weighs 6,600 pounds. This tower gives the Apollo spacecraft — without its booster — a total height of some 82 feet

— almost as tall as the combined Mercury-Atlas vehicle that orbited John Glenn.

The system would be used only in a launch emergency situation. Impending trouble is automatically indicated to the astronauts in the Command Module by indicator lights. Upon sensing an imminent catastrophe, the Command Module and tower are separated from the rest of the space vehicle by astronaut command with explosive bolts. They are propelled clear of the remainder of the vehicle by the 155,000 pound thrust of the launch escape motor while being pitched over from its vertical trajectory by the pitch control motor. At the proper time the fairing at the nose of the rocket motor extends to form canards which cause the combination to reverse itself placing the Command Module forward. The tower is then jettisoned, the earth-landing system is exposed, and the three large parachutes are deployed.

Command module

Immediately underneath the Launch Escape System is the Command Module, the only section that returns to earth (*Figure 3.3*). Along with the Service Module, it has been designed and manufactured in two configurations, Block I and Block II. The earlier configuration will be used in earth orbital work. The latter, Block II, is nearly identical in appearance but incorporates later design modifications. Only the Block II configuration is suitable for lunar flights. The Command Module contains the crew's living compartment, plus all controls for the various in-flight manoeuvres including an extensive guidance and navigation system and a stabilization and control system. Through 12 small reaction motors dispersed on the periphery of the Command Module, as well as on the sides of the Service Module, the assembled structure can be made to assume and hold any orientation within very close tolerances. Shaped like a flattened cone, this module has a bottom width of 13 feet and stands about 11 feet high. Take-off weight is about 11,000 pounds. The double walled pressurized chamber has three windows in front of the astronauts' couches, and two side windows. It is capped with an integral nose section which contains the forward access tunnel to the Lunar Module. Around this tunnel are packaged the three parachutes of the earth landing

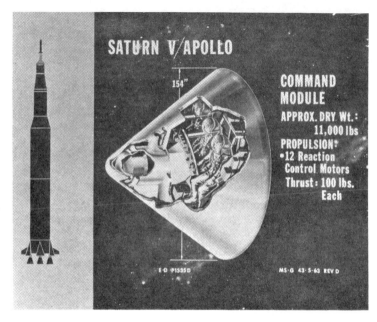

Figure 3.3.   The Saturn V/Apollo — Command Module.

system, mortars to deploy these parachutes and all of the recovery equipment. The Command Module also incorporates an ablative heat shield similar to that of the Gemini and Mercury spacecraft which dissipates the extreme heat of re-entry into the earth's atmosphere.

As with Gemini, the Apollo Environmental Control System supplies pure oxygen in the cabin at 5 pounds per square inch, conditioned to a temperature of approximately 75 degrees with a humidity index between 40 and 70 percent. The Apollo Command Module is a compact version of a pilot cockpit for three astronauts. It is more extensively equipped for human comfort than either the Mercury or Gemini spacecraft.

Depending primarily upon the Service Module for its support, the Command Module includes those redundant items which permit it to function during re-entry separated from the supporting module.

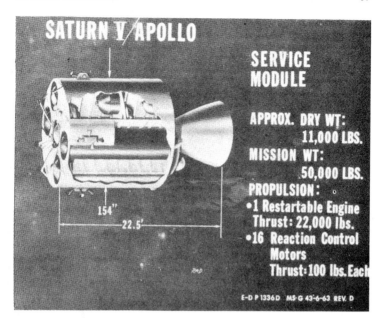

Figure 3.4. The Saturn V/Apollo — Service Module.

A separate electric power system of batteries, environment control system, consumables, water, fuel and oxidizer for the reaction control system are carried, to mention a few.

Service module

Beneath the crew's Command Module is the Service Module (*Figure 3.4*), a cylindrical unit 13 feet in diameter and 14 feet tall, weighing 50,000 pounds. The interior is unsymmetrically divided into six sectors by radial beams. One of these sectors is devoid of equipment. This has been done to permit the installation of individual palletized in-flight experiments to be determined at a later date. The main apparatus within is the primary propulsion system, which produces 22,000 pounds of thrust. Its stop-and-restart engine is used for several important manoeuvres — mid-course correction during the outward-bound phase, slowing down to go into lunar orbit, take-off from lunar orbit to earth, and mid-course corrections while earthbound. The Service Module also contains the primary electrical power supply for the spacecraft. It is made up of three fuel cells, any two of which can supply the full requirements. One fuel cell is adequate for emergency power only. The by-product of this electrical generation is water which will be the source of drinking water for the astronauts. This module also houses the main supplies of the Environmental Control System, the cryogenics for the fuel cells and the fuel and oxidizer for the service engine. On the outer surface of this module are the Electrical Power System and Environmental Control System radiators used to dissipate the heat generated in these systems. The groups of four reaction control motors, called "quads", function to position the combined Command and Service Modules in roll, pitch and yaw, according to commands from the Stabilization and Control System.

Having fulfilled all these functions during the round trip, the Service Module is finally jettisoned just before the Command Module re-enters the earth's atmosphere.

Lunar module

The Lunar Module (*Figure 3.5*), which weighs approximately 30,000 pounds, is the flight unit that will detach from the orbiting Command and Service Modules and descend to the moon's surface with two of the three astronauts aboard. It has two windows, hatches for astronaut ingress and egress, and landing gear struts for support after lunar touchdown.

The Lunar Module has its own complete guidance, propulsion, computer, control, communications, and environmental control systems, all with one or more back-up systems. These precautions are necessary because landing on the moon will be the lunar mission's most critical phase.

The Lunar Module's descent propulsion system can be throttled. Its rocket engine's thrust power can be varied from a low of 1,050 pounds to a high of 10,500 pounds so as to control the lunar touchdown flight with great precision. The astronauts will utilize this engine for the actual lunar landing.

The final descent can be slowed to just a few feet per second. The Lunar Module's four jointed steeltruss legs contain crushable

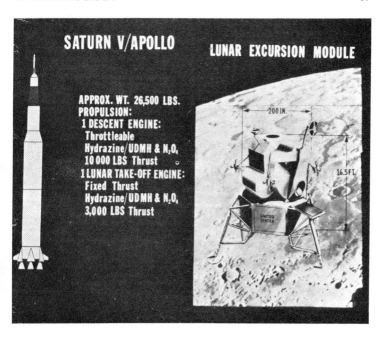

Figure 3.5.   The   Saturn V/Apollo, showing the Lunar Excursion Module.

material designed to absorb the landing shock without adverse effects to the craft or crew. The legs are also designed to land on slopes up to 12 degrees and retain balance of the spacecraft in this position.

The Lunar Module is a two-stage vehicle. The lower stage contains the descent engine and the landing gear for lunar landing. This is detachable for the lunar take-off and forms the "launch platform" for the upper stage, which is a cabin for the astronauts. Attached to the upper stage, or astronauts' cabin, is the ascent engine to propel the stage from the lunar surface to the awaiting Command and Service Module in lunar orbit. Once the rendezvous has been made and the astronauts and their lunar samples have been transferred to the Command Module, the Lunar Module is discarded and left in a lunar orbit.

Guidance and navigation

The moon-bound Apollo's space navigation system includes two relatively conventional units — an inertial guidance platform, and a flight computer. A third unit will be an optical space sextant with which the astronauts will take sightings of the earth, Moon and reference stars to check-out their position before each manoeuvre with their rocket engines, during any leg of the round trip.

Launch vehicles

Three Saturn launch vehicles are included in the Apollo Program (*Figure 3.6*). Development and operations of the first of the Saturn series, the basic Saturn I, was completed in July, 1965, with ten successful launches in ten attempts.

Saturn I developed 1.5 million pounds of thrust in its first stage through the clustering of eight rocket engines burning refined

Figure 3.6. The three Saturn launch vehicles in the Apollo Program.

Figure 3.7. The NASA's first Saturn 1B rocket successfully launched in February, 1966. The 45,900 lb. spacecraft was the heaviest "payload" launched to that time by NASA. This two-stage rocket will be used later in conjunction with manned spacecraft and in lunar landing.

kerosene and liquid oxygen (LOX). Its second stage had six engines burning liquid hydrogen and LOX, producing 90,000 pounds total thrust. This two-stage vehicle delivered a payload of 11 tons into low earth orbit. As noted earlier, the last three flights carried the Pegasus micro-meteoroid detection satellite into orbit.

The uprated Saturn I, or Saturn IB, has an improved first stage version of the Saturn I, and a new and more powerful second stage. The uprated Saturn I will launch the first manned Apollo flights into earth orbit. *Figure 3.7* shows the first launch of the Apollo/Uprated Saturn I space vehicle in February 1966.

The second stage has one liquid hydrogen — LOX-burning engine of 205,000 pounds thrust. Payload capability in low earth orbit for the uprated Saturn I will be 20 tons, enough to launch the Apollo spacecraft into earth orbit to allow the crew to practise rendezvous and docking.

The Saturn V is a vehicle of gigantic size and power. The first stage, will have a diameter of 33 feet and will be powered by a cluster of five engines, each developing thrust equal to the Saturn I's 1.5 million pounds, for a total of 7.5 million pounds. The second stage, clustering five engines, will furnish 1 million pounds of thrust. The third stage will be essentially the same as the uprated Saturn I's second stage, generating 205,000 pounds of thrust.

This immense three-stage booster, topped by the three-module Apollo spacecraft plus escape tower, will stand 365 feet high at the launch pad and weigh 6 million pounds fully fuelled (*Figure 3.8*).

The mighty Saturn V launch vehicle will be capable of delivering more than 140 tons into earth orbit — more than the weight of a fully loaded jet-liner, and the equivalent of 40 Gemini spacecraft — or of driving 48 tons — the equivalent of two freight cars — to the moon.

Test and launch facilities

In the development testing of the Apollo flight hardware, NASA was faced with the decision of how much testing could be conducted on the ground as compared with how much flight testing

Figure 3.8. The three-stage booster, topped by the three-module Apollo spacecraft, plus escape tower, stands 365 feet high and weighs 6,000,000 lb. fully loaded.

would be required to qualify the flight systems. In the early phase of rocket propulsion and launch vehicle technology, it was necessary to conduct a considerable number of flight tests to develop the flight system. In these early days, the philosophy of testing was to launch, fix, and launch again to verify the fix. As technical knowledge has been gained in the space environment, the number of launches to complete development has been steadily reduced. This is so because NASA has learned how to reproduce the space environment for ground testing and to achieve advances in equipment design and performance. Therefore, in the Apollo Program NASA is conducting much ground testing and using the flight tests for final verification. This approach has been confirmed by the experience with the Saturn I series of launch vehicles where 13 launches have been made and 13 successes have been achieved. This unprecedent-

*Figure 3.9. The Marshall Space Flight Centre, Huntsville Alabama,
Test Area.*

ed record of success reflects the results of heavy emphasis on
extensive ground testing at all equipment levels.

This ground testing philosophy plus the enormous size and power
of the Apollo hardware has given rise to a set of facilities unparalleled in scope by earlier U.S. space programs. These facilities
are to be found in widely distributed parts of the United States.

Major spacecraft test facilities are located at the White Sands
Test Facility in New Mexico. The Saturn S-IVB stage, which is the
second stage of the uprated Saturn I and the third stage of the
Saturn V, is tested in facilities located at Sacramento, California.
At the Marshall Space Flight Centre in Huntsville, Alabama,
facilities have been built for research and development test firings
of the Saturn V first stage and for dynamic testing of the Apollo/
Saturn V space vehicle (*Figure 3.9*). At the Mississippi Test Facility
acceptance test firings of Saturn V first and second stages are
conducted (*Figure 3.10*). These test facilities are but a few examples
of the overall facility requirements of the Apollo program. For
launch operations, an enormous Apollo/Saturn V launch facility,
called "Launch Complex 39", has been constructed at the United
States "space-port" at the John F. Kennedy Space Centre in Florida.

Figure 3.10. The Mississippi Test Facility — Saturn V Second Stage Static Test Stand.

Here the entire Apollo/Saturn V space vehicle is assembled some 3½ miles from the launch pad in the Vehicle Assembly Building — the largest building in the world *(Figure 3.11)*. This building stands over 525 feet high. It is almost as wide as it is tall, is 716 feet in length, and has an internal volume of over 129,000,000 cubic feet. The launch vehicle and spacecraft are then moved in a vertical position to the launch pad on the world's largest and heaviest land vehicle, a tractor-crawler with a flat horizontal surface almost the size of a football field. *Figure 3.12* shows the first "roll-out" of this vehicle, carrying a test model of the Apollo/Saturn V, from the Vehicle Assembly Building to the launch pad. This milestone "earth-bound" trip took place on May 25, 1966.

Astronaut garments

The Apollo crewmen will have different garments for wear at different times. On the outward bound trip, two of the men (in rotation with the third) will wear "constant wear garments", which are unpressurized and provide more comfort and ease of movement than the Apollo space suit.

*Figure 3.11. The Kennedy Space Centre Vehicle Assembly Building —
Launch Complex 39.*

The third man will be in the Apollo space suit (*Figure 3.13*), featuring flexible joints for ease in walking, bending, or moving his limbs, and a helmet with a pivoted visor for quick closing and sealing.

The same space suit will be worn by the two Lunar Module astronauts who step forth on the moon. But underneath will be a special undergarment interwoven with a fine network of water-circulating tubes to carry away body heat. A "thermal garment", a white "monk-like" coverall with hood, which protects the astronaut from the airless moon's blistering sunshine, is worn over the entire spacesuit. Finally, a "meteoroid cape" on his back will fend off small micrometeoroid dust which may fall on the moon at high speed. Larger meteoroids that would penetrate the cape are calculated to be extremely rare.

An important added unit of the Apollo space suit system will be the strap-on backpack for lunar exploration, including 4-hour oxygen supply, two-way radio, heating dumping radiator, and dosimeter. Partial radiation protection is built into the space suit fabric

Figure 3.12. The 365-foot-high Apollo-Saturn V facilities vehicle is here shown being moved from the vehicle assembly building and will be transported to the launch complex. This vehicle, Apollo Saturn 500-F, will never make the journey to the moon; it is being used to verify launch facilities, train launch crews and develop test and checkout procedures.

Figure 3.13. The Apollo space suit.

Figure 3.14. Training activities in the Apollo Program.

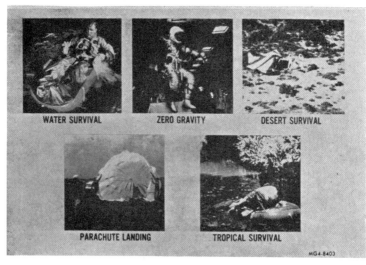

Astronaut training

Astronaut training for the Apollo Program includes the "basic space training" of the Mercury and Gemini Programs, including practice in survival techniques in the water, desert and tropics; experience in the weightless environment, and so forth *(Figure 3.14)*. In addition, new Apollo specialties are being added from time to time. Among them are:

● "Moon Trips" in simulator trainers that create the realistic illusion of travel through space, descent on the moon, and return to earth.

● "Lunar Obstacle Course", a 328-foot-wide simulation of the moon's rugged surface, complete with craters up to 50 feet wide and 15 feet deep, large boulders, a dust layer, and fissures over which to jump. A suspension harness reduces the astronaut's weight to the moon's value of 25 or 30 pounds, $\frac{1}{6}$ of his earth weight. The trainee, making long leaps across this moon-patch, experiences conditions near to those he will meet on the moon.

Figure 3.15. The network of tracking stations established around the world for Project Mercury.

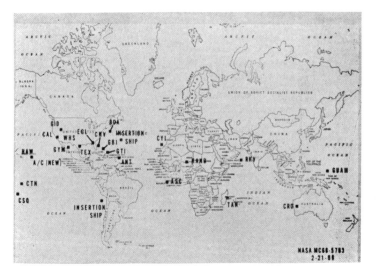

Figure 3.16. Manned Spacecraft Centre, showing the Mission Control Centre, Houston, Texas.

• "Space Suit Workouts", during which astronauts wear experimental Apollo pressure garments to practise movements such as walking, bending, and opening of visor.

Manned Spaceflight Tracking Network

A network of tracking stations was established around the world for Project Mercury. This network was augmented for Gemini and is being further augmented for Apollo (*Figure 3.15*). Ground stations and ships are included. Three of the ground stations will be linked directly to the Mission Control Centre in Houston by a communication satellite. *Figure 3.16* shows the Houston Control Centre in operation during the course of a mission.

All these stations will track and monitor the Apollo spacecraft at the beginning and end of the lunar mission — during launch into earth orbit and during the final re-entry after return from the moon.

As soon as the spacecraft leaves earth orbit beyond normal tracking station range, tracking will switch to stations located at Goldstone, California; Madrid, Spain; and Carnarvon, Australia.

Figure 3.17. An aerial view of the tracking station at Carnarvon, Western Australia.

These stations are situated about 120° apart (going east and west), so that as the rotating earth cuts off one station's direct line contact with a deep space vehicle, the next station rises above the horizon and takes over.

Unbroken day and night surveillance of the Apollo spacecraft can thus be kept by those stations. Their huge 85-foot dish antennas and sensitive equipment are similar in appearance to those which have received signals from millions of miles away in space (e.g., Mariner/Venus, Mariner/Mars).

When the returning Apollo speeds toward earth at 25,000 miles per hour, the chain of land and ship tracking stations will gear in to monitor the vital re-entry and recovery operation.

Figure 3.17 shows an aerial view of the Manned Space Flight Tracking Station located at Carnarvon in North-West Australia. At the right is the radio frequency command and UHF voice systems used to send coded commands and maintain voice communication

Figure 3.18. Lift-off from launch pad.

Figure 3.19. Saturn V — first stage separation.

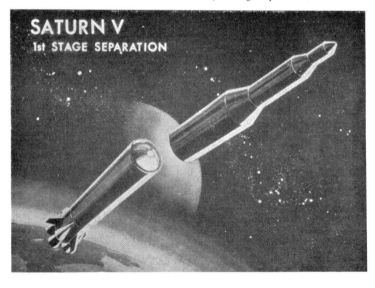

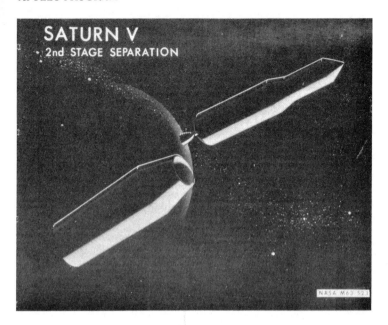

SATURN V
2nd STAGE SEPARATION

NASA M63 523

Figure 3.20.

with the spacecraft. The system is fed information by the digital command system for such missions as resetting the spacecraft's clock, firing the retrorockets, etc.

Lunar landing mission

Sometime before the end of this decade, the United States will send two astronauts to the surface of the moon. The lunar journey will begin at Launch Complex 39 at NASA's Kennedy Space Centre. Here the assembled Apollo/Saturn V space vehicle is moved by the crawler-transporter from the Vehicle Assembly Building out to the launch pad, some $3\frac{1}{2}$ miles away. At the pad, the mammoth Saturn V moon rocket and Apollo spacecraft combination towers as high as a 36-storey building, and weighs as much as a Nautilus submarine or a light cruiser.

At lift-off (*Figure 3.18*) the five engines of the first stage flame into life, and the giant rocket starts consuming its fuel at the rate of almost 3,700 gallons per second. In only 2½ minutes the rocket has consumed the entire 550,000 gallons of fuel in the first stage.

At approximately 30 miles altitude the first stage separates (*Figures 3.19*) and the five engines of the second stage ignite, providing an additional one million pounds of thrust. After the second stage burns and separates (*Figure 3.20*), the third stage ignites and places itself and the spacecraft into an earth "parking" orbit about 100 miles high (*Figure 3.21*). After a thorough checkout of men and equipment, the third stage will re-ignite at the proper time to reach earth escape velocity (*Figure 3.22*).

As the spacecraft and third stage coast towards the moon, the combined Command and Service Modules push away from the Lunar Module, turn around in space and dock with the Lunar Module (*Figure 3.23*). After the manoeuvre is completed, the Saturn V third stage is discarded. The astronauts may, if necessary, fire the Service Module engine to make the proper corrections in their trajectory.

Figure 3.21.

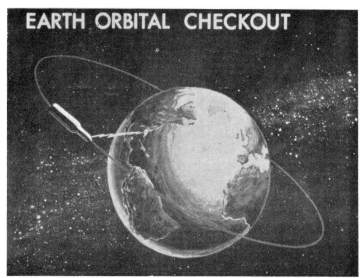

EARTH ORBITAL CHECKOUT

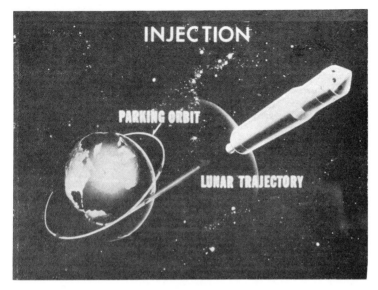

Figure 3.22.
Figure 3.23.

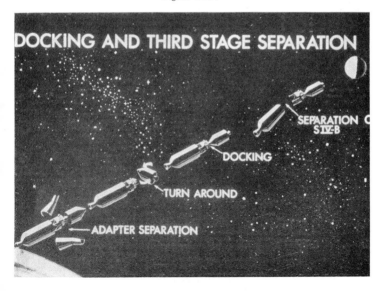

Figure 3.24.

Figure 3.25.

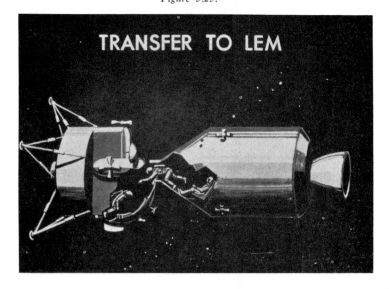

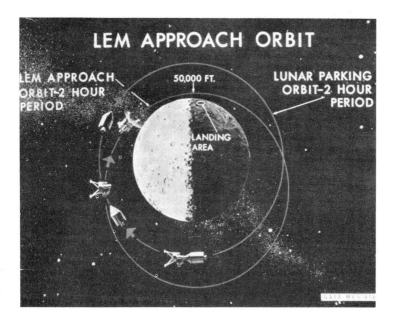

Figure 3.26.

Some 64 hours after leaving earth, as the spacecraft approaches the moon, the Service Module engine will be fired for about six minutes to brake the spacecraft into a circular lunar orbit (*Figure 3.24*). Two of the astronauts will crawl through the docking hatch into the Lunar Module (*Figure 3.25*), which will uncouple from the "mother" ship and descend to an elliptical orbit nearer the moon's surface (*Figure 3.26*). The Lunar Module coasts until an altitude of about 50,000 feet is reached and powered descent begins (*Figure 3.27*). Powered descent continues to the hover altitude of about 300 feet, when either a manual or automatic hover-to-touch-down is completed (*Figure 3.28*).

Present plans call for the two Lunar Module astronauts to stay about 18 hours on the moon's surface. After checking all systems on the Lunar Module, the two astronauts will disembark through the docking door and begin the manned exploration of the moon (*Figure 3.29*). During their 18-hour stay-time, the astronauts will

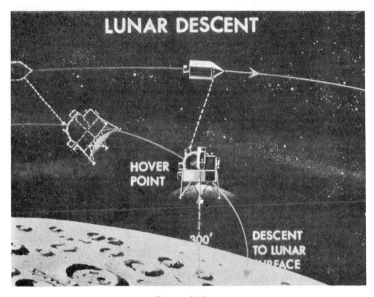

Figure 3.27.

Figure 3.28.

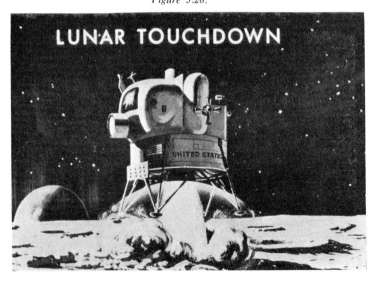

Figure 3.29.

perform two explorations of three hours each, providing a total of 12 man-hours on the moon. As a margin of safety, their life-support backpacks will be good for four hours, supplying oxygen, air conditioning, and cooling. In between these two periods of exploration, the astronauts will return to the Lunar Module for a period of about seven hours, during which they will eat, sleep, and recharge their backpacks.

The astronauts will perform a number of scientific experiments on the surface of the moon. Collection of surface and terrain samples for return to earth is the most important single scientific objective, and will therefore be completed first and in the most expeditious manner during the first period of exploration. This will permit post-mission analysis regarding basic questions in the fields of geochemistry, geology, and bioscience.

Second in importance only to sample collection is the deployment of the Apollo Lunar Surface Experiments Package (ALSEP), to

Figure 3.30.

obtain continued scientific measurements and recording of lunar phenomena for one year after the departure of the astronauts. The second phase of the first excursion will thus be devoted to the deployment and emplacement of the ALSEP. This package must be deployed approximately 300 feet from the Lunar Module in order to avoid the influences of the ascent engine operation, dust, and exhaust flow patterns.

The ALSEP will contain both a passive and an active seismometer, a magnetometer, an ion detector, and instruments to measure solar wind and heat flow.

The second period of exploration will be devoted to field geology. Activities conducted during this phase will include systematic examination, photographing, description, and collection of geologic samples and units, and determination of field relations such as shape, size, range, and patterns of alignment or distribution of all types of topographic features. Near and far field photography, mapping of

Figure 3.31.

major features and landmarks, and measurement of the diameter of visible craters will be conducted. If the landing site allows, the astronauts will also photograph the "full earth", equal in brightness to 80 full moons.

It should be emphasized that throughout the entire mission, the astronauts will be alert to the possibility of lunar phenomena unsuspected by earthly scientists. Visual observation is inherent, starting with the initial visual contact with the moon while still in-flight and extending throughout the operational and scientific activities of the lunar stay until departure.

When the time arrives for rejoining the orbiting Command and Service Module the lower stage of the Lunar Module serves as a launching pad, and is left behind on the surface of the moon (*Figure 3.30*).

Figure 3.32.

Timing the launch to co-ordinate with the Command and Service Module, the Lunar Module ascent stage will meet it 83 miles high for rendezvous and docking (*Figure 3.31*). After the three astronauts are once again together in the Command and Service Module, the Lunar Module is jettisoned and left in lunar orbit. The Service Module's rocket engine is ignited to build up to lunar escape velocity (*Figure 3.32*). Some 29,000 miles outward, the spacecraft passes out of the moon's gravitational field. Then, under the earth's pull, the Command and Service Module returns at ever mounting speed. At about 198 hours after launch, the spacecraft reaches the same velocity with which it left earth — about 24,600 miles per hour.

After the Service Module's propulsion has been used for final course corrections, this segment is jettisoned and the Command Module plunges into the earth's atmosphere (*Figure 3.33*).

Above: Figure 3.33. Below: Figure 3.34.

With a velocity of 24,600 miles per hour, Apollo re-entry will be at a higher speed than Gemini and Mercury, which were less than 17,000 miles per hour. Retrorockets are not used, since a de-orbiting manoeuvre is not required. Apollo's air friction heat will be 5,000 degrees Fahrenheit, but, quite like Mercury and Gemini, the bottom heat-shield protects the crew as air resistance rapidly cuts velocity to a safe point for parachute deployment and landing (*Figure 3.34*).

From earth launch to earth touchdown, the total trip time will be about 8 days.

Thus, we have witnessed a typical Apollo mission—landing men on the moon and returning them safely to the earth. But I want to emphasize that this lunar mission is only one of many possible missions using the capabilities which are being created in the Apollo Program. In the Apollo Program, the United States is developing the capability to send manned vehicles anywhere within a zone extending at least a quarter-million miles from the earth.

The elements being created in the Apollo Program thus constitute a resource of incalculable and enduring value which will provide a broad capability for operation in space. With this capability, it will be possible to carry out a wide variety of missions of practical and scientific value. These future manned space missions will be conducted in earth orbit, in lunar orbit, and on the lunar surface.

In the first time phase of development beyond the initial Apollo lunar landings is the Apollo Applications Program, which represents maximum utilization of the equipment and experience gained in the Apollo Program. I will discuss this Program, along with the wide spectrum of other possible missions of the future, in my next and final lecture.

CHAPTER 4

The Future

The first three lectures in this series have dealt with the present U.S. space program. The first covered the background of the program and the events associated with its establishment. The second reported the results of the first two man-in-space programs, Mercury and Gemini. The third reviewed the significance, content and status of the Apollo program leading to the beginning of manned lunar exploration.

This final lecture will consider the alternatives that lie ahead as the work to achieve the Apollo program objectives proceeds toward a conclusion. It will discuss the prospects for continued international competition and international co-operation, the benefits from our space program, experiments, the opportunities for exploiting the capabilities provided by the Apollo program, and the possible programs that might follow. Let us turn first, therefore, to the competitive aspects of the situation.

INTERNATIONAL COMPETITION

As observed in the first lecture, the era of space exploration began in an atmosphere of intense international competition. This competition has involved more than national prestige and pride. The industrial, scientific and engineering communities in a number of countries of the world have become increasingly concerned about the technological leadership they believe is accruing to the United States and the Soviet Union as the result of their space programs.

The United States has been interested from the beginning in co-operating with other countries in space exploration and obtaining benefits for all mankind. Co-operative efforts have been undertaken with Australia and more than seventy other nations. The success of these programs forms a solid base for expanding scientific and

LAUNCH VEHICLE POWER

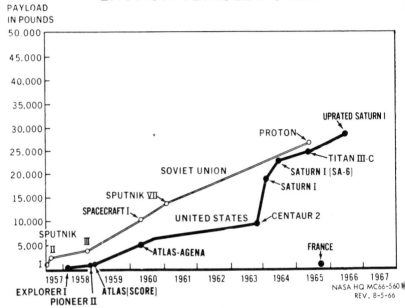

Figure 4.1.

technical co-operation to tackle problems in many areas of common international interest here on earth.

The determination of technically advanced countries to participate in space activity is illustrated by the co-operative efforts of the European Launcher Development Organization — of which Australia is a member as you know — in developing at the Woomera range an independent capability to launch satellites into orbit. In addition, France has launched satellites from its base in the Sahara Desert, and Japan is moving forward with plans to launch a satellite from its site at Kagoshima.

In addition to these national efforts, Canada, Great Britain, France, Italy and Germany are engaged in bilateral space projects with NASA, and the European Space Research Organization (which includes Great Britain, France, Italy and Germany) is engaged in satellite projects in co-operation with the United States.

The desire for technological leadership—and through it *ideological* leadership, but without significant co-operation with other countries — is causing the Soviet Union to invest resources that are of the same order as ours. As a result of these investments the pace of the Soviet space program almost doubled in 1965, including the launching of a new booster of which we still do not know the full potential.

Since the first satellites were launched, both the United States and the Soviet Union have continued to increase the power of their launch vehicles (*Figure 4.1*). The most recent significant event was the success of the uprated Saturn I launch vehicle in orbiting the heaviest weight to date on July 5, 1966. The flight demonstrated that this vehicle is capable of placing 29,000 pounds in orbit, exclusive of the final stage of the launch vehicle. The comparable figure announced by the Soviet Union for its Proton launch vehicle is 25,000 pounds.

Up to now, four different craft have been used in the Soviet and American program to place man in space *(Figure 4.2)*. The first was the one-seat Soviet Vostok, which carried men five times and a woman once. Then there was our one-man Mercury, which placed men in orbit four times. The next Soviet spacecraft was the Voskhod, flown twice — the first time with three men and the second with two. Then our two-man Gemini, which has been flown eight times with men. The latest spacecraft, which has not yet flown men, is our three-man Apollo.

The Soviets have made it clear that they intend to continue the competition in space. An example of the many statements they have made was that of Lt.-Col. Vladimir Komarov, commander of the three-man Voskhod I mission, during a visit to a Japanese school in July, 1966. He is reported to have said:

"The problem now is how to bring back to earth an exploring machine which has been soft-landed on the moon. In the case of a trip to the moon by man, a guarantee is needed that he can return safely to earth, and the Soviet Union will check this technology soon with an unmanned moon-exploring machine. Next in the program will be a similar try with a spaceship carrying a dog . . . I can state positively that the Soviet Union will not be beaten by the United States in the race for a human to go to the moon."

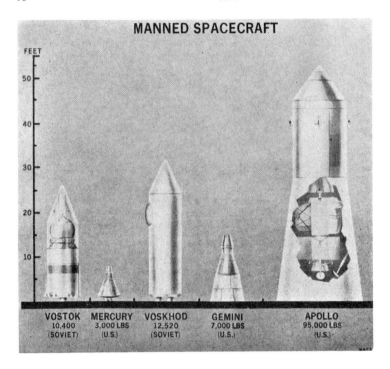

Figure 4.2.

We prefer not to consider it as a race. NASA programs are geared to scientific needs and represent a logically phased step-by-step solution to a series of very difficult scientific and engineering problems. However, we certainly do keep Soviet competition in mind as we study what next steps to take in the U.S. space program.

BENEFITS FROM OUR SPACE PROGRAM

What benefits have we received from our explorations into space, in addition to the accomplishment of the program goals? There are hundreds of examples; I will mention but a few.

The use of computers is prevalent throughout industry and government. They make it possible to produce more and to perform routine, time-consuming work at less expense and with fewer people. This clearly gives more people more time to use, to the fullest extent, their ability to think and to create.

Transistors and other very small components are facilitating the rapid introduction of an enormous quantity of new products in the electronic industry.

Reliability is becoming more and more of a by-word in the production of consumer goods. The 50,000-mile guarantee is standard practice with automobile manufacturers. Comparable improvements in reliability are being developed by household appliance manufacturers.

Space communication is a commercial enterprise. Weather observation from space is being conducted on an operational basis.

All-weather navigation is provided to ships at sea by navigation satellites.

Photographs from space have increased man's knowledge of the earth. Medicine has improved its understanding of the workings of the human body. In fact, the development of practical applications of space technology is one of the principal objectives of the space program.

Also being explored is the use of space technology, as well as analytical and management techniques, to solve more mundane earthly problems. For example, both government and industry in the United States are examining how systems analysis techniques can be applied to such problems as integrated air, rail and highway transportation; disposal of solid, liquid and gaseous wastes; and the management of the vast quantities of information needed to run our complex civilization.

EXPERIMENTS IN SPACE

Experiments conducted in the Mercury and Gemini programs have demonstrated that man plays successively more advanced roles as our ability to operate in space develops. At first, he was merely a sensor, using his eyes, ears and touch to supplement his instruments. Then he became a manipulator, steering his craft and pointing instruments. Next, he was an evaluator, judging on the scene what his senses and equipment told him, to determine what steps to take next. Now, he has become an investigator, responding creatively to unexpected situations, postulating theories and hypotheses, and devising systematic measurements. To assure the continued availability of space investigators, scientist-astronauts have been and will continue to be added to the space program.

Experiments in the space program are scheduled after thorough review by specialists in the appropriate scientific and technical disciplines. The process is similar for both the manned and the unmanned flight programs. An experiment is more likely to be assigned to a manned flight if the presence of the astronaut is likely to contribute to its chances of success, or if the equipment is so heavy or bulky that the power of a manned vehicle is required to place it in space. The planning of experiments for manned space flight programs is based on the experience and results of unmanned programs.

EXPLOITING APOLLO CAPABILITY

The Apollo program is not limited only to manned lunar landings. It is advancing U.S. capability in space across a broad front. There are many elements to this capability. The program is providing launch vehicles, spacecraft, test and launch facilities, mission control facilities, a world-wide communications network and recovery techniques applicable to other programs, in addition to a highly skilled, experienced government-industry team of almost 300,000 people.

The launch vehicle is an extremely important item in this capability. The uprated Saturn I is now able to place 35,000 pounds in orbit and this total will soon rise to 40,000 pounds. The Saturn V will provide the power to place more than 280,000 pounds in earth orbit.

The Apollo spacecraft is another significant contribution. It is a three-man craft able to carry out much more extensive manoeuvres than Gemini, and to extend our sphere of operations outward a quarter of a million miles from earth. The two-man lunar module, our first spacecraft intended wholly for flight beyond the earth's atmosphere, will enable us for the first time to conduct a number of operations in earth orbit and beyond.

A major area of capability consists of operational skills. We are developing competence in vehicle assembly and automatic checkout, in launching on time, in tracking and calculating orbits with

APOLLO CAPABILITY EXPLOITATION PROGRAM

CONSIDERATIONS

- **LUNAR LANDING THIS DECADE -- PRIMARY OBJECTIVE OF MANNED SPACE FLIGHT**

- **PROGRAM EXTENSIONS**
    - **MANNED FLIGHTS**
        - **EARTH ORBIT OPERATIONS**
        - **LUNAR EXPLORATION OPERATIONS**
    - **UNMANNED FLIGHTS**
        - **SCIENCE AND TECHNOLOGY SATELLITES**
        - **PLANETARY EXPLORATION**

- **ONLY APOLLO HARDWARE--MODIFIED AS REQUIRED--WILL BE CONSIDERED FOR MANNED FLIGHT**

- **NO MODIFICATION TO LAUNCH VEHICLES**

- **COORDINATED DOD/NASA EFFORTS**

Figure 4.3.

NASA MA65-5433

precision in a few minutes, in telemetering and transmitting vast amounts of data, in making mid-course manoeuvres, in making lunar orbital captures and descent from such orbits, in landing on another astronomical body and taking off without the help of a ground crew, in accomplishing rendezvous in lunar orbit, in "lift-off" from lunar orbit, in returning to the earth's atmosphere at seven miles a second, in controlling the spacecraft's path of flight through the atmosphere, and in returning to the earth on land or water.

The initial studies of possible activities following the Apollo program led to the recommendation that we exploit the investment in the Apollo program by applying its wide range of possibilities to other potential missions (*Figure 4.3*). Utilizing these capabilities now under development will enable us to produce hardware and fly it for future missions at a small fraction of the initial development cost.

In these studies, we have kept in mind that the Apollo lunar landing is the primary mission objective for this decade. Program extensions considered have been manned flights in earth orbit and to the moon, and unmanned earth-orbital and planetary flights. Only Apollo hardware was considered for manned flight. Modifi-

PRESENT APOLLO CAPABILITY

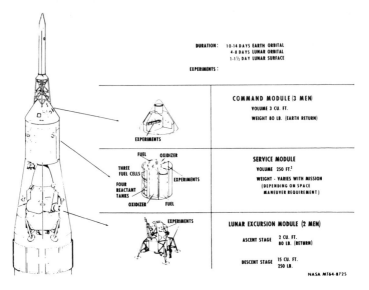

Figure 4.4.

cations as necessary were allowed in the spacecraft, but not in the launch vehicles. And we co-ordinated these studies closely with the Department of Defence.

The present Apollo spacecraft is capable of flying in any earth orbit for durations of 10 days to two weeks. With the present experimental payload capabilities *(Figure 4.4),* the command module can accommodate three cubic feet of experimental payload and can return to earth with up to 80 pounds of lunar material or other experimental payload. The service module can accommodate up to 250 cubic feet of experimental equipment. The weight limitation varies with the space manoeuvring requirement of the specific mission. The lunar module could provide an additional volume of 17 cubic feet for experimental payloads, weighing up to 330 pounds.

Now what can we do with the Apollo system besides the manned lunar landing? We can carry out a wide variety of flights in earth

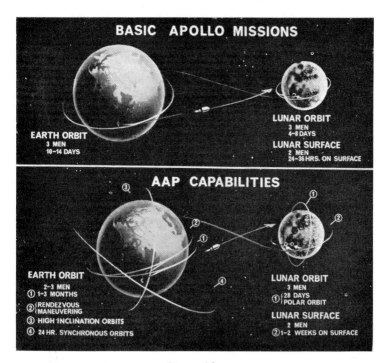

Figure 4.5.

orbit, in lunar orbit and to the lunar surface (*Figure 4.5*). The basic Apollo mission will develop the capability for three men to operate in earth orbit for up to 14 days. Basic Apollo will also develop the capability to place three men in lunar orbit for four to eight days if no landing is involved or two men on the lunar surface from 24 to 36 hours.

Added capabilities include the ability to place two or three men in earth orbit for six weeks on a single launch mission and up to three months through rendezvous resupply.

It is possible to place a manned spacecraft in a synchronous orbit over any point of the earth's equator so that it can maintain its position above a fixed point on the ground. This would be similar to the orbit, described in the first lecture, of the unmanned communication satellites.

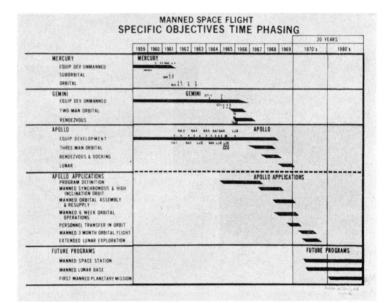

Figure 4.6.

It is also possible to place three men in lunar orbit for periods up to 28 days, and to sustain two men on the lunar surface for periods of up to two weeks. The studies indicate that these added capabilities are inherent in the Apollo system without major modifications.

Next, what about the time phasing of these potential activities? Under present plans (*Figure 4.6*), manned synchronous and high inclination orbits could begin by 1968, orbital assembly and resupply operations by 1969, and long duration flights in 1969. Extended lunar exploration missions could begin by 1971. These applications of Apollo capability would provide a firm operational and technological basis for future programs that might begin in the 1970s and 1980s.

In considering these possible applications of Apollo capability, it is important to keep in mind that the basic Apollo program has first call on the launch vehicles and spacecraft now being produced and tested. Only after the Apollo requirements have been met will alternate missions be considered. Thus it is possible that some of these activities will not begin as soon as indicated in the previous paragraph.

Now what objectives can be met in such a program? Over-all, the goal would be to provide a foundation for defining and understanding the next major step in space. Specifically (*Figure 4.7*), it appears to be feasible to achieve seven individual manned space flight objectives. These are synchronous and high-inclination orbit operations, orbital assembly and resupply, six-weeks orbital flight, personnel transfer in orbit, three-month orbital flight, extended-duration lunar exploration, and extended-duration operational, scientific and technological experiments. Study of the requirements of the various alternative future program options has indicated that one basic capability is needed regardless of the selection. That requirement is experience in long-duration manned flight. Consequently, the extension of flight duration of six weeks, three months and longer would rank high among the specific objectives of any post-Apollo program.

APOLLO APPLICATIONS
SPECIFIC OBJECTIVES

- **ATTAIN MANNED SYNCHRONOUS AND HIGH INCLINATION ORBIT OPERATIONS**

- **DEMONSTRATE MANNED ORBITAL ASSEMBLY AND RE-SUPPLY**

- **ATTAIN MANNED SIX WEEK ORBITAL FLIGHT CAPABILITY**

- **DEMONSTRATE PERSONNEL TRANSFER IN ORBIT**

- **DEVELOP THREE MONTH ORBITAL FLIGHT CAPABILITY**

- **CONDUCT EXTENDED DURATION LUNAR EXPLORATION**

- **CONDUCT OPERATIONAL, SCIENTIFIC, AND TECHNOLOGICAL EXPERIMENTS**

Figure 4.7.

MISSION I

EARTH ORBIT

ALTITUDE: 22,000 MILES   **INCLINATION:** 28.5⁰

DURATION: 14 DAYS

LAUNCH VEHICLE: SATURN V

OBJECTIVES AND EXPERIMENTS:

- DEVELOP ABILITY TO FLY SYNCHRONOUS ORBITS
- WIDE-RANGING WEATHER OBSERVATIONS
- DEPLOY LUNAR MODULE FOR LATER USE

Figures 4.8 and 4.9.

MISSION II

EARTH ORBIT

ALTITUDE: 200 MILES;   **INCLINATION:** 28.5⁰

DURATION: 14 TO 28 DAYS

LAUNCH VEHICLE: SATURN IB (TWO LAUNCHES)

FIRST PAYLOAD — COMMAND SERVICE MODULES (3 MEN)
SECOND PAYLOAD — LUNAR MODULE (UNMANNED)

OBJECTIVES AND EXPERIMENTS:

- DEVELOP ABILITY TO CONDUCT EARTH-ORBITAL RENDEZVOUS OPERATIONS
- RESUPPLY AND MISSION EXTENSION
- CREW AND MATERIAL TRANSFER
- OPERATIONS WITH SPENT BOOSTER STAGE
- EXTRAVEHICULAR ACTIVITY, MANEUVERING
- POWER-TOOL OPERATIONS

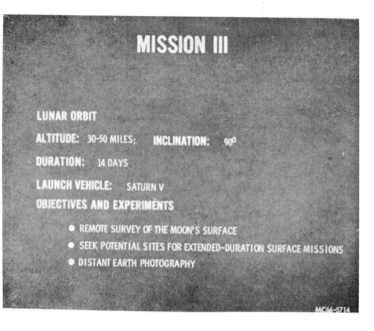

Figure 4.10.

In the event of a decision to exercise the option to carry out such a program, a number of missions could be flown. For example (*Figure 4.8*), with an Apollo spacecraft in a synchronous orbit, we could make astronomical observations with a large telescope, and we could use photographic and radar equipment for observations of the earth.

A second type of mission, in low earth orbit (*Figure 4.9*), would be to develop the procedures of resupply for a space station and to learn to transfer crew and materials between two spacecraft. Using the same techniques, it would also be possible to make rendezvous with a Pegasus unmanned satellite now in orbit detecting meteoroids. The sensing panels could be returned to earth for analysis.

A third kind of mission (*Figure 4.10*) would place the spacecraft in orbit about the moon for two weeks. Cameras and other sensing equipment could be used to survey the moon's surface for potential

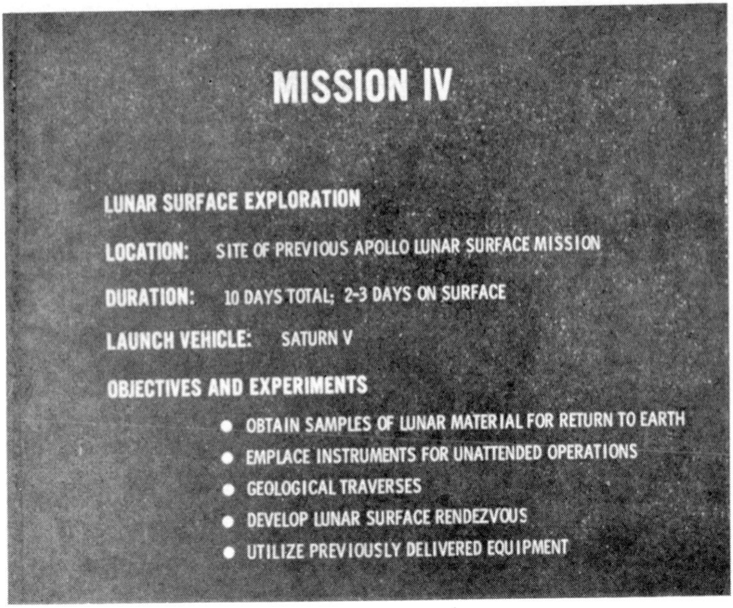

Figure 4.11.

landing sites for extended-duration surface exploration and for later analysis by land-based geologists.

A fourth possibility (*Figure 4.11*) would be to launch a spacecraft to the same place on the moon's surface where a landing has already been made. Thus it would be possible to use some of the equipment left behind on the previous flight, and to stay on the moon for several days.

Now the question is, why is it desirable to fly such missions? What are the possible applications of benefit to man on earth?

With the weight-lifting capabilities available (*Figure 4.12*), it would be possible to place both large antennae and powerful transmitters in stationary orbits. Manned with technicians, these stations would be capable of operating over long periods of time. With such equipment, it would be possible to bring live television to all countries of the world, and to receive it on ordinary home receivers.

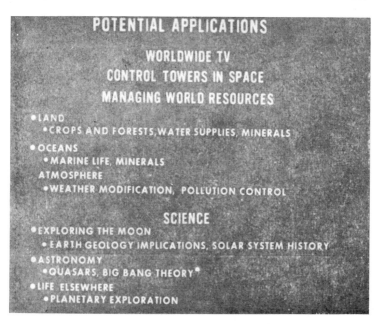

POTENTIAL APPLICATIONS

WORLDWIDE TV
CONTROL TOWERS IN SPACE
MANAGING WORLD RESOURCES

- LAND
  - CROPS AND FORESTS, WATER SUPPLIES, MINERALS
- OCEANS
  - MARINE LIFE, MINERALS
- ATMOSPHERE
  - WEATHER MODIFICATION, POLLUTION CONTROL

SCIENCE
- EXPLORING THE MOON
  - EARTH GEOLOGY IMPLICATIONS, SOLAR SYSTEM HISTORY
- ASTRONOMY
  - QUASARS, BIG BANG THEORY*
- LIFE ELSEWHERE
  - PLANETARY EXPLORATION

Figure 4.12.

An exciting related application is in the early establishment of control towers in space, both for aircraft and for ocean-going ships. From such vantage points it would be possible to provide communications and all-weather navigational systems over wide areas which are now unavailable to earthbound control systems.

An entire group of potential applications is based on the use of observations and actions by human operators in space to make fuller use of the resources of the earth, considered on a planet-wide basis. These resources consist, of course, of the land, the oceans, and the atmosphere.

The use of photography and other forms of remote sensing could supply agriculture with the information it needs on current status of crops and forests on a continental and even a world-wide basis, so that the techniques of modern analysis might be applied to cope with the food needs of an exploding world population.

APOLLO APPLICATIONS
SYNCHRONOUS ORBIT OPERATIONS
METEOROLOGICAL RESEARCH LABORATORY

Figure 4.13.

Remote sensing from space might also meet the necessity for information on water supplies, the resources to be extracted from the oceans, and mineral reserves. For example, on his Mercury flight Astronaut Gordon Cooper photographed an oil-bearing area in Northern Tibet.

Another application is to the weather. As Mark Twain observed, everyone talks about it but nobody ever does anything about it.

In 1966, a group established by the U.S. National Academy of Sciences issued a report indicating that the time may well have come to do something about the weather. Also in 1966, President Johnson recommended to the U.S. Congress a long-range program to accomplish weather modification. The Apollo/Saturn flight hardware is capable of assisting in this effort. An early step (*Figure 4.13*) might be to employ the Apollo spacecraft as a meteorological research laboratory.

Finally, there are the applications to science. In 1965, scientists associated with the U.S. National Academy of Sciences and other leaders recommended the exploration of the moon (*Figure 4.14*) and the placing of large telescopes and other astronomical instru-

Figure 4.14.

ments in space (*Figure 4.15*). The reports from these studies expressed the belief that the presence of man in space, close to these instruments, can greatly improve the ability of science to increase man's knowledge about the origin of life and the history of the earth, the sun, the planets and the universe around us.

But it is important to emphasize that the first task to be performed, before these benefits can be provided to the potential users, is to learn to operate in space. Before we can deliver people and equipment to the place where this work is to be done, we must investigate the conditions and the problems associated with operations in the weightless, vacuum environment of space. For example, the experience of Gemini has shown the need to gain a great deal of additional experience with extravehicular activity (*Figure 4.16*). Of equal importance are the efforts to develop skills in cargo and personnel transfer operations (*Figure 4.17*) and the handling of

APOLLO APPLICATIONS
SYNCHRONOUS ORBIT OPERATIONS
ORBITAL TELESCOPE

NASA MC66-52

Figure 4.15.

propellants for the assembly and resupply of space vehicles in orbit about the earth (*Figure 4.18*).

One of the experiments under consideration to develop operational skills is the use of a spent Saturn upper stage as a habitable structure. In 1966, we awarded a contract to produce an airlock through which astronauts could enter the empty hydrogen tank of the second stage of an uprated Saturn I.

The airlock will be stacked on the space vehicle between the second stage of the Saturn and the lower portion of the spacecraft. In orbital flight, the command and service modules would separate from the Saturn stage, rotate, and dock with the airlock unit (*Figure 4.19*). Then the astronauts would activate systems to pressurize the hydrogen tank for habitation. The hydrogen tank, 21 feet in diameter and 30 feet in length, has more than 10,000

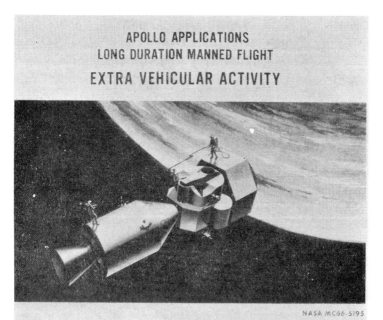

APOLLO APPLICATIONS
LONG DURATION MANNED FLIGHT
EXTRA VEHICULAR ACTIVITY

NASA MC66-5195

Figure 4.16.

cubic feet of internal volume. The airlock unit will carry additional hydrogen and oxygen to extend the lifetime of two Apollo spacecraft sub-systems, the fuel cells for electrical power and the life support devices. The airlock is to be delivered in time for use in 1968.

Now who are the potential users of these space capabilities (*Figure 4.20*)? There are the world communications media—television, telephone, cable and data transmission. There are the airlines and the shipping lines. There are the people throughout the world who are concerned with the earth's resources, in addition to Government agencies, such as, in the United States, the Department of Agriculture, the Environmental Science Services Administration, the U.S. Coast and Geodetic Survey, the U.S. Geological Survey, the Navy Oceanographic Office and others. There are the world's weather services. There is the scientific community, with its special interest in astronomy, the exploration of the moon and life sciences in space.

NASA MC66-51

Figure 4.17.

Looking back on history, we see that the voyages of the great mariners of the Age of Exploration — Columbus, Magellan, Drake, Cook — captured the imagination of men of their time even though they found lands and peoples quite different from what they had expected. Yet the real contributions which these new lands were to make were certainly far beyond even the wildest imagination of men of that time. So far as the American continent is concerned, it was not until many ships had travelled regularly from Europe to America that men truly began to exploit the full potential and promise of the new land.

Similarly, I believe that men will have to live and work in the space environment for some time before they can begin to exploit fully this new resource that is becoming available. The Apollo/Saturn flight equipment will enable us to proceed from *man-hours*

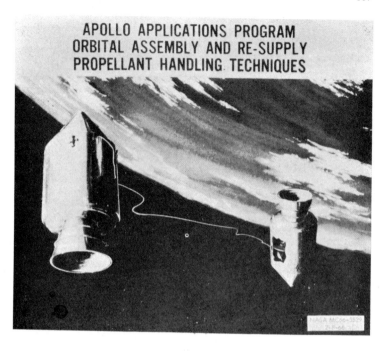

APOLLO APPLICATIONS PROGRAM
ORBITAL ASSEMBLY AND RE-SUPPLY
PROPELLANT HANDLING TECHNIQUES

Figure 4.18.

to *man-days* and then to *man-years* of flight experience. In the period immediately following the accomplishment of the Apollo program, a most important task will be to gain this experience and to develop advanced operational techniques for use in future programs.

Future alternatives

Careful study is under way to determine what major programs to undertake after the Apollo program is completed and after the capabilities of the Apollo vehicles have been fully exploited. The studies have focused attention on five major program alternatives. These do not exhaust all possibilities, but they do cover the most promising.

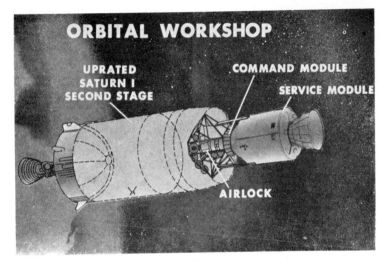

Figure 4.19.

The five alternatives are:

1. Direct economic benefits, with emphasis on extensive earth-orbital activities.
2. Lunar exploration and science.
3. Planetary exploration and science.
4. Maximum effort aimed at pre-eminence in earth orbital, lunar and planetary activities.
5. Balanced combination of economic benefits, lunar and planetary exploration, and science.

The direct economic benefits program would call for the construction of an orbital space station, which would lead into efforts to develop an "Applications Centre" in orbit, a research facility, modules for use in planetary flight, and later to an assembly and launch facility in orbit.

The lunar exploration and science program would require an orbital space station, mobility and power systems for the lunar surface, and a system for direct flight to the moon.

The planetary exploration and science program would involve an orbital space station, a temporary station on the moon, a near-planet flyby system and, later, a planetary development facility on the moon.

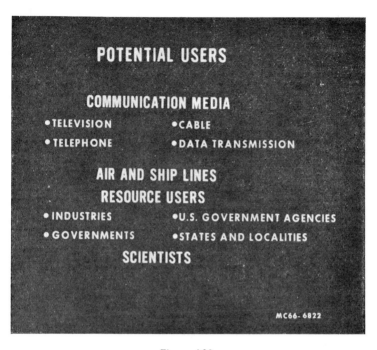

Figure 4.20.

In a maximum effort, we would proceed rapidly along all three of these courses.

In a balanced program, we would have to choose from the many alternatives, those that can give us the greatest return for the funds invested.

Examination of the alternatives discloses that an orbital space station is an early requirement of whatever program alternatives might be selected (*Figure 4.21*). We are, therefore, concentrating attention in current studies on establishing just what kind of space station can best meet our needs and how much time and funding will be required to develop such a station.

Summary and conclusion

To summarize, we have seen that international competition was a primary initial motivation of the United States space program

MSF PROGRAM EVOLUTION

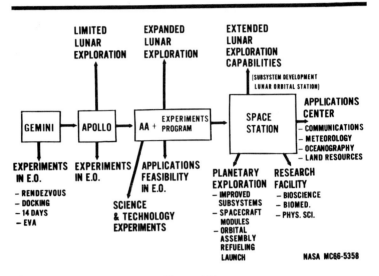

Figure 4.21.

and that considerable results were attained by adapting military rocket boosters to launch unmanned spacecraft for the purposes of scientific investigations and early applications of space technology.

At the same time, as indicated in the second lecture, we were developing a broad capability for the manned exploration of space. In the Mercury program, we established man's capabilities in short space flights and we laid the foundation for manned space flight technology. In the Gemini program, we gained operational proficiency, learned about man's capabilities in flights lasting up to two weeks, and developed new techniques. These included rendezvous, docking, the use of a separately launched rocket stage for space manoeuvres, astronaut activities outside the spacecraft, and controlled flight to a selected landing point. In addition, both Mercury and Gemini permitted man to conduct scientific activities in space.

The Apollo program, the largest and most complex scientific and engineering program ever undertaken by the United States, is leading to the landing of men on the moon and their safe return to earth in this decade. As shown in the third lecture, more than a quarter of a million people in every part of the United States are working on this program, which has now reached the flight-test phase. Major steps leading to the lunar mission have been taken and the program is proceeding on schedule. If all goes well, we will accomplish our goal before the end of the decade.

In this final lecture, I have indicated that we assume that the competition will continue, and that it will not be limited to the United States and Russia. Considerable returns from our investment in space are already at hand, and we expect greater returns as the technology and techniques are further employed by industry and government to make better products, to operate more efficiently and to solve earthly problems.

An attractive next step, following the initial manned lunar landing, is to continue to use our Apollo launch vehicles and spacecraft for missions of direct earthly benefit and of significant scientific value. These flights both in earth orbit and to the moon, would extend through to 1971. The most important task during this period would be to gain flight experience and to develop advanced operational techniques necessary for use in the future.

For the next decade, the options before us include emphasis on direct economic benefits, exploration of the moon, and exploration of the planets. But whatever route we choose, a space station would appear to be an early step after the conclusion of the Apollo Program.

As we look to the future we realize that history will look back on this century and this decade as a time when man took his first steps to explore the universe beyond this planet.

Will he succeed? For such an answer perhaps, we should turn to the great writers and philosophers. Sixteen years ago the late American writer William Faulkner made a comment that may apply. He said:

"I believe that man will not merely endure; he will prevail. He is immortal . . . because he has a soul, a spirit capable of compassion and sacrifice and endurance."

In the exploration of space, I believe with Faulkner that man will prevail.

The Evolution Of Stars

And The

Origin Of The Elements

by

E. E. SALPETER

Professor E. E. Salpeter.
Professor of Theoretical Physics,
Cornell University, Ithaca, N.Y

CHAPTER 1

The Sun as a Star

My main aim is to describe the evolution of stars, from their birth to their death, and how most of the chemical elements and their many isotopes were made and destroyed inside stars. The main theme is change and yet I will start with a single snapshot-picture, the present state of our sun. After reviewing a number of observational facts about the sun, we shall ask a central question—is there some good theoretical reason explaining many of these observational facts? Since I am a theorist myself you will not be surprised when I answer this question in the affirmative.

Our study of the present-day sun in the first chapter will introduce us to the theory of Stellar Structure—what the inside of a star is like and why. In the second chapter we shall review a bit of Nuclear Physics in order to understand thermonuclear reactions and the way these reactions transform chemical elements. We shall investigate just which reactions are most important at various temperatures, all high compared with temperatures we are used to on the earth and yet some too low for some purposes. Finally, in the third chapter we shall put together what we have learned in the first two chapters in order to understand the very slow changes taking place during stellar evolution and which nuclear transformations occur at various stages of this evolution.

(a) The observational facts

I want to discuss some, but not all, of the interesting observational facts about our sun. Some of the most beautiful observations (such as sunspots, granulation, flares, corona and solar wind) have to do with the very outermost layers of the sun and with the solar system and that we shall not discuss at all. We shall be interested in some facts which are much less spectacular but will eventually give us some information about the deep interior of the sun. Typically we shall be concerned not with qualitative observations

115

but with the numerical measurement of a number of quantities such as the mass M, radius R, energy output L, surface temperature T_s and age of the sun. These numerical values will all come out very large compared with values we are most familiar with. And yet we shall see that each such measurement is, at least in some indirect way, a comparison with some quantity we are familiar with on the earth.

Let us start with an "invisible" quantity, the age of the sun or, more correctly, the age of the earth and other solid components of the solar system. The details of geochemistry and of dating by means of radio active decay is very complex but the basic idea is simple: Some isotopes undergo radioactive decay and one can measure with very sensitive detection apparatus the minute fraction of a sample that decays in a second or a day or month. In this way one can measure the "half-life" of the radioactive decay, i.e., the time you would have to wait for half of the sample to have decayed away. Detection techniques are so sensitive that half-lives can be measured even though they are as large as many billions of years. Imagine, for instance, a radioactive decay where the decay-product is volatile and will diffuse away in a hot molten sample but will remain trapped in a cold solid sample. If you know the half-life of the decay and you measure the amounts of the radio-active material and of the decay-product in a piece of rock (or of a meteorite which hits the earth) you can figure out for how long the rock has been in a cold, solid form. We learn from geochemists that "the solar system is about 4·5 billion ($4·5 \times 10^9$) years old", which really means that the earth and planets were formed or solidified about as long ago as that.

We have good theoretical reasons to believe that the sun itself was formed at about the same time as the planets. There are no direct observations to back up this assertion that the sun is 4 or 5 billion years old, but we do have evidence that for the last 2 billion years or so the sun not only has been around, but has been radiating energy at about the same rate as at present. The evidence for this comes from paleontologists who have studied fossils of animals and plants which lived up to 2×10^9 years ago. Animals and plants are very sensitive to temperature, so we know that our atmosphere, as heated by the sun, has been about as warm as now for at least this length of time. We shall discuss later theoretical arguments suggesting that the sun has radiated at *roughly* a constant rate not only the last 2 billion but the whole 4 or 5 billion years (but we shall also argue for a *slight* change in the rate).

Measuring the radius $R_\odot$ of the sun is relatively easy: The apparent angular size (about $\frac{1}{2}°$) of the sun as seen from the earth is, of course, well-known and $R_\odot$ could be obtained from simple trigonometry if the earth-sun distance (called the astronomical unit or a.u.) were known. The ratios of the astronomical unit to other lengths in the solar system are also well-known, such as to the sun-Venus or earth-Venus distance, so an accurate measurement of any of these distances will suffice. A number of methods have been used, but the most accurate and recent method involves sending a radar-signal to Venus and measuring the elapsed time till the return of the echo-signal. Radar travels with the speed of light c, which had already been measured accurately on the earth some time ago ($c = 3 \times 10^5$ km/sec). In this way the astronomical unit (about 8 light-minutes or $1 \cdot 5 \times 10^8$ km) is now known with very great precision and the radius of the sun is $R_\odot \approx 7 \times 10^5$ km, which is about a hundred times the radius of the earth.

The mass $M_\odot$ of the sun can also be obtained accurately, but some theoretical physics has to be invoked to do so. Newton's Law of Gravitation states that any body (independent of its mass m) at a distance r from a heavy body M suffers a gravitational acceleration g towards that body, given by

$$g = GM/r^2 \tag{1.1}$$

where G is a *universal* constant (i.e., the same for all bodies and all distances). From this Law and from his three Laws of Motion, Sir Isaac Newton derived all the properties of gravitational orbits which planets describe as they revolve about the sun (or moons about a planet or a man-made satellite about the earth, etc.). Some of these properties had been described previously by Kepler as purely empirical relations, but Newton's complete derivation was historically the first triumph of Theoretical Physics and, possibly, its greatest to this day. One of the specific derivations relates the period of one orbit (the year for our earth) to the mass M of the central body, multiplied by the universal constant G. To derive the mass $M_\odot$ of the sun from the earthly year we merely need the numerical value of G and this was found by Cavendish by measuring in the laboratory the gravitational acceleration (as in *Equation 1.1*)

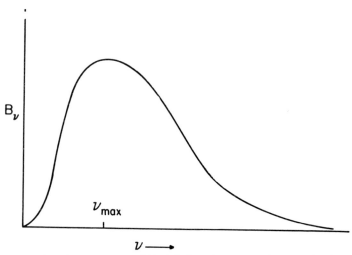

Figure 1.1.   The intensity B_v of black-body radiation as a function of radiation frequency v.

due to a metal sphere of known mass.   Note that this derivation of $M_\odot$ is essentially a roundabout way of comparing the mass of the sun with that of the metal sphere.

Numerically, of course, these two masses differ enormously since $M_\odot = 2 \times 10^{33}$ gm, which is about three hundred thousand times the mass of the earth (and a thousand times the mass of Jupiter). From $M_\odot$ and $R_\odot$ one can easily derive the average density $\bar{\rho}$. Although $M_\odot$ and $R_\odot$ are enormously large on a terrestrial scale, $\bar{\rho} = 1 \cdot 4$ gm/cm³ happens to be not very different from the density of water.

Another quantity we are interested in is the luminosity $L_\odot$ of the sun, i.e., the total amount of energy the sun radiates per second. One can easily measure the amount of sunlight which falls on the earth and we already know the earth-sun distance (the a.u.) so we can easily calculate $L_\odot$ (after applying a small correction for the ultra-violet and infra-red radiation which does not penetrate the earth's atmosphere).   One finds the enormously large value of $L_\odot = 4 \times 10^{33}$ erg/sec for the sun's luminosity.   This rate of energy-release sounds much less impressive when expressed per unit mass of the sun,

$\bar{\epsilon} \equiv (L/M)_\odot = 2$ erg/gm sec. In fact, per unit body-weight you and I produce heat from animal metabolism at a rate about a thousand times $\bar{\epsilon}$ for the sun. Lest you get too unimpressed by the sun's slow simmering, however, remember how often you and I refuel at the dinner table, whereas the sun has been going strong for billions of years. We shall, of course, return to the mysterious source of the sun's energy.

The sun's radiation has another property which we can crudely describe as "its colour". In reality the sun emits radiation of all different wavelengths (or frequency or colours), with an intensity distribution something like that shown in *Figure 1.1*. One can talk of the wavelength or colour where the intensity has a maximum and for the sun this is, of course, in the yellow. On the earth very hot bodies emit radiation in a similar manner with the "colour" changing from infra-red to red to yellow to blue to ultra-violet as the temperature increases. The sun's radiation corresponds to a "colour temperature" T of roughly 5,600°K.

I finally want to mention the chemical composition of the sun, although we shall have much more to say on this subject in the second and third chapters. For the earth (and for meteorites) the abundances of the various chemical elements can, of course, be obtained directly by chemical analysis and methods have also been worked out for measuring the abundances of the various isotopes of most elements. We shall return to details later, but note now that medium-light elements such as carbon, nitrogen, oxygen (and the somewhat heavier metals) are common on the earth with the two lightest elements hydrogen (H) and helium (He) relatively rare. For the sun and other stars one can find the abundances of at least some of the chemical elements by analyzing the so-called "Fraunhofer lines". These are absorption lines in the spectrum of sunlight produced by atoms of various elements as the sunlight passes through the outer (slightly cooler) layers of the surface of the sun. The relative proportions of elements and isotopes of carbon and all heavier elements are (with some important exceptions) similar to those on the earth. The startling difference is that *all* these elements together constitute only about 5% (by mass) of the material of the sun! By far the most important constituent of the sun is hydrogen, followed by helium (about 70% and 25%, respectively, by mass).

(b) Theoretical explanations

We now have values or the age, chemical composition, mass $M_\odot$, radius $R_\odot$, luminosity $L_\odot$ and surface colour temperature T for the sun. I now want to ask the question whether it is just an accident that these quantities have the numerical values they have or are there some good theoretical reasons for at least some relationships between them? In this chapter I shall try to show that, given age, composition and mass, the other three quantities R, L and T *must* have the values they have. We shall return later to questions regarding age, composition and mass.

Hydrostatic Equilibrium and the Central Temperature. Before we discuss theoretical relations connecting the observed quantities we have a relation for a quantity which is important but cannot be measured directly, the central temperature T_c. Although methods exist for actually calculating T_c as well as the temperature at other points in a star's interior, I shall give only an estimate for $\bar{T}$, the average temperature in the sun's interior which is smaller than T_c by a factor of about two.

Basically, the relation we want comes from the fact that the sun seems to be in perfect equilibrium in the sense that it neither contracts nor expands even on the time-scale of many millions of years. We have already discussed the gravitational acceleration g and if we substitute $M_\odot$ for M and $R_\odot$ for r in *Equation 1.1* we get the value of g at the sun's surface. Although g would be zero at the exact centre of the sun, its value at a "typical point in the interior" (for instance, a point r such that half the sun's mass is below it and half is above) is not much smaller than its value at the surface. We shall therefore approximate g by its surface-value $g = GM/R^2$ (I am dropping the solar subscript $_\odot$, because our theoretical considerations apply equally well to many, but not all, other stars).

If you dropped a marble into an imaginary tunnel drilled through the sun it would fall freely under gravity and one can easily calculate from the laws of mechanics the time t_{ff} it takes to reach the centre. Leaving factors of two or three out of the actual formula, one has an order of magnitude relation

$$t_{ff} \sim \sqrt{R/g} \sim \sqrt{R^3/GM} \sim (G\bar{\rho})^{-\frac{1}{2}} \qquad (1.2)$$

and for the sun this time turns out to be about a day. There are no tunnels through the sun but, if there were no pressure to hold up

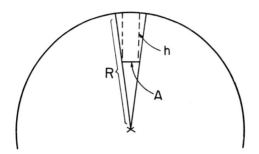

Figure 1.2. A schematic of a portion of the sun of radius R.

the matter, all the atoms in the sun would fall freely under gravity
and the sun would collapse in a time approximately equal to t_{ff}.
We shall not make use of the actual expression in *Equation 1.2* for
t_{ff}, but shall often use the fact that t_{ff} is enormously short compared
with time-scales over which conditions in the sun (or other stars)
change-equilibrium must be maintained with great precision!

If the interior of the sun is hot the thermal motion of the atoms
provides pressure and this pressure must balance the gravitational
acceleration. Consider a small horizontal area A drawn through
a "typical" point in the sun's interior as shown in *Figure 1.2*. We
want only order of magnitude relations so we can replace the cone
(solid) above area A by a cylinder (dotted) whose mass is then $\bar{\rho}Ah$
and further replace the height h by the full radius R ($\bar{\rho}$ is the average
density). The full downward gravitational force (or "weight") is
then $g(\bar{\rho}Ah)$ and this must be balanced by the upward force $\bar{P}A$
on the area A due to the thermal pressure $\bar{P}$. The area cancels out
and we have

$$\bar{P} \sim g\bar{\rho}R \sim GM\bar{\rho}/R . \qquad (1.3)$$

Now we merely need some general results from thermodynamics
which relate thermal pressure P (and thermal energy) to density ρ
and temperature T. We shall often come across a fundamental
constant k, the "Boltzmann constant" (with dimensions of energy
divided by temperature) such that

$$k \times 11{,}560°\text{K} = 1 \ eV = 1 \cdot 6 \times 10^{-12} \text{ erg} \qquad (1.4)$$

(where 1 eV is the energy a potential of one volt gives to an electron, a convenient energy unit in atomic physics). In a "perfect" gas each atom or free ion or free electron or other free particle in one cubic centimetre contributes kT towards the pressure and its average thermal kinetic energy is $(3/2) kT$. These two statements are true, independent of the mass m of the particle (which we shall often describe as "molecular weight" μ in units of the mass H of the hydrogen atom, $m = \mu H$). For a mixture of particles we denote the mean molecular weight by μ such that the total number of free particles (per cm³) is $\rho/\mu H$ (with ρ the density in gm/cm³). The "perfect gas law" then reads (with v_{th} the "thermal velocity")

$$\frac{1}{2} m\, v^2_{th} = \frac{3}{2} kT, \qquad P = \frac{\rho}{\mu H}\, kT \;. \tag{1.4}$$

Substituting this expression for $\bar{P}$ (using $\bar{\rho}$ and the average temperature $\bar{T}$) into *Equation 1.3* the density $\bar{\rho}$ cancels out and one can rewrite the result in the form

$$k\bar{T} \sim GM(\mu H)/R \;. \tag{1.5}$$

Equation 1.5 is the expression for average interior temperature in terms of mass and radius which we had wanted to derive. The right-hand side of *Equation 1.5* is the "potential energy" of a particle of mass μH which is the work required to remove the particle from the (surface of the) sun to infinity against the gravitational attraction. The left-hand side of *Equation 1.5* is (except for a factor of $2/3$) the average kinetic energy of thermal motion for one free particle. We have thus shown that at equilibrium the ratio of the average potential energy to the average kinetic energy is of order unity. From thermodynamics and mechanics one can derive an accurate relation, the Virial Theorem, which shows by how much this ratio differs from unity. We shall see in *Chapter 3* that the value of this difference is important for stellar evolution, but for our present purposes *Equation 1.5* is sufficient.

In the interior of the sun the hydrogen and helium are almost fully ionized. Since the free electrons have a small mass $(m_e = H/1837)$ the mean molecular weight is actually less than unity, $\mu \approx 0\cdot6$. Substituting the solar mass and radius into *Equation 1.5* one finds a very high value for the mean temperature, $\bar{T} \sim 10^7 {}^\circ K$, so that $k\bar{T}$ is of the order of a kiloelectron-volt ($1\ keV = 10^3\ eV$). The actual central temperature T_c of the sun is about $15 \times 10^6 {}^\circ K$.

I would like to mention, as a side-remark, the question of escape of light gases from a planet or a star. For a fixed temperature, *Equation 1.4* shows that the thermal velocity v_{th} of an atom is the larger, the smaller its mass is. The "escape velocity"—the lowest initial velocity which enables a particle to escape from the earth's (or sun's) surface—on the other hand, is independent of the particle's mass and equals 11 km/sec for the earth. For the earth the lightest atoms, hydrogen and helium (but not any others), have largely escaped from the earth's warm upper atmosphere during the earth's long lifetime. This explains the low abundance of these two elements on the earth and nearby planets (the outer major planets such as Jupiter are heavier and colder and they contain a large abundance of hydrogen and helium). For the sun with its much larger mass the escape velocity is much larger, about 600 km/sec. Even for hydrogen one would require temperatures of the order of $10^{7}°$K for the thermal velocity to be comparable with the escape velocity. Although the interior temperatures are this large, the surface temperature ($<6000°$K) is lower by a factor of more than a thousand. Consequently *none* of the chemical elements have escaped from the sun to any great extent.

The colour-luminosity relation. I want to discuss next the relation between luminosity L and the colour temperature of a star's surface. For this purpose, as well as a number of others, we need a little of the theory of "black-body radiation". Imagine a closed hollow oven which is heated to a uniform temperature T. Radiation will be emitted by some atoms on the hot wall, reabsorbed by others and so on. After a while a "dynamic steady state" will be built up, which means that individual bits of radiation come and go but the kinds of radiation present in one cm³ inside the cavity do not change with time. To appreciate the properties of this radiation even in a crude qualitative manner, one has to appreciate the quantum nature of light. In fact, it was the properties of black-body radiation which prompted Planck to postulate that light (or other radiation) of frequency v and wavelength λ can occur only in quantized chunks of energy E_v given by

$$E_v = hv = hc/\lambda \tag{1.6}$$

where h is a fundamental constant (now known as *Planck's constant*). One of these chunks of energy is called a photon and, no matter what the circumstances, photons can be created or destroyed, few or many photons may be present but one can never have a fraction of a photon.

From Planck's postulate and from the theory of statistical mechanics one can derive the intensity B_ν as a function of frequency ν of black-body radiation (or the number of photons per cm^3 of different frequencies). A sketch of this function is given in *Figure* 1.1 which shows a maximum at some frequency ν_{max}. I cannot discuss the correct derivation for the formula for B_ν, but we can at least make some of the salient features plausible. We have seen that any atom or molecule at temperature T has an average thermal energy of order kT and it is not surprising that "typical" black-body photons have similar energies. One finds

$$h\nu_{max} \sim 4kT, \ \lambda_T \equiv c/\nu_{max} \sim ch/4kT \tag{1.7}$$

where λ_T is the wavelength of a "typical" photon of frequency ν_{max} and c is the speed of light. We are also interested in the total energy content U per cm^3 of the black-body radiation photons, so we need the number density of photons. I think you will not be too surprised to find that there is about one photon per cube of side $\lambda_T \propto T^{-1}$ so that the number of photons per cubic centimetre is proportional to T^3. The energy density U is simply the number density of photons times their average energy (which is of order $h\nu_{max}$ or kT). The correct expression is

$$U = (4\sigma/c)T^4 \tag{1.8}$$

where σ is a constant (actually it is $2\pi^5 k^4/15c^2 h^3$) called the *Stefan-Boltzmann constant*.

For simplicity we have thought of the black-body radiation in the cavity of a hollow body, but the same kind of radiation is present also throughout a hot black-body and on its surface—the photons and the atoms co-exist peacefully and their interaction maintains a common temperature for both. Consider now the black-body photons near the body's surface with temperature T_s. Half of these photons are moving towards the surface and one can show that the mean velocity normal to the surface of this half is $c/2$. The photon energy which passes through unit area of the surface per second is called the flux F and equals half the energy content in a column of unit area and height $c/2$.

This then gives for the emitted flux

$$F = (c/4)U = \sigma \ T_s^4 \tag{1.9}$$

The sun does not have a completely sharp surface like a solid body, but the photons that escape from the sun come from a surface layer whose thickness is finite but very small compared with the sun's radius. To a good (but not excellent) approximation one can replace this finite layer by a sharp black-body surface at temperature T_s. The total surface area is $4\pi R^2$ and, using *Equation 1.9*, one finds for the total luminosity L

$$L = 4\pi R^2\, \sigma\, T_s^4 \ . \tag{1.10}$$

We have already discussed the colour temperature in terms of the frequency ν_{max} at which the emitted radiation intensity has a maximum. If we are really dealing with black-body radiation this colour temperature should be the same as T_s in *Equation 1.10* and for the sun (and most other stars) this is at least approximately true. *Equation 1.10* is then the desired relation between luminosity L and colour. We shall see next that the *interior* conditions determine L (and R), so that the surface layer must always adjust its temperature to a value dictated by the interior conditions according to *Equation 1.10*.

The Luminosity L. We ask ourselves next whether, for fixed mass M, radius R (and chemical composition), there is some way to predict the luminosity L. You will not be surprised to hear that the answer is "Yes", but you probably will be surprised that it is *not* really questions of nuclear physics and energy production which determine L but merely questions of heat flow, i.e., the transport of photons. This concept goes against one's intuition but it is very important for an understanding of stellar structure and evolution. So, for a little way, let us pay no attention to any sources which replenish the sun's energy and let us remember merely that its interior is very hot, according to *Equation 1.5*, and that there is a lot of energy stored in the form of black-body radiation photons, according to *Equation 1.8*.

More specifically we should concentrate on the fact that there is a temperature *gradient* throughout the sun, since the centre is so very much hotter ($T_c < 10^{4\circ}$K). We all know that heat flows from hot to cold whenever there is a temperature gradient, for instance, along a copper bar one end of which has been heated. In the case of the copper bar the heat is mainly carried by the free electrons ("electron conduction") and the same happens in a special class of stars called "white dwarfs" (see *Chapter 3*). For the majority of ordinary stars including the sun, however, electron conduction is less important than the energy carried outwards by the photons of the black-body radiation. How big the heatflow is for a given temperature gradient depends on the "mean-free path" l of the photons, the distance a photon travels on the average before it is scattered or absorbed (and another photon re-emitted). For each point in the star one can write down an equation connecting the temperature gradient to the heat-flux near this point. I shall estimate only crudely the total luminosity L by estimating how long it takes the energy content of the black-body radiation to leak out of the sun.

Consider a "typical" photon in the sun's deep interior. It can be scattered by free electrons, absorbed by some atom or absorbed during the collision between an electron and a proton (photons of similar or lower frequency are then quickly re-emitted). The calculation of the mean-free path l for the photon is complicated but has been carried out by atomic physicists for different conditions of density and temperature and chemical composition. At the moment we note only that l is enormously smaller than the star's radius R. In this case one is dealing with the so-called "random-walk" problem, i.e., the photon starting in the deep interior zigzags back and forth (each step having length l) many times before it finally happens to get to the surface from which it then escapes. The total number of steps taken is clearly much larger than the straight-line ratio (R/l) and it can be shown that the actual number of steps is close to $(R/l)^2$. This random-walk process is illustrated in *Figure 1.3* for a fictitious case of $(R/l) = 5$. For the sun (R/l) is more like 10^{12} and the average time t_{ph} taken for a photon to leak out,

$$t_{ph} \sim (R/l)^2 \, (l/c) = R^2/lc \;, \tag{1.11}$$

is about 10^7 years. This time is enormously long compared with the few minutes light takes to travel (in a straight line) from the sun's surface to the earth, but note that it is much shorter than the age of the sun. We finally get a rough estimate for the luminosity radiated away by noting that the energy content of the black-body radiation (of density U) throughout the sun (volume $4\pi R^3/3$) is radiated away in time t_{ph}. Using *Equation 1.8* for U and *Equation 1.11* for t_{ph} we have

$$L \sim (4\pi R^3/3)U/t_{ph} \sim (16\pi/3) \, (lR) \, \sigma \overline{T}^4 \tag{1.12}$$

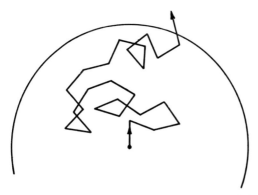

Figure 1.3. The "random walk" of a photon zig-zagging out of the interior of the sun.

and $\overline{T}$ in turn is given roughly by *Equation 1.5*. Our expression for L in *Equation 1.12* is meant only as a rough order of magnitude relation and it gives a value fairly close to the observed L for the sun when the appropriate values for *l* and the other quantities are substituted.

Note the similarities and differences between *Equations 1.10* and *1.12* for L. Mathematically they differ by one R being replaced by one *l* and T_s being replaced by $\overline{T}$, so that

$$T_s/\overline{T} \sim (l/R)^{1/4} \ll 1 . \tag{1.13}$$

Physically, remember that the star's gravitational equilibrium determines $\overline{T}$ via *Equation 1.5* and that $\overline{T}$ determines L via *Equation 1.12*. *Equation 1.10*, on the other hand, has to be read in the opposite direction in the sense that L is now fixed and determines the surface conditions and T_s via *Equation 1.10*.

The mass-radius relation. Assume a given mass M and chemical composition and assume that this composition is the same at all points of the star. We have so far not restricted the value of the radius R and can envisage a whole series of models, one for each value of R. Whatever value of R you pick out of this series, $\overline{T}$ will then be given by *Equation 1.5* ($\overline{T} \propto 1/R$) and (T_s and) L will then be given by *Equation 1.12*. Although L as given by *1.12* depends on the value of R it turns out not to vary very much. Now, finally, we have to

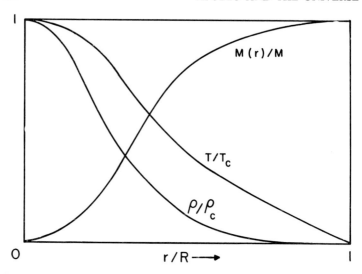

Figure 1.4. The density ρ, temperature T at radial distance r from the sun's centre (ρ_c and T_c are ρ and T at the centre, R is the sun's radius). M(r) is the mass lying below r and M ≡ M(R) is the total mass.

consider the question of energy production. We have seen that the sun's luminosity has remained constant over a much longer period $(>2 \times 10^9$ ys) than the time taken for the sun's photon energy to leak out ($\sim 10^7$ ys), so some source of energy must continuously replenish the energy L that is being radiated away each second. In the next chapter we shall see that the energy source for the sun is the nuclear transformation of hydrogen into helium and that the rate for this energy release depends extremely strongly on temperature $\overline{T}$. If you picked an arbitrary value for R in the series of imagined models you would find that the total energy release per second would be much less than L if $\overline{T}$ is less than some critical value (or much too large if $\overline{T}$ is larger). In this whole series of imagined models there is only one for which R is just right so that $\overline{T}$ has just the critical value so that the nuclear energy release exactly equals the energy radiated away. For the nuclear rates in the sun one requires about $\overline{T} \sim 10^{7}$°K and it is this nuclear requirement which fixes the radius R to have the value it has.

To summarize the theoretical results of this chapter: Given a mass M and uniform composition and a star fully in equilibrium, the rest can be determined including radius R, luminosity L and surface temperature T_s. I have given only order of magnitude estimates, but tedious and accurate calculations can and have been carried out to calculate these quantities accurately and also to calculate the internal structure in detail. By detailed structure I mean $\rho(r)$ and $T(r)$, the density and temperature as a function of radial distance r from the centre for all values of r between 0 and R. In such calculations one is dealing with a number of simultaneous "differential equations". For instance, the assumption of hydrostatic equilibrium at each point r gives an equation for the derivative of pressure or of $\rho(r)$ and photon mean-free-path considerations give an equation for the derivative of $T(r)$, i.e., for the temperature gradient. With modern electronic computers these calculations can be carried out quite accurately. The latest calculations for a star of solar mass and uniform composition give a theoretical value for the luminosity about 25% lower than the observed value $L_\odot$ for the sun. We shall see in *Chapter 3* that even this small discrepancy is not due to any numerical inaccuracies but rather to the fact that the composition of the sun is not quite uniform.

E

CHAPTER 2

Element Cooking and Nuclear Energy Production

We saw in the last chapter that the sun has been shining steadily for a few billion years even though its internal heat content leaks out in about ten million years, so the sun must be steadily burning some kind of fuel. We are familiar with many different kinds of chemical fuels which are used to initiate chemical reactions in which some atoms and/or molecules undergo some transformations which release chemical binding energy. In any kind of fuel burning there are two questions: (i) the *rate* at which energy is released per second which can depend drastically on the detailed set-up used and (ii) the maximum *total* amount of energy that can be released by unit mass of the fuel which depends only on the released binding energy per atom and cannot be increased by any trickery. Even the most efficient chemical fuels (somewhat better than the fuels we use in animal metabolism and the fuels automobiles use) release only a few *eV* (electron Volts energy) per reacting atom. If the sun were made of such a chemical fuel, it could supply the sun's luminosity for at most ten thousand years, which would, of course, be quite useless.

Some nuclear reactions also release energy and when they do the energy release is often several *MeV* (million electron Volts) per nucleus, so that nuclear fuels can be millions of times more efficient than the best chemical fuels. This could be quite adequate and we shall see in fact that the sun uses up only one per cent of its mass in nuclear fuel every billion years. We shall first discuss the question of (a) the binding energy of various nuclei to see which kinds of nuclear transformations could lead to energy release and then study (b) how the rates of thermonuclear reactions in general depend on temperature and (c) look at the specific chain of reactions which supply the sun's energy. These reactions in the sun, besides releasing energy, also transform hydrogen into helium and other reactions can transform helium into a large variety of isotopes of other chemical elements. We shall finally discuss the fascinating subject of "element cooking".

(a) Nuclear binding energy and structure

All nuclei are built up out of protons and neutrons. The proton
is the nucleus of the hydrogen atom and provides most of its mass H
and has a positive electric charge equal and opposite to the charge e
of the electron. The neutron has almost the same mass as the
proton but is electrically neutral (it decays into a proton plus an
electron plus a neutrino in the free state but not inside stable nuclei).
For a complex nucleus we call the number of protons Z, the atomic
number and the total number of protons plus neutrons (nucleons
for short) A, the atomic weight (or atomic mass number). Each
chemical element has a fixed value of Z, but it usually can have various
nuclei with different values of A, the different isotopes. A is usually
added as a superscript (and Z sometimes as a subscript) to the
symbol for the chemical element as $_{26}Fe^{56}$ for the most common
isotope of iron with 56 nucleons in all.

Only some combinations (less than a thousand) of A and Z lead
to "absolutely stable" nuclei which can live forever (if left alone).
Other combinations lead to radioactive nuclei and we shall be
particularly interested in "beta-decaying" nuclei. In a beta-decay
the atomic weight A of the nucleus remains the same but the atomic
charge Z changes up or down by one when a neutrino plus electron
or positron is emitted. The time-scale of beta-decays varies from
case to case but is typically in the range of seconds to hundreds of
years, short compared with "astronomical" time-scales of millions
to billions of years. Other combinations of A and Z are completely
unstable and if you tried to put together a nucleus of this kind it
would simply fly apart in something like 10^{-21} sec! This unbelievably
short time is typical of "nuclear time-scales" since typical nuclear
sizes are only a few times 10^{-13} cm and at typical speeds of a few times
10^8 cm/sec (say, one hundredth the speed of light c) the transit time
is simply 10^{-13-8} sec.

I want to mention specifically some of these non-existing unstable
nuclei. In particular, $_2He^2$ does not exist and would fly apart into
two protons; neither $_2He^5$ nor $_3Li^5$ exist and would fly apart into
$_2He^4$ plus a neutron or a proton (the $_2He^4$-nucleus is also called an
alpha-particle). An interesting case of intermediate nature is $_4Be^8$,
which can break up spontaneously into two alpha-particles but this
break-up is extremely slow on a nuclear time-scale (although faster

than beta-decays). These facts have an important although negative effect on the course of nuclear reactions in stars. Starting with common hydrogen, $_1H^1$, the most natural reaction would be to form $_2He^2$ out of two protons but that is impossible. In a mixture of hydrogen $_1H^1$ and helium $_2He^4$ it would be natural to combine one proton and one alpha-particle to form $_3Li^5$, but that is impossible, and so on.

Let us return to the more positive side of the structure of stable nuclei. Except for the very lightest nuclei, one gross feature of nuclear structure is the phenomenon of "saturation", which means crudely that as A is increased the volume of the corresponding nucleus increases but that the properties per unit volume remain pretty much the same (at constant nuclear density, nuclear radii are of order $A^{1/3} \times 10^{-13}$ cm). In particular, saturation implies a constant value for the "binding energy per nucleon" B, i.e., the total energy required to break the nucleus up into free neutrons and protons divided by the total number A of nucleons. In reality B varies fairly drastically from one nucleus to another and, even if one averages B over a few adjacent stable nuclei, B is not completely constant but is something

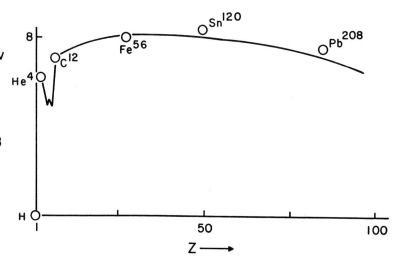

Figure 2.1. The binding energy B per nucleon (in MeV) plotted against atomic charge Z.

like the curve in *Figure 2.1*. One feature of this curve is the slow
increase of B with A or Z for light nuclei up to a maximum value of
about $8 MeV$ for medium-weight nuclei (the common metals with
$_{26}Fe^{56}$ having the largest B of any nucleus). This increase for light
nuclei is due to the fact that nucleons near the surface of a nucleus
have much lower binding energy than interior ones and the *fraction*
of nucleons near the surface decreases with increasing A (since surface
area is proportional only to $A^{2/3}$ and not to A). The other gross
feature is an even slower decrease of B with increasing A or Z for
nuclei heavier than Fe^{56}. This decrease is due to the electrostatic
repulsion between all the Z protons which decreases the binding
energy B by an amount which is larger for larger Z. For the light
nuclei where the electrostatic (or "Coulomb") repulsion is unimportant the most stable nuclei have equal numbers of neutrons
and protons ($Z = 0.5 A$) whereas for the heavier nuclei the electrostatic repulsion makes nuclei with larger number of neutrons than
protons ($Z \approx 0.4 A$) more stable.

We also shall need some more detailed features of the binding
energy curve. Most important is the great stability of the alpha-
particle, the $_2He^4$-nucleus, compared to neighbouring nuclei. In
fact, it has a value for B of about $7 MeV$, only one MeV less than the
maximum value (compared with $B \approx 1.2 MeV$ for $_1H^2$, for instance).
Nuclei with $Z = 2n$, $A = 4n$ can be thought of as a combination of
n alpha-particles and are usually also particularly stable—$_6C^{12}$,
$_8O^{16}$, $_{10}Ne^{20}$, $_{12}Mg^{24}$, $_{14}Si^{28}$, etc. "Even-even nuclei" (both A and Z
even) in general are more stable than those with odd A and/or Z
(but usually not as much as the special class of "n-alpha" nuclei).
Nuclei which have Z and/or the neutron number (A-Z) equal to one
of the so-called "magic numbers" of the nuclear shell-model theory
(which I cannot describe in these lectures) also have slightly larger
B than their neighbours. These magic numbers are the integers
20, 50, 82 and 126 so that all the many isotopes of tin ($_{50}Sn$) have a
"magic" proton number and the most abundant isotope of lead
($_{82}Pb^{208}$) is even "doubly magic" with $Z = 82$ and $A - Z = 126$.

Before we look at individual reactions and their rates we can
already guess some general trends merely from knowing which nuclei
are stable and how B varies from one nucleus to another. In any
chain of nuclear reactions where one set of nuclei is transformed into
another set, the total number of nucleons (neutron *or* proton) remains

the same—they are merely reshuffled from one nucleus to another. What matters then is not the total binding energy of individual nuclei but how the average binding energy B *per nucleon* of the original nuclei compares with that of the final ones. If B increases in the process we call the reaction chain *exothermic* and an energy equal to the increase ΔB in B is released for each nucleon which takes part in the reaction.

By definition the nucleus of common hydrogen $_1H^1$, being a single proton, has zero binding energy whereas common helium $_2He^4$ has $B \approx 7\ MeV$. Hydrogen is also the major constituent of interstellar gas and of stars, so by far the largest potential source of energy lies in the conversion of hydrogen into helium and we shall have to look for ways to carry out this conversion. If we can further transform some of the helium-nuclei (alpha-particles) into the "n-alpha" nuclei (especially $_6C^{12}$ to $_{14}Si^{28}$) we could release some more energy (slightly less than one MeV per nucleon compared with 7 MeV for $H^1 \to He^4$). Finally, any transformation of the n-alpha nuclei into the nuclei of the metals in the iron-region, which have the largest values of B (especially $_{26}Fe^{56}$ itself), would release another fraction of one MeV per nucleon. It is clear that building up any heavy elements beyond the iron-region would cost some energy rather than release it, but we shall see that a little of that takes place nevertheless, and we are interested not only in energy production but also in the possibility of making the various isotopes of the other chemical elements out of hydrogen.

(b) Thermonuclear reactions

An important process is the reaction between the hydrogen-nucleus (or proton, often denoted by p) and some other nucleus. In most (but not all) cases this other nucleus can simply absorb the proton and release some energy in the form of a very energetic photon, called a γ-ray. One example of such a reaction is

$$_6C^{13} + {}_1H^1 \to {}_7N^{14} + \gamma \tag{2.1}$$

which is often abbreviated to $C^{13}(p,\gamma)N^{14}$. In most cases, such as in *Equation 2.1*, this absorption with the release of a γ-ray (called a "radiative absorption") is the *only* possible end-result which releases energy. In only a very few cases, especially when the end-result is a n-alpha nucleus, is there a competing reaction which also releases some energy in which an alpha-particle is released (denoted as a (p, a) reaction). One of these rare examples is

$$_7\text{N}^{15} + {}_1\text{H}^1 \quad \begin{array}{l} \nearrow {}_8\text{O}^{16} + \gamma \\ \\ \searrow {}_6\text{C}^{12} + {}_2\text{He}^4 \end{array} \tag{2.2}$$

Although such a (p, a) is energetically impossible in most cases, when it *is* possible it usually has a much larger rate than the competing (p,γ) reaction. In *Equation 2.2* for instance, the reaction proceeds according to the bottom (rather than the top) line more than 99% of the time.

Another kind of reaction, which does not take place in the sun but occurs in some stars which are much hotter, involves the absorption of an alpha-particle with energy being released in the form of a γ-ray. An example of such an (a,γ) reaction is

$$_6\text{C}^{12} + {}_2\text{He}^4 \rightarrow {}_8\text{O}^{16} + \gamma \tag{2.3}$$

Only rarely will we come across a reaction where both reacting nuclei are heavier than an alpha-particle, but one example of such a reaction is the formation of $_{12}\text{Mg}^{24} + \gamma$ out of two $_6\text{C}^{12}$-nuclei.

All the reactions I have just mentioned would release energy if they occurred, but in order to make them occur one has to bring a positively charged proton (or alpha-particle) close enough to another positively charged nucleus for the attractive nuclear forces to come into play. These nuclear forces are extremely strong when the separation r between the (centres of the) two nuclei is only a few times 10^{-13} cm, but they are quite negligible for separations r appreciably larger than 10^{-12} cm. We have already mentioned the electrostatic repulsion between positively charged particles. This repulsion also decreases with increasing separation r but quite slowly so that it is less important than the nuclear attraction for small r and more important for large r. The resulting potential energy curve $V(r)$ is shown in *Figure 2.2* with the region of strong nuclear attraction labelled *Nuclear Well*. The bottle-neck to the reaction is the positive (repulsive) region of $V(r)$ which has a maximum a little way outside of the nuclear well but is still appreciable at somewhat larger separations r, the infamous "Coulomb barrier".

The strength of this repulsive Coulomb barrier is proportional to $Z_1 Z_2$, the product of the atomic charge number of the two reacting nuclei, and its maximum is a few hundred *keV* even for a proton

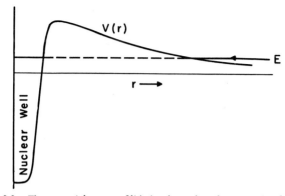

Figure 2.2. The potential energy V(r) (nuclear plus electrostatic) of a proton at distance r from another nucleus.

reacting with a light nucleus (and several *MeV* for a heavy nucleus, especially for alpha-particie reactions). You will remember that the kinetic energy of thermal motion with which two nuclei approach each other in the sun's interior is of the order of $k\overline{T}$ which is only about one *keV* and we seem to be in trouble. However, we can still get the reaction going on, but at a very slow rate, by invoking two phenomena which are both rare but not impossible. Occasionally two nuclei will approach each other with a kinetic energy E which is much larger than the thermal energy kT, but the probability for this happening is proportional to the small factor $e^{E/kT}$ (which is 10 raised to the power $[0.434\ E/kT]$). We do not have to make E quite as large as the maximum of the Coulomb barrier, because of a quantum mechanical effect called "barrier penetration", illustrated in *Figure 2.2* by the horizontal line with arrow labelled E. According to classical physics the proton would simply be reflected where the line hits the potential barrier. According to quantum theory (or wave-mechanics), however, there is a small chance for the proton to leak through the barrier along the dotted line and to enter the nuclear. The probability for such barrier penetration decrease very strongly when E is decreased or the height of the barrier is increased. For a given temperature T and reacting nuclei, a compromise situation is most favourable where E is much larger than kT but much smaller than the maximum of the Coulomb barrier.

The actual formulae for the rate of a "thermonuclear reaction" (the compromise situation discussed above) are quite complicated and vary greatly from case to case. I shall merely illustrate some of the important factors in a typical case: the reaction time t_r, the time that would be required for half the reacting nuclei to be used up, might be something like

$$t_r \sim 10^{-8} \sec \times e^{(T_o/T)^{1/3}}; \quad T_o \sim (Z_1 Z_2)^2 \times 10^{10\,°}K \qquad (2.4)$$

where Z_1 is 1 for a proton or 2 for an alpha-particle and Z^2 is the atomic charge of the other reacting nucleus. I have left out the dependence on density, abundance and mass of the nuclei in this simplified formula, but not the following features: the reaction time would be exceedingly short were it not for the temperature-dependent factor. This factor is exceedingly large, decreases rapidly with increasing temperature T and increases rapidly with increasing Z_1 and Z_2. We saw in the first chapter that reaction times of the order of 10^9 years are required in stellar interiors. For the reactions 2.1 or 2.2 this requires temperatures of the order of $10^{7\,°}K$, reaction 2.3 requires about $10^{8\,°}K$ and the reaction between two C^{12}-nuclei requires about $10^{9\,°}K$.

(c) Hydrogen burning

We have already guessed that the conversion of hydrogen into helium is the energy source for our sun and the same is true for a whole class of stars, called "main sequence stars". We have also seen already that the most obvious starting reaction, the direct absorption of one proton by another, is impossible because $_2He^2$ does not exist. There are two different chains of reactions which both achieve this H → He conversion. These two chains of reactions were first elucidated by Hans Bethe of Cornell University about 30 years ago, have been refined since and, with the aid of a number of nuclear laboratory experiments, have by now had their rates calculated quite accurately.

One of these chains is really a cycle in which the various isotopes of carbon and nitrogen act as catalysts, i.e., they are necessary to make the cycle go around but they are not permanently used up. This so-called "carbon-cycle" or "CN-cycle" is illustrated in *Figure 2.3*. Reading it from the top we start with a (p, γ) reaction on $_6C^{12}$ which results in $_7N^{13}$. The N^{13}-nucleus is radioactive and undergoes beta-decay,

$$_7N^{13} \rightarrow \,_7C^{13} + e^+ + \nu, \qquad (2.5)$$

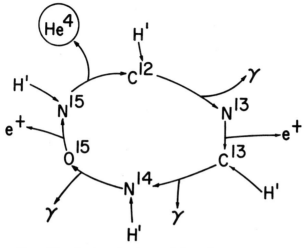

Figure 2.3. A schematic picture of the carbon-nitrogen cycle.

into C^{13} with the emission of a positron (e^+) and a neutrino (ν). This beta-decay takes about 10 minutes which is long on a nuclear time-scale but much too short for a thermonuclear reaction to compete at solar temperatures. C^{13} is a stable nuclear and waits around until it suffers a (p,γ) reaction as shown in *Equation 2.1*, N^{14} is again stable and a further (p,γ) reaction results in $_8O^{15}$. This nucleus is again radioactive and decays to $_7N^{15}$ with the emission of a positron and a neutrino. The final step is then as we discussed in connection with *Equation 2.3*: instead of yet another (p,γ) reaction, most of the N^{15}-nuclei undergo a (p,α) reaction instead so that $_6C^{12}$ reappears and an alpha-particle is produced.

Since the carbon and nitrogen isotopes reappear again we can summarize the net result of the carbon cycle in the form

$$4 \ _1H^1 \rightarrow \ _2He^4 + 2\nu + 28 \ MeV \ . \tag{2.6}$$

You might object that I have left out the two positrons which were also emitted. Actually, these positrons quickly annihilate together with two electrons from the ionized gas, so the net result is really the disappearance of two electrons. This is already included in *Equation 2.6* if you consider each side to include enough electrons to neutralize the nuclear charge (4 on the left and 2 on the right-hand side). Most of the 28 *MeV* energy gain is released in the form of γ-rays (very energetic photons) and in kinetic energy of the C^{12} and He^4-nuclei. The γ-rays are quickly absorbed, other photons re-emitted, etc., and most of the energy is simply fed into the thermal motion of the ionized gas and into black-body radiation.

The other reaction chain is the so-called "proton-proton chain" and starts with a most unusual reaction. Because of the small charge (and mass) of the proton, the temperature-dependent factor in *Equation 2.4* would be much less severe for bringing a pair of protons together than for other reactions. We have already said that the two protons normally fly apart again in a short time but there is a minute chance that one of the protons will undergo a beta-decay into a neutron (plus positron and neutrino) in this short time. A neutron and proton can be bound together to form a deuteron, the nucleus of $_1H^2$, and this is stable. The deuteron quickly undergoes a (p,γ) reaction of $_2He^3$ which is stable. There are a number of competing ways to complete the chain, but I give only one of them explicitly,

$$\left.\begin{array}{l} 2\ _1H^1 \rightarrow\ _1H^2 +\ e^+ +\ \nu; \\ _1H^2 +\ _1H^1 \rightarrow\ _2He^3 +\ \gamma \end{array}\right\} \times\ 2;$$

$$2\ _2He^3 \rightarrow\ _2He^4 +\ 2\ _1H^1 \tag{2.7}$$

The end result of this reaction chain is again *Equation 2.6*, just as for the carbon-cycle, and the same is true for the alternative ways of completing the chain.

I cannot describe how the calculations for rates of the reaction chains are carried out, but I can at least quote some results. The rate of energy production for the carbon-cycle ϵ_{CN} and for the proton-proton chain ϵ_{pp}, at temperatures near those in the sun's interior, can be approximated by

$$\epsilon_{CN} = \rho X_H (X_{CN}/0.02)(T/15\ 10^{6\circ}K)^{19.9} \times 0.039$$

$$\epsilon_{pp} = \rho X_H^2 (T/15\ 10^{6\circ}K)^{3.9} \times 0.38 \tag{2.8}$$

with ϵ in ergs/gm/sec, ρ the density in gm/cm^3, X_H and X_{CN} the abundance (by mass) of hydrogen (about 0.7 in the sun) and of the carbon plus nitrogen isotopes (about 0.02), respectively. These two rates of energy production are also plotted in *Figure 2.4* over a wider range of temperature T. Note how much more temperature-sensitive the rate for the carbon-cycle is, so that it dominates in stars hotter than the sun whereas the proton-chain dominates in stars like the sun or cooler. The low temperature-sensitivity of the proton-chain is unusual and is due to Z_1Z_2 in *Equation 2.4*, being unity which is much smaller than for all other thermonuclear reactions (the slowness of the reaction comes mainly from the beta-decay which must occur).

I have said that most of the energy released in the conversion of hydrogen into helium in the deep interior of a star is immediately absorbed and goes into thermal energy. A fraction of the energy, however, goes into kinetic energy of the two neutrinos which are released in the beta-decays. Neutrinos, unlike any other particles, do not react appreciably with anything at all and most of the neutrinos escape from the star without being scattered or absorbed. Since a neutrino passing through the earth has only a minute chance of being absorbed anywhere in the earth, it is clearly very difficult to detect the neutrinos by their absorption in a man-made detector. Nevertheless, such an experiment will be attempted soon in a huge tank in a deep mine in North Dakota. The different ways of completing the proton-chain (and the carbon-cycle) give neutrinos of different energy and the experiment, if successful, will tell us which predominates.

(d) Further reactions

Once we have produced helium out of hydrogen, can we go further and produce heavier elements yet? As in the case of hydrogen, the most obvious reactions involving $_2He^4$ will not work—a (p,γ) reaction does not work because $_3Li^5$ does not exist and a (α,γ) reaction does not work because $_4Be^8$ breaks up again into two alpha-particles after a while. We are not completely lost, however! During the short period the $_4Be^8$-nucleus holds together, there is a minute chance for another alpha-particle to be absorbed. The resultant nucleus in this case is $_6C^{12}$ which is perfectly stable,

$$2 \ _2He^4 \rightleftharpoons \ _4Be^8 \ ,$$
$$_4Be^8 + \ _2He^4 \rightarrow \ _6C^{12} + \gamma \tag{2.9}$$

Once C^{12} has been built up in this indirect way, some of the C^{12} produced will immediately react with some of the helium to form O^{16} and some of this in turn reacts immediately to form Ne^{20}. The reaction-chain in *Equation 2.9*, called the "triple-alpha reaction", requires temperatures of about $10^{8\circ}K$. This is much hotter than the interior of the sun but still not hot enough for the Ne^{20} to be pro-

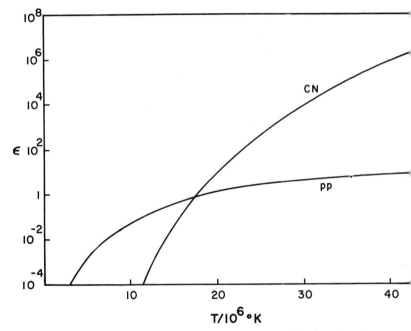

Figure 2.4.   The rate of energy production ε (in ergs/gm/sec) for the carbon-nitrogen cycle (CN) and the proton-proton chain (pp) as a function of temperature T.

cessed through to Mg^{24} or beyond.   The reactions can be summarized as

$$
\left.
\begin{array}{l}
3 \ _2He^4 \rightarrow \ _6C^{12} + 7 \cdot 3 \ MeV, \\
_6C^{12} + \ _2He^4 \rightarrow \ _8O^{16} + \gamma, \\
_8O^{16} + \ _2He^4 \rightarrow \ _{10}Ne^{20} + \gamma
\end{array}
\right\}
\qquad (2.10)
$$

where the final abundance ratios of C^{12}, O^{16} and Ne^{20} depend somewhat on the density and temperature.

We can ask what will happen if all the hydrogen and helium has been used up and the C^{12}, O^{16} and Ne^{20} are heated further.   The next reaction, requiring temperatures of almost $1 \times 10^{9}°K$, is the formation of $_{12}Mg^{24}$ (and nearby nuclei) out of two C^{12}-nuclei. At temperatures slightly above $1 \times 10^{9}°K$ the O^{16} is also used up with pairs of it reacting to form $_{16}S^{32}$ (and nearby nuclei).   At about the same temperature another process becomes noticeable which seems a step in the wrong direction: a few photons from the black-body spectrum now have enough energy to "photodisintegrate" a Ne^{20}-nucleus, which robs energy instead of releasing it and which undoes the last reaction in *Equation 2.10*. The alpha-particle released will quickly be absorbed on some nucleus (for instance Ne^{20}) and the net result is not an energy loss but the reshuffling of alpha-particles from Ne^{20} to nuclei with slightly greater binding energy B. The net change in chemical composition is the disappearance of C, O and Ne with the production of $_{12}Mg^{24}$, $_{14}Si^{28}$, $_{16}S^{32}$ and some other nuclei in this vicinity of the periodic table.

The Mg (or Si or S)-nuclei have too large a charge to react with each other at any appreciable rate. To build up even heavier nuclei from these, temperatures of about 3 or $4 \times 10^{9}\,°K$ are required. At these temperatures some of the magnesium to sulphur nuclei are photodisintegrated, some of the resulting lighter nuclei split further and further into alpha-particles and protons. Some of these alpha-particles and protons get absorbed by other magnesium to sulphur nuclei, some by the resulting nuclei and so on. A complicated network of nuclear reactions takes place and many different isotopes of the elements up to and including the "iron-region" can be built up. We shall not discuss these reactions in detail but it is time to look at the abundances of different elements and their isotopes.

(e) Abundances of elements and their isotopes

A few hundred different isotopes, from slightly more than 90 different elements, are stable. On the earth and for meteorites both the abundance ratios of different isotopes of the same element and the abundances of practically all the different chemical elements have been measured in detail. We have also seen that from spectroscopy the abundances of very many (but not all) elements can and have been measured for the outer layers of the sun (and even some isotopic abundance ratios). For the outer layers of many other stars similar measurements have been carried out for a number of elements (especially for hotter stars). Abundances have also been measured spectroscopically for the cold interstellar gas which lies in the path of light from distant stars and also for some luminous regions of gas, called "planetary nebulae".

For the earth and meteorites we have already seen that the escape of light gases have greatly depleted the abundance of hydrogen and helium. During the complicated geological history of the earth

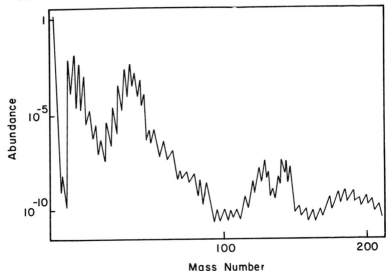

Figure 2.5. The "cosmic" abundance (by number of atoms, relative to hydrogen) as a function of atomic weight A (or "mass number").

some "chemical fractionation" has also altered the relative abundances of some chemical elements.   Nevertheless, geochemists have puzzled these effects out fairly well and isotopic abundance ratios are usually not affected.   It seems then that the abundances are pretty much the same in the inter-stellar gas today, in the surface of the sun and of all stars at least as young as the sun and in the material from which the earth and meteorites were formed. The detailed information from the earth and meteorites has been judiciously used to fill in gaps in abundance measurements for the sun, stars and inter-stellar gas.   These adjusted abundances are called the "cosmic" abundances (but we shall see that very old stars form an exception which is of great significance).

Some of the gross features of the "cosmic" abundances of the chemical elements (without distinguishing between their isotopes) is shown schematically in *Figure 2.5*.   Some of the important features are: of all the elements other than hydrogen and helium, the group of elements between $_6C$ and $_{16}S$ are the most abundant and Li, Be and B have a particularly low abundance.   The next most abundant

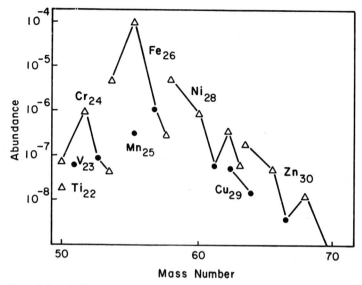

Figure 2.6.   The detailed "cosmic" abundances as a function of atomic mass number for a few elements in the "iron-region".

group of elements are the metals in the iron-region with a maximum abundance at $_{26}$Fe and abundances falling off rapidly below $_{24}$Cr and above $_{28}$Ni.   *All* the elements above $_{28}$Ni (which I shall call "heavy elements"), even when put together, have a very much lower abundance then the light elements or the iron-group, but there are at least two relative abundance peaks among the heavy elements.

To illustrate the wealth of abundance information available when isotopic abundance ratios are included, I have plotted absolute abundances against the atomic weight A of the isotopes for just a few elements in the iron-region in *Figure 2.6*.   One detailed feature which is true in most regions of the periodic table (but *not* in all) is that the abundance tends to be higher for a nucleus with a higher binding energy (compared to its neighbours).   For the elements in *Figure 2.6* with more than one isotope, for instance, the most abundant isotope is also the one with the largest binding energy B per nucleon. Nuclei with odd Z, such as $_{25}$Mn and $_{27}$Co, usually have lower B than "even-even nuclei" and the abundances for $_{25}$Mn and $_{27}$Co are indeed lower than for $_{24}Cr$ or $_{26}Fe$ or $_{28}Ni$, etc. Another detailed feature is the particularly high abundance of the five n-alpha nuclei C^{12}, O^{16}, Ne^{20}, Mg^{24} and Si^{28} (and S^{32} slightly lower).

Some of the abundance features we can already explain in a general sort of way in terms of thermonuclear reactions in stars. If some stars have exhausted their hydrogen and have attained internal temperatures of about $10^{8°}K$, helium is converted to C^{12}, O^{16} and Ne^{20} in large quantities (and small amounts of other light nuclei). If some of these stars lose their material to the interstellar gas, the gas will be enriched in these three isotopes. Other such stars might live on after exhausting their helium and reach internal temperatures of about $10^{9°}K$ in which case these three isotopes are processed to Mg^{24}, Si^{28} (and a number of other nuclei). This explains the high abundance of the five or six light n-alpha nuclei.

We have seen in *Figure 2.6* the richness of the abundance data for the iron-region. The network of reactions leading from nuclei like Mg, Si and S to the elements in the iron-region is a very complicated one, involving (p,γ) and (a,γ) as well as their inverses, the "photo-disintegrations", and also occasional beta-decays. Because of the interplay between exothermic reactions and their inverses one should expect final abundances to be strongly correlated with binding energy B per nucleon. The detailed final abundances also depend somewhat on the rates of individual reactions and quantitative calculations of the reaction network have by now been done. Although there are a few discrepancies here and there, the agreement between the theoretical predictions and the observed abundances in *Figure 2.6* is quite astounding.

None of the reactions we have discussed so far could explain any production of the heavy elements, beyond the iron-region ($Z \gtrsim 30$). These heavy nuclei have a lower value of B, have a large Coulomb repulsion (although they are neutron-rich, A - Z > Z) and could not easily be made by absorption of protons or alpha-particles. However, if the elements in the iron-region were exposed to a flux of *neutrons* such a build-up could occur: neutrons do not suffer any Coulomb repulsion and successive neutron absorptions can take place easily. If the neutrons are produced at a low rate over a long-period (the "slow" or "s-process") any beta-emitting nucleus produced has time for its beta-decay before the next neutron absorption takes place. On the "s-process" neutron-absorption then takes place along completely stable nuclei. One can calculate predicted abundances from the neutron absorption rates which have been measured in the laboratory. These calculations have been carried out and again (after adjusting two free parameters) the agreement is excellent at least with many of the observed abundances including one abundance peak among the heavy nuclei.

What could be some of the sources of a neutron-flux on a slow time-scale inside stars? When discussing thermonuclear reactions earlier I listed only the major reactions, but some of the minor ones produce neutrons. For instance, in connection with the triple-alpha reaction we discussed the absorption of alpha-particles on major constituents such as $_6C^{12}$, but small amounts of other isotopes are also present including a little $_6C^{13}$. This nucleus undergoes the reaction

$$_6C^{13} + {_2He^4} \rightarrow {_8O^{16}} + n \tag{2.11}$$

which is one of the sources of neutrons in stars.

A few of the heavy nuclei require for their formation the "r-process" (for "rapid") where neutrons are produced and absorbed at such a great and rapid rate that there isn't time for beta-decay and neutrons are absorbed even on beta-unstable nuclei. This rapid event of course took place a long time ago and beta-decays have occurred since the neutron-flux stopped, but the resulting stable nuclei are different from those produced in the s-process. Ordinary stars do not provide such a rapid neutron-flux, but we shall come to more favourable, although drastic, conditions in the last chapter.

CHAPTER 3

Evolution of Stars

So far we have concentrated on a single star at a single epoch in its development, the present-day sun. To study the evolution of stars we first have to look at the observational data for other stars. We then return to theoretical calculations of the internal structure of stars, paying more attention to the slow but steady changes with time.

(a) The colour-luminosity diagram and the initial main sequence

The earth revolves about the sun in an orbit whose diameter is 2 astronomical units. This diameter is small but not negligibly small compared with the distance to nearby stars. For a few hundred such stars one can measure accurately the "trigonometric parallax"— the apparent angular wobble back and forth (relative to very distant galaxies) of the star due to the real periodic motion of the earth. More indirect methods for determining distance of stars that are further away can also be used in some cases and calibrated against information obtained from the nearby stars.

If a star can be seen at all (many tens of thousand can be seen with even a modest telescope), the radiation from it reaching the earth per second can be measured easily. If its distance from us is known, one can then easily calculate its absolute luminosity L. The colour temperature can also be observed (by measuring the ratio of intensities at a few different wave lengths) and, after applying some small corrections, this gives the effective black-body surface temperature T_s. Each such star can then be represented as a point on a "colour-luminosity diagram" with T_s plotted horizontally and L vertically, as in *Figure 3.1*. To each point on such a diagram there corresponds a definite value of the stellar radius R, which can be calculated from *Equation 1.10*. Note that radii are smallest on the bottom left and largest on the top right of a diagram such as *Figure 3.1*.

If one plots all the stars which are near enough to have a reliable

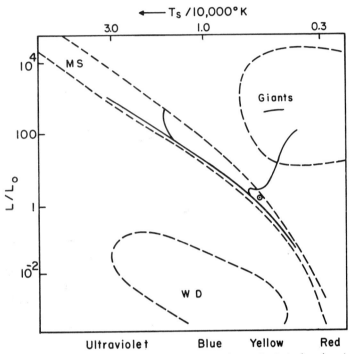

Figure 3.1.   The luminosity L (in units of the solar luminosity $L_\odot$) plotted against colour or surface temperature T_s.

distance measured for them (from trigonometric parallax or other means) on such a diagram, one finds that only some regions of it are heavily populated.   The most prominent feature is a narrow band from left top to bottom right (labelled M.S. between dotted lines) called the "main sequence".   About 80 or 90% of all stars, including our sun, are main sequence stars with most of them about as bright as the sun or fainter.   Another region of the colour-luminosity diagram is the right-top region (labelled *Giants* in *Figure 3.1*) which corresponds to rather luminous stars with very large radii R, the "red giants" which constitute only a few percent of all stars and have a rather large spread in L and R.   Finally, the left-bottom contains an elongated region (labelled WD) of the so-called "white dwarfs" with rather low luminosity but very small radii.   About

10 or 20% of all stars are white dwarfs. Finally, a more detailed point about the statistics of main sequence stars: for $L > 2L_\odot$ the number of main sequence stars (in the volume which is less than a few hundred light years away from us) decreases very rapidly with increasing luminosity L.

To get values of radius R from measurements of L and of colour, one has to know the "bolometric correction", the fraction of the total luminosity contributed by the infra-red and ultra-violet (which cannot be observed from the ground) and the conversion from colour to effective surface temperature T_s. For very cool and very hot stars which radiate mainly in the infra-red and the ultra-violet, respectively, the uncertainties are rather great. Fortunately, the stellar intensity interferometer at Narrabri can measure directly and accurately the apparent angular size and hence radius R of a few dozen stars with accurately known distances. These precision measurements of R can be used to calibrate the colour—T_s conversion. Orbiting astronomical telescopes outside the earth's absorbing atmosphere will soon measure infra-red and ultra-violet luminosities, which will give bolometric corrections accurately.

We have seen how one can calculate the mass of the sun from observations on planets revolving around the sun. We cannot observe any planets of other stars, but many stars come in pairs and in a few favourable cases of such "binaries" one can measure all the properties of the orbits the two stars describe as they revolve around each other. From analyzing these orbits one can calculate the masses of both stars. We have already said the main sequence is (almost) a line in *Figure 3.1* so that a unique luminosity goes with each radius. In addition one finds a unique mass for each point on the main sequence with mass increasing with increasing luminosity. The red giants are sufficiently rare so that there is little reliable data on their masses, but it seems to be a heterogeneous group with different masses ranging from slightly more than 1 $M_\odot$ to higher masses. There are also few direct accurate mass values for white dwarfs, but most of them probably lie between about $\frac{1}{2}M_\odot$ and $M_\odot$.

As *Figure 3.1* shows, the main sequence is really a band rather than a single line on a T_s-L plot. For reasons which will become apparent in the next subsection, the lower boundary of this band is called the "Initial Main Sequence" and is most important. In *Table 1* we find mass M, radius R and luminosity L for three points

Table 1

	$M/M_\odot$	$R/R_\odot$	$\dfrac{M}{M_\odot}\dfrac{R_\odot}{R}$	$L/L_\odot$
M.S.	0·2	0·5	0·4	0·01
M.S.	1	1	1	0·8
M.S.	25	7	3·5	10^5
R.G.	~2	~100	~0·02	~100
W.D.	~0·7	~0·02	~50	~0·001

on this initial main sequence. Note that luminosity L is a very rapidly increasing function of M whereas M/R increases only very slowly.

We can now compare these observational facts about stars on the initial main sequence with the simple theoretical considerations of stellar structure in *Chapter 1*. Remember that these considerations were based on two assumptions, i.e., that the star has (i) a uniform chemical composition throughout it and (ii) an internal pressure which obeys the "perfect gas law" in *Equation 1.4* as predicted by *classical* statistical mechanics. *Equation 1.5* showed that internal temperatures $\overline{T}$ are proportional to M/R and *Table 1* implies that $\overline{T}$ varies rather little along the main sequence (between about 4 and 30 million °K, say). The luminosity L is given in terms of the photon mean free path l by *Equation 1.12*. This quantity l depends in a complicated way on temperature $\overline{T}$ and density $\bar{\rho}$ and one finds that l increases fairly rapidly with increasing stellar mass M (more massive stars have somewhat larger $\overline{T}$ and lower $\bar{\rho}$). The predicted L is then a rapidly increasing function of M, something like

$$L/0{\cdot}8L_\odot \sim (M/M_\odot)^{4 \text{ or } 5} . \qquad (3.1)$$

We also saw in *Chapter 2* that the thermonuclear rate of energy production from the conversion of hydrogen into helium increases extremely rapidly with temperature (see *Equation 2.8* and *Figure 2.4*), which reconciles the rapid variation of L with the slow variation of $\overline{T}$.

Accurate stellar structure calculations for uniform stars have now been carried out for a number of different masses. The agreement with the observations of the initial main sequence is excellent. Our own sun actually lies slightly above the *initial* main sequence line in *Figure 3.1* (but well inside the main sequence *band*). The calculations for solar mass predict close to $0\cdot8\ L_\odot$, the value on the observed initial main sequence!

The situation is radically different for the red giants and for the white dwarfs. *Table 1* gives only one example of each, but for *all* red giants the ratio M/R is very much smaller than for any main sequence star and for *all* white dwarfs this ratio is very much larger. The theoretical models for stars we have discussed so far clearly cannot explain such stars—one or both of the assumptions I mentioned earlier must be wrong for these stars! We shall see that (i) red giants do *not* have a uniform chemical composition and (ii) densities inside white dwarfs are so high that the perfect gas law of classical mechanics breaks down and has to be replaced by a quantum mechanical pressure law. These two statements are true but not self-evident and we shall first have to consider the evolution of stars. One clue is provided by observations on star clusters.

(b) Star clusters and stellar populations

Many of the stars in our galaxy do not occur singly but are part of a cluster of stars. Some of these clusters have an irregular shape and contain a rather small number of stars (a few hundred, say) and are called "open clusters". A different type are the "globular clusters" which are tight spherical collections of stars, each containing as many as 100,000 stars.

On a larger scale still, different parts of our galaxy have different properties: (I) Our sun and the "open clusters" are situated in the "spiral arm" region of the galaxy which contains a lot of gas and dust and rotates about the centre of the galaxy. (II) The globular clusters and individual stars called "high velocity" stars are often (but *not* always) situated far above the spiral arms and are characterized by high random velocities rather than galactic rotation. I cannot discuss here theories of the evolution of a whole galaxy but these theories give us a clue that stars in "population II" were all formed at about the same time and are the oldest stars (of age

t_o , say), whereas some star formation is still going on from the gas and dust in population I (so that these stars have ages ranging from almost zero to t_o).

Instead of plotting *all* nearby stars on a colour-luminosity (or T_s-L) diagram, let us plot merely the stars in one particular cluster. This has two advantages: if there are errors in distance measurements, the stars in one cluster are all at nearly the same distance from us so there will be little scatter in the T_s-L points (although there may be a small common shift). Secondly, we believe that all stars in one cluster must be practically the same age (but the value of this age differs from one open cluster to another). In *Figure 3.1* you will find just two examples of the diagram for an individual cluster (thin black curves) but they illustrate the general features: the lower part of the main sequence follows the "initial main sequence" (lower left boundary of the main sequence band) at low luminosities, above some luminosity L_{c1} the curve starts to deviate from the initial main sequence and to cross the main sequence band. The curve then moves into the red giant region (usually after a "gap" which represents merely a paucity, not an absence, of stars in this region).

The value of L_{c1}, the "turn-off" from the main sequence, varies greatly from cluster to cluster. More precisely, this is true for the "open clusters" or even smaller star groups in stellar population I with L_{c1} having the largest values for the youngest clusters (some are only a few million years old). The globular clusters typical of stellar population II, on the other hand, all have almost the same turn-off at $L_{c1} \sim 2L_\odot$. The *oldest* of the open clusters of population I also have their turn-off near $2L_\odot$ (with a curve through the red giant region similar to, but not identical with, that of globular clusters).

These colour-luminosity diagrams for different clusters, together with *Equation 3.1*, give us enough clues about the basic features of stellar evolution: the rate of energy production per unit mass of a star is proportional to L/M and, according to *Equation 3.1*, this ratio increases with increasing M and L. Since the nuclear energy reservoir per unit mass is fixed it is plausible that stars of low mass and luminosity should "live longer" than bright massive ones. Stars with $L << L_{c1}$ in a given cluster have used up very little of their nuclear fuel and are still on the "initial main sequence", as the name implies, whereas stars with $L >> L_{c1}$ have long since "died" (in a fashion we shall discuss later). The early evolution away from the main sequence, after a star with $L \sim L_{c1}$ has burned some but not all of its nuclear fuel, must therefore be into the red giant region.

By carefully counting the number of stars in different parts of the colour-luminosity diagram one could, in principle, get more quantitative but empirical information on evolution including even the speed of evolution. For instance, individual stars must cross the "gap" between the main sequence band and red giant region quite rapidly, since the "snapshot picture" we take of the whole clusters shows so few stars in this gap. The curves for open clusters are also compatible with the colour-luminosity diagram for nearby stars in general. In fact, if we superimposed the curves for open clusters of all ages up to the oldest observed one we would get a picture very similar to the main sequence band plus giant region of the nearby stars. Even the frequency of occurrence of nearby stars of different types can be understood: *all* main sequence stars of $L \lesssim 2L_\odot$ are still on or near the main sequence, whereas of the more luminous stars only those born more recently are still present (the rest have evolved into the giant region or beyond).

Besides stars in the main sequence and giant regions most clusters also have a smaller number of other kinds of stars, including white dwarfs. These represent later stages of evolution and we shall return to that later.

I still have to mention a most important observational fact on chemical abundances: we have seen that the present-day interstellar gas has about the same relative abundances of helium and heavier elements as the atmospheres of the sun and of younger population I stars. The situation is quite different for the population II stars which have lower abundances of the elements heavier than helium (the situation with helium is uncertain at the moment). The numerical values of these abundances vary from one population II star to another, some of them have these elements *under*abundant by factors of about one hundred! This certainly must have something to do with "element cooking" in stars, especially in old population II stars. You might be puzzled, however, that the oldest stars show the lowest rather than the highest abundances. I shall explain this later on.

(c) Early evolution and red giants

We have seen that our sun is about 5 billion years old and converts about 1% of its total mass from hydrogen into helium per billion years. We shall see that our galaxy and stellar population II stars are about 10 billion years old. Near their "turn-off" in the luminosity-colour diagram (slightly brighter than the sun) stars have converted 10 or 15% of their hydrogen into helium when they move toward the red giant region. *If* the helium produced were mixed uniformly throughout the star, its position on the colour-luminosity diagram would be altered only slightly—furthermore, this small change would be to the left ("bluer") instead of to the right ("redder") of the initial main sequence!

To resolve this puzzle we have to return to a finer detail of the internal structure and the thermonuclear reactions in a main sequence star. You will remember that (a) the temperature drops from its maximum value at the centre of the star as one moves outwards and that (b) the nuclear reaction rates (even for the proton-chain) increase rapidly with increasing temperature. Most of the nuclear reactions, and hence most of the build-up of helium, therefore takes place in the innermost regions of the star which contain only a few per cent (less than 20% even for the proton-chain) of the mass of the star. This will tend to build up a high concentration of helium in the inner regions and very little further out. We only have to make sure that nothing can mix the outer with the inner regions.

We are used to the phenomenon of "convection" where atoms move large distances by simply being carried along in some bulk motion, as in the wind in our atmosphere or the motion of the water in a boiling pot. Such convection can be very efficient at "turning over" material, *if* it can take place at all. Detailed theoretical studies of stellar interiors show that there may be some convection very close to the centre of a star, and possible again very close to its surface, but *not* in the in-between regions. So convection cannot transport helium out from the centre, but how about diffusion of individual He-nuclei? We have already discussed such diffusion by "random walk" of photons and saw that it requires about 10^7 years for a photon to diffuse out towards the surface of the sun. For nuclei and electrons, however, the process is much too slow (would require at least 10^{11} years). We can therefore confidently assert that the high concentrations of helium built up in the innermost "core" of a star will remain there.

We already have an explanation why one could not see from spectroscopic studies of the *outermost* layers any trace of the helium built up in the inner. The rather drastic change from mainly helium in the inner core to predominantly hydrogen further out has also another effect which is easy to describe but hard to explain: ionized H^1 and He^4 have different mean molecular weights μ and μ occurs in the equation of hydrostatic equilibrium. As the inner core becomes richer in He, its value of μ increases slightly and slowly and we are not surprised to find that detailed calculations for such stars predict slow and slight changes in the interior conditions such as central temperature and luminosity. For the sun, for instance, these calculations predict a luminosity increase of about 20% after 5 billion years which explains the discrepancy between our sun and the initial main sequence. One result of these detailed calculations is surprising, however: these slight changes in the interior are eventually accompanied by a *drastic* increase in radius of the outermost layers—the surface is puffed out like a balloon! I cannot give any qualitative physical explanation for this—we merely have to accept the results of these calculations.

When we observe the radius R of a star we mean that outermost layer of it from which the light-photons escape. The mass of this layer is a negligibly small fraction of the total mass of any star. In *Chapter 1* we assumed that this R is not much larger (a factor of two or so) than the radius r_{typ} of a "typical point" such that half the mass is below ($r < r_{typ}$) and half is above ($r_{typ} < r < R$). For main sequence stars this assertion is backed up by the real calculations but as the outer surface "puffs out" r_{typ} changes little while R increases greatly. *Equation 1.5* should have r_{typ} in it instead of R and these stars with a giant outer radius can have quite high central temperatures. On the other hand, *Equation 1.10* refers to the outermost layers so that, for given luminosity, the surface temperature for these giants is lower ("red giants" compared with our yellow sun).

I have said that the interior of a star changes relatively little in its early evolution away from the main sequence and toward the red giant region. However, when the hydrogen in the star's inner core is completely exhausted, the core also has to change appreciably:

we now have no nuclear energy source but the star keeps shining on with about the same luminosity. We have seen that the star's internal heat content is radiated away in about 10^7 years and you might think that the interior would cool off then. It is true that the interior temperature $\overline{T}$ takes about this time scale to change appreciably but it *increases* instead of decreasing! As energy is radiated away the pressure lags slightly behind the gravitational acceleration, the inner core contracts and thereby releases some gravitational energy and, according to the so-called Virial Theorem, only half of this energy release is radiated away while the other half heats the interior further.

(d) Later evolution and white dwarfs

The last remarks can be summarized crudely but in general as: "When in doubt" (i.e., when it has no adequate nuclear energy production) a star (or at least its inner core) will contract and heat up until "something else happens". Except for some drastic possibilities I will discuss at the very end of this chapter, the "something else" is the onset of another thermonuclear reaction.

For stars whose inner core has been converted from hydrogen into helium and has started to contract and heat up, the situation is slightly complicated as follows. The layers just outside the inner core still contain lots of hydrogen and they also heat up as the core does and eventually become hot enough for hydrogen burning. We then have a thin "shell-source" of nuclear energy—inside the shell there is no hydrogen left and outside the shell the temperature has dropped so that the rate of energy production is rather low. As more hydrogen is converted into helium the location of this shell moves outwards and detailed calculations show that the temperature T_c at the centre of the inner core keeps on increasing.

Finally T_c increases sufficiently (to about $10^{8\circ}$K) so that helium-burning by means of the triple-alpha reaction starts at the centre of the star. The star then has a rather complicated structure with two energy sources as shown in *Figure 3.2*. For stars with mass less than about $1 \cdot 5 \; M_{\odot}$ the onset of helium-burning changes the structure of the whole star appreciably. In *Figure 3.3* a part of the colour-luminosity diagram for stars in a globular cluster (solid line) is shown in more detail: The point with the highest luminosity and lowest surface temperature is reached when helium-burning is

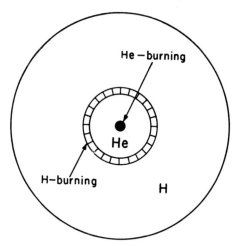

Figure 3.2. The various layers in an evolved star.

just barely starting at the centre. When the energy production rate due to helium-burning becomes appreciable the luminosity and outer radius both decrease suddenly but slightly, leading to the discontinuity in *Figure 3.3* (the horizontal portion in this figure is appropriately called the "horizontal branch").

After the helium has been exhausted in the inner core from the triple-alpha reaction, this core will again contract and heat up. After a while the central temperature is sufficient for carbon-burning at the centre simultaneously with a shell-source of helium-burning and another shell further out of hydrogen-burning. In principle, this process can continue with the most advanced thermonuclear reaction at the centre and more and more other reactions in successive shells with hydrogen-burning in the outermost shell. The star is then made up of many different layers, reminiscent of an onion, possible with iron and its metal-group nearest the centre, elements like Mg to S next, then C to Ne, followed by He and finally an outer layer consisting still of the material (mainly hydrogen) from which the star was originally formed.

The early evolution of a main sequence star into the red giant region and the onset of helium-burning have been calculated for stars of

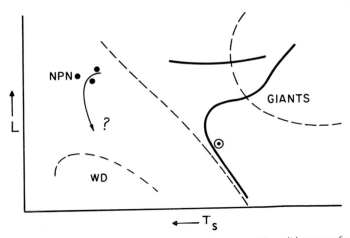

Figure 3.3. A portion of the colour-luminosity diagram. The solid curve refers to stars in a globular cluster.

different masses. For each assumed age of a cluster one can then calculate a theoretical colour-luminosity curve. For most clusters one of these theoretical curves agrees well with the observations, which gives us confidence in the theory and also gives us the actual age of the cluster. The globular clusters, and hence our galaxy, are about 10 billion years old. For the later stages calculations can and have also been carried out in spite of the more complicated structure. Uncertainties build up rapidly as the evolution progresses, not because of the complex internal structure which can be handled by modern electronic computations but because of a phenomenon we have disregarded so far—mass-loss from a star. We know our sun loses some of its mass in the form of "corpuscular radiation", i.e., the outermost parts of the very tenuous solar corona are somehow shot out into the solar wind. For the sun the rate of loss amounts to very little even after many billions of years, but there is some evidence that the rate may be enormously greater for some stars, especially for some red giant stars with their "puffed-up" envelopes.

The phenomenon of mass-loss is not understood well at the moment and its rate probably depends greatly on quantities such as magnetic fields and rotation, which can be different for otherwise similar stars. It is then possible that some stars lose a considerable fraction of their mass steadily and continuously as they evolve while others lose little. We shall see later that the stars which lose little mass eventually end in a most spectacular explosion (supernova) but let us now follow the stars that have lost much of their mass (relatively quietly).

I have said that a star's interior temperature $\overline{T}$ increases proportionally to M/R as a star's radius R decreases. For sufficiently massive stars ($M \gg 1.5\ M_\odot$) this is always true, but not for stars of low mass and the mass remaining after steady mass-loss for many stars is likely to be less than 1 $M_\odot$. As a star shrinks a purely quantum-mechanical phenomenon takes over, the so-called "electron-degeneracy": Let r be the average distance between "neighbouring" electrons, which decreases in proportion to radius R as the star shrinks. According to quantum mechanics most electrons then have an additional momentum (called the Fermi momentum p_F) which can be estimated from the Heisenberg uncertainty principle to be about h/r, where h is Planck's constant. The corresponding energy per electron (the Fermi energy E_F) is then of the order of

$$E_F = \frac{1}{2m}\ p_F^2 \sim \frac{(h/r)^2}{2m} \propto \frac{1}{R^2} \tag{3.2}$$

The Fermi energy thus increases with two powers of $1/R$ where $k\overline{T}$ increases with only one power of M/R. For a mass below about 1 $M_\odot$ the Fermi energy E_F eventually exceeds the thermal energy $k\overline{T}$ (per electron), the electrons are becoming "degenerate" and the correct pressure no longer obeys the "perfect classical gas law" which we had assumed in *Chapter 1* and *Equation 1.5* for the temperature $\overline{T}$ is now simply wrong. In fact, as R decreases steadily, $\overline{T}$ reaches a finite maximum value at a *finite* value of R and then decreases toward zero temperature which it would reach at another (slightly smaller) value R_{cr} of the radius.

Degeneracy effects are more important for stars of lower mass so that R_{cr} actually increases with decreasing mass. Chandrasekhar proposed about 30 years ago that the white dwarfs are stars in which the electrons are highly degenerate and most of the pressure is "degeneracy" rather than thermal pressure. The predicted radii should then be close to R_{cr} which Chandrasekhar also calculated as a function of mass, $R_{cr} \approx 0.05\ R_\odot$ for $M = 0.3\ M_\odot$ and

$R_{cr} \approx 0.01\ R_\odot$ for $M = 1\ M_\odot$, for instance. The observed radii of most white dwarfs fall in this expected range of 0.01 to $0.03\ R_\odot$.

Another interesting although rare type of star are the "nuclei of planetary nebulae" which have radii almost as small as white dwarfs but much larger luminosities. Typical positions for them in *Figure 3.3* are labelled NPN. These are thought to be a "half-way stage" in a star's progress towards the white dwarf stage. This progress (or decline) can be summarized as follows.

Consider a star which has lost an appreciable fraction of its mass in a continuous manner during its red giant stage (or later phases). This mass-loss probably took place in a mild enough manner so that the outer layers were shed which are rich in hydrogen, whereas the inner regions had all their hydrogen (and probably even their helium) converted into heavier nuclei. We may typically be dealing with a star remnant of mass about $0.7\ M_\odot$ consisting of C^{12} or heavier elements in its interior, a little helium further out with negligible amounts of hydrogen left. Such a remnant star has little change for any thermonuclear source of energy production and consequently must contract slowly. Near to the NPN position in the colour-luminosity diagram in *Figure 3.3*, the interior material begins to show signs of electron degeneracy and the luminosity reaches a maximum value and so does the central temperature (a few times $10^{8\circ}$K, not quite sufficient to burn carbon). After that the radius keeps decreasing (slightly) towards the finite limiting value R_{cr} (about 0.02 $R_\odot$) while the luminosity and central temperature T_c both decrease. The time-scale of the cooling of the star is determined by the luminosity L and increases as L becomes small. A star in the NPN region, for instance, will cool appreciably in less than 10^6 years whereas a typical white dwarf (with T_c only a few times $10^{6\circ}$K) would require 10^{10} years or so to decrease T_c by another factor of two. The final fate of such a star is then no dramatic death—it "merely fades away" at constant radius to lower and lower temperature at a slower and slower rate.

(e) Supernovae and element cooking

I want to end this series with a big bang, the violent star deaths known as "supernovae". These are gigantic explosions of a star in which most of the star is shattered and the debris mixed into the interstellar gas. For a few weeks after the onset of such an explosion the luminosity can be as high as $10^8 L_\odot$. In our galaxy, supernovae explosions occur only about one every hundred years or so, but nevertheless about 10% of all "star-deaths" are of this type (the rest ending as white dwarfs).

Consider now stars which have managed to evolve rather far without having lost very much mass along the way, so that the remaining mass is larger than $1 \cdot 5 M_\odot$, say. For these larger masses the electron degeneracy effects, which are all-important for white dwarfs, are less severe and relativistic effects come into play as the radius decreases further. These relativistic effects modify the quantum mechanical effects in such a way that a *massive* star never suffers from high electron degeneracy, so that the radius can decrease and the internal temperature $\overline{T}$ increase *indefinitely*. In other words, the two effects of relativity and quantum mechanics, both of which we had omitted in *Chapter 1*, almost cancel each other and *Equation 1.5* remains fairly good always for stars of large enough mass.

One of these massive stars can have quite a complicated structure after sufficient evolution: the nuclei in the iron-region make up its inner core, then medium-light elements followed by helium but with plenty of hydrogen still remaining in the outer regions. Since the nuclei in the inner core have the largest possible binding energy per nucleon, *any* nuclear transformations in the core can only rob energy rather than produce it. Such energy loss can lead to the rapid collapse of the inner core under gravitation and the layer outside this core will start falling in on itself (since there is no pressure holding it up from below). During this falling in the gas (rich in helium and hydrogen) is compressed and heated greatly, somewhat like in the triggering of a hydrogen bomb, and H, He and other light nuclei can be "ignited". The energy release from the nuclear transformations in these outer layers is large and rapid, so that an explosion ensues which shatters much of the star.

This thermonuclear explosion has a profound effect on the chemical abundances in the universe, in two ways. Most important, much of the isotopes from C^{12} to the iron-region nuclei (which had been produced *previously* in various layers of the star) are fed into the inter stellar gas during the explosion. As discussed before, the surfaces of surviving very old population II stars show that the interstellar gas contained very little of the elements heavier than He when our galaxy was very young. Estimates of the rate of occurrence of supernovae explosions at different epochs of our galaxy indicate that the interstellar gas was already appreciably enriched when the later population II stars were formed from it and that gradual, slight further enrichment has taken place since then.

Supernovae explosions also solve the puzzle as to where in the universe the "r-process" can be occurring. We have seen that such an explosion involves many different nuclear reactions occurring simultaneously (with H, He, C^{12}, iron-nuclei, etc., having been mixed together and heated) and on a very rapid time-scale. As discussed in connection with the s-process, some of the (minor) nuclear reactions produce a flux of neutrons. Since all reactions during the supernova explosion proceed rapidly, the neutron flux is also very great but lasts only a very short time. Plenty of nuclei in the iron-region are present and can undergo many successive neutron-captures with insufficient time for beta-decays between neutron-captures. Radioactive nuclei are thus formed in this "r-process" and fed into the inter-stellar gas, together with the other supernova debris, where they eventually decay.

In this narrative of a supernova event I have left the inner core of the star when it started to collapse. The eventual fate of the inner core is a fascinating question to which we do not yet know the correct answer, although we are aware of a number of possibilities. The collapse is helped (and our calculations of it hindered) by processes in which pairs of neutrinos are produced which take away energy rapidly from the core. It is possible that the collapse is halted when nuclei start touching and are pressed together, but it is also possible that the collapse keeps on going. If the collapse continues, very strange phenomena involving General Relativity take place, including the eventual vanishing from view of the collapsing object. If the collapse is halted by nuclear effects one is also dealing with a strange object. The internal density is many millions of times higher still than in a white dwarf star. At these densities most of the electrons are absorbed by the nuclei and one has a "neutron star" consisting largely of neutrons. This neutron matter is surrounded by an outer layer of more or less ordinary material, but the radius of the whole neutron star is only a few kilometers. Such a neutron star would mainly radiate X-rays (rather than visible light) which are absorbed in the earth's atmosphere, but rocket and satellite experiments will soon search for such neutron stars.

The Transuranium

Elements

by

DR. GLENN T. SEABORG

Dr. Glenn T. Seaborg
Chairman of the U.S. Atomic Energy Commission,
Washington D.C.

The Transuranium Elements

Introduction

An exciting branch of science, which started as recently as World War II and has a clearly discernible future of great promise, is that of the "transuranium elements". These are the man-made chemical elements with atomic numbers greater than that of the heaviest natural element, uranium, which has the atomic number 92 (that is, it has 92 protons in its nucleus). The transuranium elements are, for all practical purposes, synthetic in origin and must be produced by transmutation, starting in the first instance with uranium. The key to the discovery of these "synthetic" elements was their position in the periodic table.

93	NEPTUNIUM, Np
94	PLUTONIUM, Pu
95	AMERICIUM, Am
96	CURIUM, Cm
97	BERKELIUM, Bk
98	CALIFORNIUM, Cf
99	EINSTEINIUM, Es
100	FERMIUM, Fm
101	MENDELEVIUM, Md
102	——
103	LAWRENCIUM, Lr
104	——

Figure 1. The Transuranium Elements.

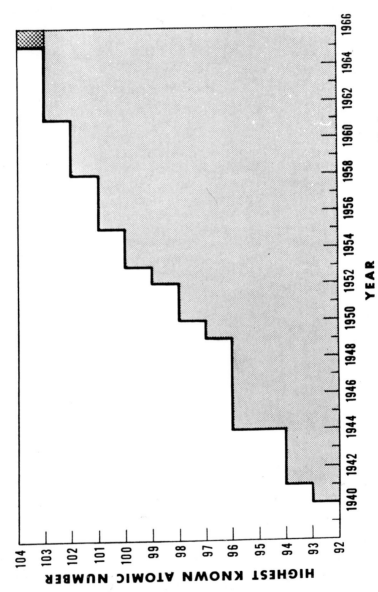

Figure 2. Increase in number of known transuranium elements with time.

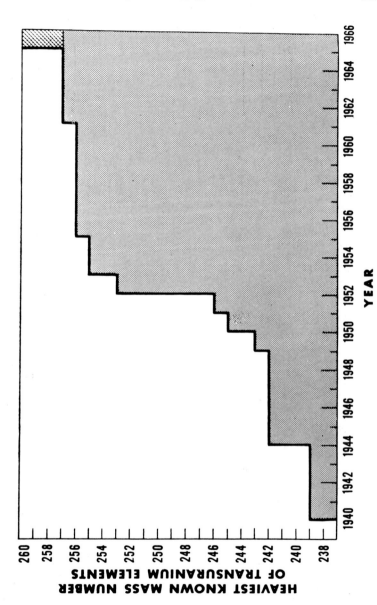

Figure 3. Increase in known mass number of transuranium isotopes with time.

At the present time, eleven and perhaps twelve transuranium elements have been created and discovered with a total of nearly 100 isotopes. All the transuranium elements are shown in *Figure 1;* they are unstable and, therefore, are radioactive. The half-life of the various isotopes decreases in general with increasing atomic number — this means that as we create heavier and heavier elements they exist for shorter and shorter periods, and as a result their production, separation and identification become progressively more difficult.

It is interesting to observe how the discovery of the individual elements has been spread over time. The pace of discovery is shown in *Figure 2* where the atomic number (the number of protons in the nucleus) of each new element is related to the time of its discovery during the last 25 years. In terms of mass number (the sum of protons and neutrons in the nucleus) we have been able to synthesize isotopes as high as mass number 257 in easily detectable quantity, and perhaps as high as mass number 260 in quantities of a few atoms. The advancement of mass number with time is shown in *Figure 3*.

Many radioactive isotopes have been synthesized for each of the transuranium elements, giving us today a total of about 100 transuranium isotopes. The increase with time of the total number of transuranium isotopes is shown in *Figure 4*.

The transuranium elements up to and including element 99, einsteinium, have been isolated in weighable quantities — those beyond element 99 have been investigated only with tracer quantities, that is, quantities not visible to the eye and too small to be weighed. Element 98, californium, was available in 1966 in only rather small quantities — microgram quantities — and element 99, einsteinium, was available only in submicrogram or what we call *nanogram* (billionths of a gram) quantities, but within a few years, as a recently initiated AEC program for the production of these elements gets under way, larger quantities, perhaps grams of californium and milligrams of einsteinium, will become available.

Prior to the discovery of the transuranium elements, the relationship of the heaviest naturally occurring elements, actinium, thorium, protactinium and uranium, in the periodic table was not clearly understood. Today we know that the transuranium elements fit in

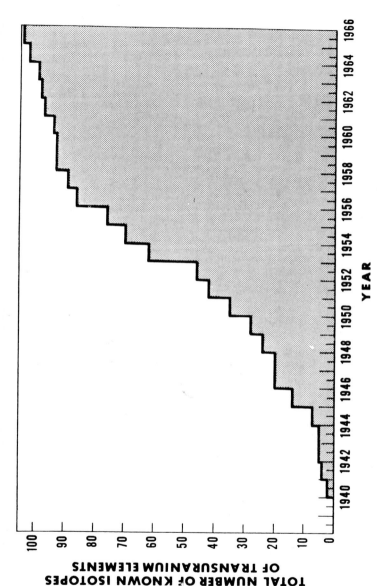

Figure 4. Increase in total number of known transuranium isotopes with time.

as a separate row at the bottom — as shown in *Figure 5* — set apart from the periodic table along with the previously known naturally occurring elements — actinium, thorium, protactinium and uranium.

These 14 elements constitute what is known as the "actinide" series, and are analogous to the previously known rare-earth series — the lanthanide series. An inner-electron shell, the 5f shell, is being filled as we go across this actinide series just as the inner 4f electron shell is being filled as we successively build up the members of the "lanthanide" series. We have an element-by-element analogy of the chemical properties between the two series and this has made it possible to predict the chemical properties of these elements.

Recognition of the fact that the transuranium elements represented a whole new family of actinide elements (that is, "like actinium") analogous to the rare-earth series of elements, the lanthanides, permitted the discoverers to predict the chemical properties of the unknown transuranium elements, and thereby enabled them to discover and separate them from all the other elements in the periodic table, which, incidentally, is the classical test for the discovery of a new chemical element.

Prediction of the chemical properties of the yet undiscovered transuranium elements is quite straightforward. Lawrencium, the element with the atomic number 103, completes the actinide series. Accordingly, the elements with atomic numbers greater than 103 are known as transactinide elements. One of these, element 104, may have been discovered in some recent Soviet research work. It is expected that these transactinide elements will fit into the periodic table as shown. Thus we can predict the chemical properties of the "transactinide" elements 104 to 118, inclusive, and we suggest that they will have an element-by-element chemical analogy with the elements immediately above them in the periodic table. In other words, element 104 should chemically be like hafnium, element 105 like tantalum, element 106 like tungsten, and so on across the periodic table to element 118, which should be a noble gas like radon. You may notice that element 102 is in the table without a name and I will come back to that later.

Let me briefly review some of the history of the discovery of the transuranium elements. The efforts of men to change one element

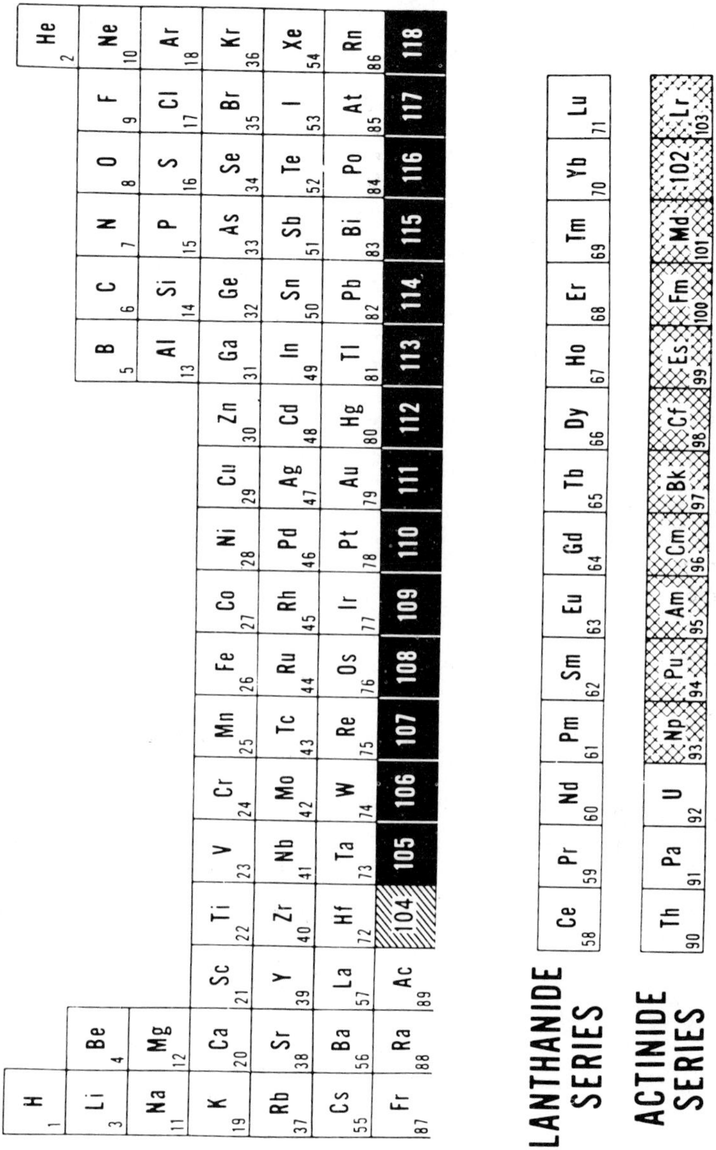

Figure 5. Periodic Table of the Elements

into another, or to create new elements, date back to the time of the alchemists. But the first serious scientific attempts to go beyond the heaviest of the known elements — uranium — and explore the transuranium region were those of Enrico Fermi, Emilio Segrè, and their co-workers in Rome, Italy, in 1934, shortly after the existence of the neutron had been discovered. This group bombarded uranium with slow neutrons with the hope that the uranium nucleus would "capture" a neutron. A number of radioactive products were found. In the immediately following years, many more such radioactive species were observed. However, chemical investigations led to the discovery that these were not transuranium elements — but rather products of the fission process (i.e., the splitting of the uranium nucleus into two nearly equal parts). The discovery of fission by Otto Hahn and F. S. Strassman, in December, 1938, which led to the "atomic age", was in a sense a dividend or by-product of man's quest for the transuranium elements.

Neptunium

As fate would have it, the discovery of the first transuranium element — element No. 93, neptunium — was a by-product of studies of the fission process conducted by E. M. McMillan. Mc-Millan, working at the University of California at Berkeley, in the spring of 1940, was trying to measure the energies of the two main fragments from the neutron-induced fission of uranium. He placed a thin layer of a uranium compound — uranium oxide — on one piece of paper; and next to this he stacked very thin sheets of similar paper to stop and collect the fission fragments recoiling from uranium. The paper he used was ordinary cigarette paper — the kind that people who roll their own cigarettes use. In the course of his studies, he found that there was another unstable, radio-active product of the reaction — one which did not recoil sufficiently to escape from the thin layer of uranium undergoing fission. He suspected that this was a product formed by the capture of a neutron in the uranium. McMillan — and P. H. Abelson, who joined him in this research — were able to show, on the basis of their chemical work, that this product was an isotope of the element with atomic number 93 — neptunium-239, formed by neutron capture in uranium-238, followed by electron emission (beta-decay).

McMillan's and Abelson's investigation of neptunium showed that it resembles uranium — not rhenium, as predicted — in its chemical properties. Therefore, analogous to uranium — which was named after the planet Uranus — element 93 was named neptunium, after the next planet, Neptune. This was the first definite evidence that an inner electron shell (the so-called 5f electron shell) is filled in the transuranium region.

The first isolation of a weighable amount of neptunium in the form of the long-lived ($2 \cdot 2 \times 10^6$ year half-life) neptunium-237 took place in October, 1944, when L. B. Magnusson and L. B. La Chapelle were able to isolate the material at the wartime Metallurgical Laboratory of the University of Chicago.

Plutonium

The element with the atomic number 94 was next to be discovered. By bombarding uranium with deuterons — the heavy isotope of hydrogen raised to a high energy in the 60-inch cyclotron at the University of California at Berkeley — E. M. McMillan, J. W. Kennedy, A. C. Wahl, and I, in late 1940, succeeded in preparing a new isotope of neptunium, neptunium-238, which decayed to plutonium-238.

The first bombardment of uranium oxide with the 16 million electron volt (Mev) deuterons was performed on December 14, 1940. Alpha radioactivity was found to grow into the chemically-separated element 93 fraction during the following weeks, and this alpha activity was chemically separated from the neighbouring elements — especially elements 90 to 93, inclusive — in experiments performed during the next two months. These experiments constituted the positive identification of element 94, plutonium.

The chemical properties of elements 93 and 94 were studied by the so-called "tracer method" at the University of California for the next year and a half. This meant that invisible amounts of these elements were followed in chemical studies by their tell-tale radioactivity. These first two transuranium elements were referred to by the group simply as "element 93" and "element 94", or by code names, until the spring of 1942, at which time the first detailed reports on them were written. The early work, even in those days, was carried on under a self-imposed cover of secrecy. Throughout 1941, element 94 was referred to by the code name of "copper", which was all right until it was necessary to introduce the element copper into some of the experiments. This posed the problem of distinguishing between the two. For a while, plutonium was referred to as "copper" and the real copper was "honest-to-God copper". This seemed clumsier and clumsier as time went on, and element 94 was finally christened the element "plutonium", after the planet Pluto and analogous to the naming of uranium and neptunium.

The plutonium isotope of major importance is the one with mass number 239 — that is, the nuclear species having 94 protons and 145 neutrons. The search for this isotope, as a decay product of neptunium, was being conducted by the same group, with the collaboration of E. Segrè, simultaneously with the experiments leading to the discovery of plutonium. The isotope plutonium-239 was identified, and its possibilities as a nuclear energy source were established during the spring of 1941.

Using neutrons produced by the 37-inch cyclotron at the University of California, the group first demonstrated, on March 28, 1941, with a sample containing 0.5 microgram of plutonium-239, that this isotope undergoes slow neutron-induced fission.

The realization that plutonium, as plutonium-239, could serve as the explosive ingredient of a nuclear weapon, and that it might be created in quantity in a nuclear reactor or "atomic pile" — as it was called — followed by chemical separation from uranium and the highly radioactive fission products, made it imperative to carry out chemical investigations of plutonium with weighable quantities, even though only microgram quantities could be produced using the cyclotron sources of neutrons available at that time. On August 18, 1942, B. B. Cunningham and L. B. Werner, at the wartime Metallurgical Laboratory of the University of Chicago, succeeded in isolating about a microgram of plutonium-239 — less than one ten-millionth of an ounce — which had been prepared by cyclotron irradiations. Thus, plutonium was the first man-made element to be obtained in visible quantity. The first weighing of this man-made element took place on September 10, 1942, and was performed by investigators Cunningham and Werner. The actual sample weighed at that time is shown in this photograph of the highly magnified plutonium compound (2.77 micrograms of oxide),

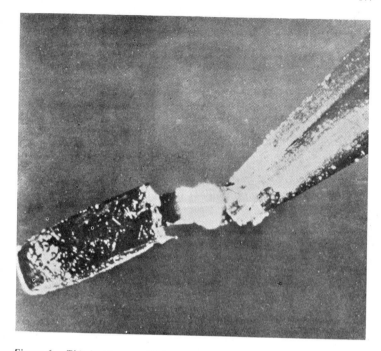

Figure 6. This highly magnified plutonium compound (2·77 micrograms of oxide) is the first to be weighed by man (September 10, 1942) and is here shown on a platinum weighing boat. The picture is magnified approximately 35-fold. The plutonium oxide appears as a crusty deposit (lower left-hand part of the photograph) near the end of the platinum weighing boat, which is held with forceps that grip a small handle (upper right-hand part of photograph).

shown in *Figure 6* on a platinum weighing boat. The plutonium oxide appears as a crusty deposit (lower left-hand part of the photograph) near the end of the platinum weighing boat, which is held with forceps that grip a small handle (upper right-hand part of photograph).

These so-called "ultramicrochemical" studies conducted by the research workers on plutonium were remarkable. It was possible to perform many significant studies with almost invisible amounts of material — work that was carried out under a microscope. *Figure 7* is a photograph of the first laboratory for the study of pure

Figure 7. First laboratory for the study of pure plutonium (University of Chicago, fall of 1942).

plutonium at the University of Chicago in 1942. If extremely small volumes are used, even microgram quantities of material can give relatively high concentrations in solution; and with the development of balances of the required sensitivity, micrograms were also sufficient for gravimetric analysis.   Liquid volumes in the range of 1/10th to 1/100,000ths of a cubic centimetre were measured with an error of less than one per cent by means of finely-calibrated capillary tubing. Chemical glassware, such as test tubes and beakers, was constructed from capillary tubing and was handled with micromanipulators.

Plutonium is now produced in much larger quantities than any other synthetic element. The large, wartime chemical separation plant at Hanford, Washington, was constructed on the basis of these investigations performed on the ultramicrochemical scale; the scale-up between ultramicrochemical experiments to the final Hanford plant corresponds to a factor of about one *billion* — surely, a scale-up of unique proportions. *Figure 8* is a view of Hanford Chemical Extraction Plant which used the Bismuth Phosphate Process developed with ultramicrochemical techniques during the Second World War at the Metallurgical Laboratory, University of Chicago.

The crucial experiments in the discovery and demonstration of the great value of plutonium were performed during the late winter and spring of 1941, over 25 years ago. The key experiment in its discovery was conducted in a little chemistry laboratory, Room 307, Gilman Hall, on the campus of the University of California at Berkeley, on February 23, 1941, and as you may know, this room was dedicated as a National Historic Landmark last February. The demonstration of the value of plutonium as an energy source took place on the same campus on March 28, 1941, when it was first shown that its important isotope can be split in half — that is, it undergoes fission — when bombarded with thermal or slow neutrons. And on May 18, 1941, the first quantitative measurement was made of the probability (or cross-section) for this so-called fission reaction. The original sample of plutonium-239 upon which this demonstration and this measurement were made has been preserved and was presented to the Smithsonian Institution on March 28, 1966, the 25th anniversary of the fission demonstration.

The intervening 25 years have seen a tremendous scale-up in

Figure 8. View of Hanford Chemical Extraction Plant which used the Bismuth Phosphate Process developed with ultra-microchemical techniques during the Second World War at the Metallurgical Laboratory, University of Chicago.

the production of plutonium. In fact, this scale-up amounts to a billion-billion-fold, an unprecedented increase in available quantity for a chemical element. These 25 years have shown that plutonium has almost unlimited potential for use to the benefit or to the detriment of man — that is, use as a nuclear fuel to produce unlimited quantities of electricity or as the explosive ingredient in a nuclear weapon.

Americium and curium

After the completion at the wartime Metallurgical Laboratory of the most essential part of the investigations concerned with the chemical processes involved in the production and separation of plutonium, attention turned to the problem of synthesizing and identifying the next-heavier transuranium elements. As my collaborators in this endeavour, there were A. Ghiorso, R. A. James and L. O. Morgan.

There followed a period during which the attempts to synthesize and identify elements 95 and 96 bore no fruit. The unsuccessful experiments were based on the premise that these elements should be much like plutonium, in that it should be possible to oxidize them to a higher oxidation state and utilize this oxidation in the chemical isolation procedures. It was not until the middle of the summer of 1944, upon the first recognition that these elements were part of an "actinide" transition series (i.e., were chemically very similar to the element actinium and to the long-known rare-earth elements) that any advance was made; and then progress came quickly. Incidentally, this element-by-element analogy in chemical properties between the actinide and lanthanide (rare-earth) elements has been the key to the chemical identification — and hence, discovery — of most of the subsequent transuranium elements.

As soon as it was recognized that these same elements could be oxidized only with extreme difficulty, if at all, the identification of an isotope then thought to be due to element 95 or 96 followed immediately. Thus, the isotope of element 96 — now known to be curium-242 — was produced in the summer of 1944 as a result of the bombardment of plutonium-239 with 32-Mev helium ions in the cyclotron at Berkeley.

The identification of element 95, americium, in the form of isotope americium-241, followed, during late 1944 and early 1945, as a result of the bombardment of plutonium-239 with neutrons in a nuclear reactor.

Some comments should be made here concerning the rare earth-like properties of these two elements. Our hypothesis that they should greatly resemble the rare-earth elements in their chemical properties proved to be so very true that, for a time, it appeared to be unfortunate. The better part of a year was spent in trying, without success, to separate chemically the two elements from each other and from the rare-earth elements; and although we felt entirely confident, on the basis of their radioactive properties and the methods of production, that isotopes of elements 95 and 96 had been produced, the chemical proof was still undemonstrated. The elements remained unnamed during this period of futile attempts at separation (although one of our group referred to them as "pandemonium" and "delirium", in recognition of our difficulties). The key to their final separation, and the technique which made feasible the separation and identification of these and subsequent transuranium elements, was the so-called ion exchange technique which I shall describe later. The elements were named americium, after the Americas, and curium, in honour of Pierre and Marie Curie, by analogy to the naming of their rare-earth counterparts (i.e., homologues) europium (after Europe) and gadolinium (after the Finnish chemist, Gadolin).

Chemical identification

I would now like to mention the basic chemical reactions that have been key factors in the discovery of the transuranium elements beyond curium. The importance of these chemical reactions is that they provided a means to separate elements which are chemically very similar.

Most of the transuranium elements heavier than curium, element number 96, up through mendelevium, element 101, were chemically identified through the use of simple chemical reactions — shown in *Figure 9*. These, of course, are prototype chemical reactions in which I have written M^{+3} to stand for the metallic ion representative of any actinide or lanthanide element. These basic chemical reactions, commonly called ion exchange reactions, were those used to separate each new element from all previously known elements.

The first equation is an ion exchange adsorption equation in which the M^{+3} ion in solution, the actinide or lanthanide ion, exchanges with the ammonium ion connected to the resin, R, whose formula need not further concern us, to go on to the resin in the form MR_3 shown on the right-hand side, releasing the three ammonion ions.

The second equation is an equation by which the actinide ion, M^{+3}, is dissolved back off the resin. It is the equation which we refer to as the elution equation whereby the chemical element of

$$M^{+3}_{(aq)} + 3NH_4\,R_{(s)} \rightleftharpoons MR_{3(s)} + 3NH^+_{4(aq)}$$

$$MR_{3(s)} + 4A^- \rightleftharpoons MA^-_{4\,(aq)}$$

Figure 9. Idealized chemical reactions involved in the separation of the actinide and lanthanide elements by the ion exchange technique. M^{+3} represents the tripositive actinide or lanthanide ions. NH_4R represents the ion exchange resin with exchangeable cation NH_4^+ and a polymer residue R^-, A^- represents the anion which forms complex ions with the actinide or lanthanide ions, and MA_4 represents an example of a formula for the complex ion formed.

interest is separated from the ion exchange resin. In this equation A^- represents a simple or complex anion, something like nitrate ion or chloride ion, or perhaps something as complex as citrate ion or the alphahydroxisobutyrate ion. It does not really matter what the exact formula is; the point is that this A^-ion combines with an M^{+3} ion, the actinide ion, to form a complex anion shown on the right-hand side of the second equation as MA_4^- and thus dissolves the actinide or lanthanide off the resin.

In actual practice, a portion of the ion exchange resin and the actinide ions to be separated are thoroughly mixed and contacted, until the actinide ions are all adsorbed on the resin. The mixture is then put on top of a resin column. *Figure 10* shows such a simple ion exchange column. The mixture of resin and actinide ions is put on the top of the black resin column and then the solution labelled *eluant* containing the A^-ion, to which I referred, is passed through the column, dissolving the actinide ion from the resin.

The actual separation procedure is accomplished by a repetitive process in which the various actinide M^{+3} ions go back and forth between the ion exchange resin and the solution while they move slowly down the column of resin. Those two chemical equilibrium distributions make it possible to effect through this repetitive action a complete separation, in ideal cases, of one actinide element from another, and a pure actinide element comes out at the bottom of

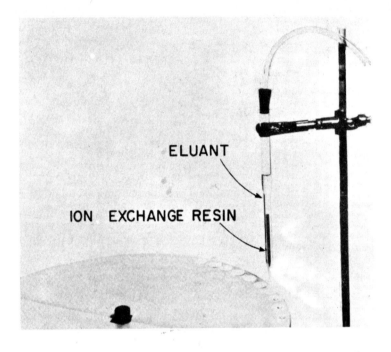

Figure 10. Experimental apparatus for ion-exchange separation used in the chemical separation and identification of actinide elements. The drops of eluant are collected on the metal discs, and their radiations are analyzed.

the column. By this process, then, with very simple apparatus, it is possible to separate these chemically very similar elements — the actinide elements and the lanthanide elements — from each other in a short time and quite completely. *Figure 11* shows a comparative example of the separations which can be achieved with the actinide and lanthanide elements using the simple technique. This includes elements whose discovery I shall describe presently.

But more than this, it has been possible for years to predict the chemical properties of the undiscovered heavier actinide elements so as to make it feasible to design experiments ahead of time and

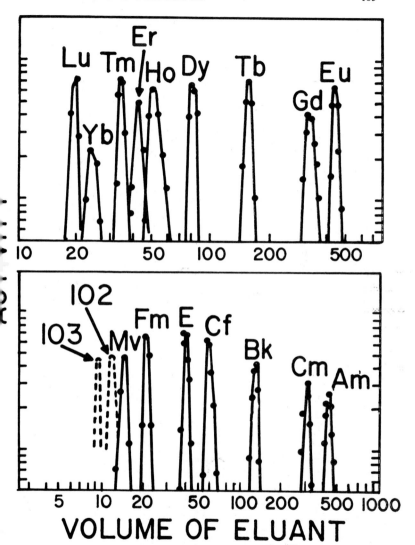

Figure 11. Example of experimental data obtained in ion-exchange method of chemical separation and identification of actinide elements based upon their analogous behavior to the lanthanide elements.

actually predict where these new elements will come out of the ion exchange resin column in the discovery experiment with that new element.

These actinide elements elute from a resin column analogously to the lanthanide elements. Thus, the actinide element, americium, comes off in a position about very similar to that of the lanthanide element, europium. The americium is designated by the symbol, Am, while europium is designated by the symbol, Eu. The other elements come off the resin in the order of their atomic numbers with the element having the highest atomic number in both the actinide series and the lanthanide series coming off first.

The chemical elution experiment using this technique for elements 102 and 103, whose discovery I shall describe presently, has not yet been carried out because the half-lives of the known isotopes of these elements are too short and therefore these elements are represented by dotted lines. The known isotopes of elements 102 and 103 have half-lives of only a few seconds. Other actinide elements had been put on this chart with dotted lines in previous years — for example, before the discovery of berkelium, californium, einsteinium, fermium or mendelevium, they were on the chart in dotted lines showing their predicted position. When they were discovered it was found that they came out of the column in the predicted positions. You can see, therefore, the effectiveness of this method for predicting the chemical properties of an element even before it is discovered.

Berkelium and californium

The most important prerequisite to the process for making the transcurium elements (i.e., the still-heavier elements beyond curium) was that sufficiently large amounts of americium and curium had to be manufactured to serve as starting materials. Because of the intense radioactivity of these starting substances, even in milligram or submilligram amounts, it was necessary to develop extremely efficient chemical separation methods in order to obtain the enormous separation factors needed for the isolation of the new elements from the starting material, so that it would be possible to detect the very small amounts of radioactivity due to the new transcurium elements. The dangerous radioactivity of the source material made it necessary to develop complicated methods for remote control operation to keep the health hazards at a minimum.

These production, separation, and protection problems were solved, and successful experiments were performed at the end of 1949 and the beginning of 1950. Americium for target material was prepared in milligram amounts by intense neutron bombardment of plutonium over a long period of time, and curium target materials were prepared in microgram amounts as the result of the intense neutron bombardment of some of this americium. Both of these neutron bombardments took place in a high-power reactor having a high neutron density output.

Element 97, berkelium, was discovered by S. G. Thompson, A. Ghiorso and G. T. Seaborg in December, 1949, as a result of the bombardment of the milligram amounts of americium-241 with 35 Mev helium ions accelerated in the 60-inch cyclotron of the University of California at Berkeley. The first isotope produced has the mass number 243 and decays with a half-life of 4.5 hours.

Element 98, californium, was first produced and similarly identified by Thompson, Ghiorso, K. Street, and Seaborg, in February, 1950, at the University of California at Berkeley. The first isotope produced is now assigned the mass number 245 and decays with a half-life of 44 minutes. This isotope was produced by the bombardment of microgram amounts of curium-242 with 35 Mev helium ions accelerated in the 60-inch cyclotron. It is interesting to note that this identification of element 98 was accomplished with a total of only some 5,000 atoms. Someone remarked, at the time, that this number was substantially smaller than the number of students attending the university.

The naming of elements 97 and 98 presents an interesting story. Element 97 was called berkelium after the city of Berkeley, California, where it was discovered, by analogy to the naming of its rare earth counterpart, terbium, which was named after the city of Ytterby in Sweden. Element 98 was named californium after the university and state where the work was done.

Upon learning about the naming of these elements, the "Talk of the Town" section of the New Yorker magazine had the following to say:

New atoms are turning up with spectacular, if not downright alarm-
ing, frequency nowadays, and the University of California at Berkeley,
whose scientists have discovered elements 97 and 98, has christened
them berkelium and californium, respectively. While unarguably suited
to their place of birth, these names strike us as indicating a surprising
lack of public relations foresight on the part of the university, located
as it is in a state where publicity has flourished to a degree matched
perhaps only by evangelism. California's busy scientists will undoubtedly
come up with another atom or two one of these days, and the
university might well have anticipated that. Now it has lost forever
the chance of immortalizing itself in the atomic tables with some
such sequence as universitium (97), ofium (98), californium (99),
berkelium (100).

The discoverers sent the following reply:

"Talk of the Town" has missed the point in their comments on
naming of the elements 97 and 98. We may have shown lack of
confidence but no lack of foresight in naming these elements 'berkelium"
and "californium". By using these names first, we have forestalled
the appalling possibility that after naming 97 and 98 "universitium"
and "ofium", some New Yorker might follow with the discovery of
99 and 100 and apply the names "newium" and "yorkium".

The answer from the *New Yorker* staff was brief:

We are already at work in our office laboratories on "newium" and
"yorkium". So far, we just have the names.

In 1958, S. G. Thompson and B. B. Cunningham at Berkeley
succeeded in isolating, for the first time, macroscopic amounts of
berkelium (as berkelium-249) and californium (as a mixture of
californium 249-252), which were synthesized by the long-term
irradiation of plutonium-249 and its transmutation products with
neutrons. *Figure 12* shows a photograph of the first pure compound
of californium isolated in 1960 by B. B. Cunningham and J. C.
Wallmann, using californium-249 — obtained via the decay of
previously separated berkelium-249. The compound was three-
tenths of a microgram ($\cdot$0000003 of a gram) of californium oxychloride ($CfOCl$). Later, the trichloride and oxide were also
prepared. This experimental work was the first carried out on a
"submicrogram" scale as a result of new techniques and represented
an order-of-magnitude scale-down from the ultramicrochemical
work done during the last war.

Einsteinium and fermium

The story of the discovery of elements 99 and 100, einsteinium
and fermium, represents an outstanding example of the unexpected

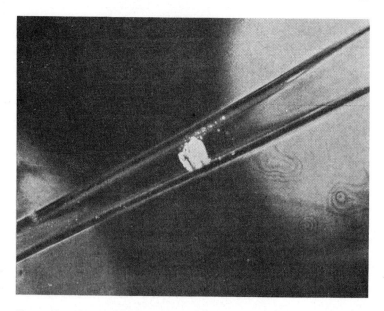

Figure 12. Photograph of the first pure californium compound isolated in 1960 (0.3 ug of californium as the oxychloride, CfOC1), magnified about 90-fold. The californium was in the form of the isotope Cf²⁴⁹.

in science. The seventh and eighth transuranium elements were discovered in debris from "Mike", the first, large thermonuclear or "hydrogen bomb" explosion which took place in the Pacific in November 1952. *Figure 13* shows a photograph of the event. Debris from the explosion was collected, first, on filter papers attached to airplanes which flew through the clouds and, later in more substantial quantity, gathered up as fallout materials from the surface of a neighbouring atoll. This debris was brought to the United States for chemical investigation in a number of laboratories.

Initial investigation of this debris at Argonne National Laboratory in Chicago, and at Los Alamos Scientific Laboratory of the University of California in New Mexico, led to the unexpected observation of heavy isotopes such as plutonium-244 and plutonium-246. At that time, the heaviest known isotope of plutonium was

Figure 13. The first large thermonuclear explosion — in the Pacific, November, 1952. Einsteinium and fermium, elements 99 and 100, were first discovered in the debris from this test.

plutonium-243. Since this pointed to the capture of many successive neutrons by the uranium-238 in the device, and thus the presence of neutron-rich isotopes in greater abundance than expected, a group at the University of California Radiation Laboratory undertook to look for isotopes of transcalifornium elements in this material. Ion exchange experiments of the type previously mentioned immediately demonstrated the existence of a new element. Later, in order to secure a larger amount of source material, it was necessary to work up many hundreds of pounds of coral from one of the atolls adjoining the explosion area. Eventually, such coral was worked up by the ton in a pilot-plant operation which went under the name of "Paydirt".

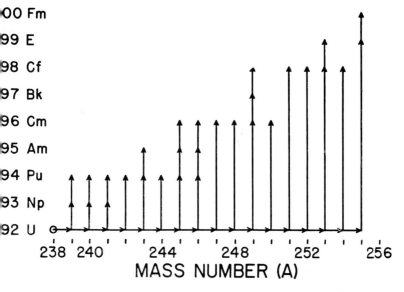

Figure 14. Nuclear reactions for the synthesis of einsteinium and fermium, elements 99 and 100, in the first thermonuclear explosion. The horizontal arrows represent the almost instantaneous capture of neutrons and the vertical arrows represent the subsequent beta-decay (electron emission).

Without going into the details, it may be pointed out that the experiments by the research groups at the three laboratories led to the positive identification of isotopes of elements 99 and 100 by the ion exchange adsorption elution technique that I described earlier. A radioactive isotope, with the mass number 253, which decayed with a half-life of 20 days, was identified as an isotope of einsteinium, element 99, named in honour of Albert Einstein. A radioisotope, with the mass number 255 and a half-life of about 20 hours, was identified as an isotope of fermium, element 100, named in honour of Enrico Fermi.

The successive instantaneous capture of many neutrons by uranium-238 had led to heavy uranium isotopes. The heavy uranium isotopes then decayed into the isotopes appearing beyond them in the periodic table, hence increasing the atomic number in successive steps, as illustrated in *Figure 14* showing the nuclear reactions for the synthesis of einsteinium and fermium, elements 99 and 100, and other heavy isotopes, in the first thermonuclear explosion. The horizontal arrows represent the almost instantaneous capture of neutrons and the vertical arrows represent the subsequent beta decay (electron emission). The first identification of element 100 was made with only about 200 atoms. The most striking previous accomplishment in this category was the positive identification of element 98 with a total of about 5,000 atoms.

It was not until 1961 that sufficient einsteinium had been produced through intense neutron bombardment in reactors to permit separation of a macroscopic and weighable amount. B. B. Cunningham, J. C. Wallman, L. Phillips, and R. C. Gatti, at Berkeley, were able to separate — working on the new, submicrogram scale — an extraordinarily small amount of einsteinium-253. A total amount of only a few hundredths of a microgram — a billionth of an ounce — was weighed on a special, magnetic-type balance.

Mendelevium

Beginning with element 101 the discoveries of transuranium elements have been based on experiments in which the elements have been produced and identified literally one atom at a time. This atom-by-atom identification of new elements has been, in my opinion, one of the outstanding achievements in the history of science. When you realize that it takes about a million billion atoms to make a speck barely large enough to see, you may get some glimmering of the difficulties involved with identifying a new element one atom at a time.

These extremely small yields of the highly sought-after product are the result of three factors. The first is the very small amount of starting material available for the transmutation process. The second factor is the very small probability that a nuclear bombarding projectile will strike the target nucleus. And finally, in the overwhelming majority of the rare instances when the bombarding projectile actually strikes the starting nucleus, it causes it to split in half in the fission reaction, rather than to absorb the projectile in a fusion reaction, with the formation of the particular sought-after isotope of a new heavier element. Added to these obstacles is the tremendous level of radioactivity which is often present in the starting, target material, and which greatly complicates the handling problems. (I recall vividly an incident of accidental release of target isotope curium-244 at Berkeley in 1959, which we referred to as the "curium explosion" and which contaminated the laboratory for weeks.)

The fundamental methods worked out for this successful experiment have served as the basis for the production and discovery of the elements heavier than mendelevium, and will doubtless continue to serve as a basis for many of the experiments designed to discover still further elements. In view of this significance of the mendelevium (element 101) experiment, I would like to describe it in some detail.

The discovery of mendelevium by A. Ghiorso, B. G. Harvey, G. R. Choppin, S. G. Thompson, and G. T. Seaborg, was in many ways the most dramatic of them all. It was decided to make an attempt in a situation which would have been regarded by most sensible people as very premature. All of the previous discoveries of transuranium elements had been based on starting with weighable amounts of target materials; however, it was thought that techniques had advanced to a point where it might be possible to identify the element with the atomic number 101 in a target of unweighable amount.

The plan of attack involved the bombardment of the maximum available quantity of einsteinium, element 99, in the form of the isotope einsteinium-253, with helium ions in the Berkeley 60-inch cyclotron, utilizing the reaction.

$$_{99}\text{Es}^{253} + _{2}\text{He}^{4} \longrightarrow _{101}\text{Md}^{256} + n$$

On gathering together all of the einsteinium-253 that was available as a result of its production in nuclear reactors, the total quantity was found to amount to about 10^9 atoms — that is, one billion atoms — or less than one trillionth (or one million millionth) of an ounce (10^{-12}). The question was whether this constituted a sufficient amount of material to make an attempt at bombardment realistic.

$$N \cong N' \sigma I t$$

$$(10^9)(10^{-27})(10^{14})(10^4) \cong$$

One atom per experiment

Figure 15. Calculation used to determine the feasibility of experimentally producing mendelevium, element 101.

Certain calculations were carried out at that time in 1955 before the bombardment in order to ascertain what the yield of the new element, element 101, might be. In the equation in *Figure 15* the symbol N on the left represents the number of atoms of element 101 that were expected to be formed in the bombardment. On the right-hand side of the equation, N' represents the number of atoms of target material, that is, the 10^9 atoms that I mentioned before. Sigma represents the probability for the reaction, that is the cross-section of the target atom — the einsteinium 253 — which is estimated to be 10^{-27} square centimeters in the units used in this work. I represents the intensity of the helium ion beam and that was measured to be 10^{12} particles per square centimetre per second, and t is the reasonable time of bombardment related to the estimated half-life of the product — which is 10^4 or about 10 thousand seconds or 3 hours.

By filling in the values for N' and sigma and I and t, (10^9), (10^{-27}), (10^{14}), and (10^4), respectively, then multiplying them together, which means we add exponents, we have $+9$ and -27, giving us -18, and then $+14$, giving us -4, and then $+4$, giving us zero for an answer of 10^0, which, of course, is equal to one. This indicates that we could expect to produce only one atom of element 101 in the experiment!

Actually, that is the way it turned out. The calculation was

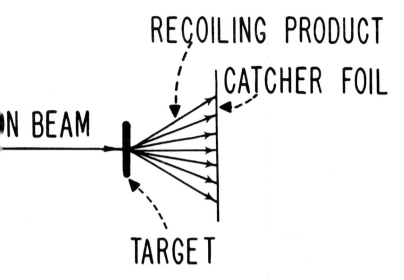

Figure 16. Schematic drawing illustrating the recoil technique.

correct. We did produce just about one atom per experiment and still it was possible to identify chemically, by the adsorption elution technique described earlier, and announce to the world the discovery of this new element. Adding significantly to the complexity of the experiment, of course, was the absolute necessity for the chemical separation of this one atom of element 101 from the 10^9 atoms of einsteinium in the target, and its ultimate complete chemical identification by separation with the ion exchange method.

This separation and identification would presumably have to be done in the period of an hour or less because of the short half-life that was expected. These requirements indicated the desperate need for new techniques, together with some luck. Fortunately both were forthcoming. The new technique involved the separation of element 101 by the, at that time, untried recoil method of separation as illustrated in *Figure 16*.

The discovery process was described soon after the discovery in a Soviet journal called *Priroda* (meaning *Science*), as shown in *Figure 17*. First, we have the alpha particle beam labelled *1* in

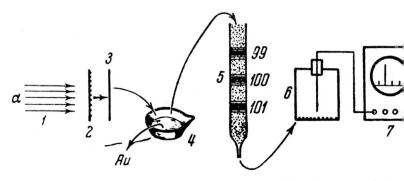

Figure 17. Schematic drawing of the experimental techniques used in the discovery of element 101, mendelevium. The beam of alpha particles (1) strikes the target (2) from which the produced atoms of mendelevium recoil to a catcher foil (3). A chemical dissolution (4) and ion-exchange separation (5) are performed. The pure sample is counted in a detection chamber (6) and observed with a recorder (7). (Drawing from the Soviet journal Priroda).

the *Figure*. The helium ion beam strikes the target with the einsteinium on the back side of the target, labelled *2* in the *Figure* and not the front side as had usually been the case up to this time.

The helium ion beam produced in the cyclotron was sent through the back of the foil in order that the atoms of element 101, recoiling due to the reaction with the impinging helium ions, could be caught on a second thin gold foil, number *3* in the diagram. This second gold foil containing the recoiled atom, which was relatively free of the einsteinium target material, was dissolved in the chemical operation, labelled *4* in the *Figure*.

Bombardments were made as I indicated. The discovery of radioactive decay by spontaneous fission was an element of luck since decay by spontaneous fission is easy to detect and there is not much of a background due to spontaneous fission to obscure the results. It was thus found that the chemical identification could be made as shown using the adsorption-elution column, labelled number *5* in the picture.

You will notice that the element with the highest atomic number, element 101, came out first and then that was presented to the

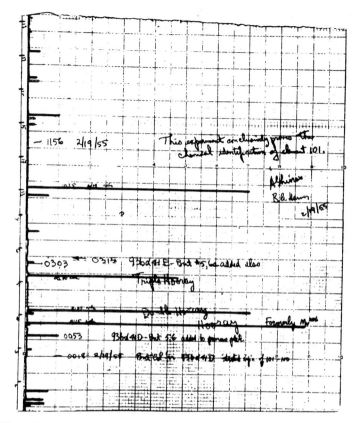

Figure 18. Reproduction of original data sheet showing stylus tracing (and various annotations) from a spontaneous fission recording system, corresponding to discovery of mendelevium, element 101 (February 19, 1955).

detection system labelled number 6, where the spontaneous fissions could be found.

We may see in *Figure 18* the original data sheet obtained and marked in the lab the night of the discovery. You will notice that the size of the pulse is represented by the length of the line that goes across the sheet from the axis at the left toward the right. The lines of small length indicate decay by alpha particles, while the line long-length indicates decay by spontaneous fission in this unusual process.

You will notice that the first long line is labelled "hurray", which was about 1:15 in the morning, and then see the next line which was at about 1:30, labelled "double hurray", and then a little higher line labelled "triple hurray". There is also a fourth long line at the top, the fourth spontaneous fission count. This line is without a label.

This indicates the obtaining of four spontaneous fission counts in this all-night definitive experiment and these were chemically identified in the proper elution sequence to establish that the atomic number of the new element was element 101. And you will notice the inscription, "this experiment conclusively proves the chemical identification of element 101", by A. Ghiorso and B. G. Harvey dated February 19, 1955. These all-night experiments are typical of such research at the frontiers of science — very little is accomplished by scientists who work only from 9 a.m. to 5 p.m.

Element 101 was named *mendelevium* in honour of the Russian scientist Dmitri Mendeleev, who was the first to use the periodic table of the elements to predict the chemical properties of undiscovered elements, a principle which has been the key to the discovery of so many of the transuranium elements.

Element 102

The next element, element 102, was also produced and identified one atom at a time using the recoil technique. However, the difficulties that had to be surmounted here were even greater and show what the future holds as research progresses at the far-out frontiers of the transuranium elements. In this case, the half-life of the product nucleus was so short that a direct chemical identification was not possible. Consequently, a "double recoil technique", involving the chemical identification of a daughter isotope, was used.

It has been necessary to use so-called "heavy ions" as bombarding projectiles, positively charged atoms of an element heavier than helium, in order to reach the desired atomic and mass number — that is, in order to add the required number of protons and neutrons to the starting material (the target nucleus). The heavy, positively charged ions must be accelerated to high velocities in a special accelerator so that they can force their way into — that is, fuse with — the heavy target nucleus despite the repulsion due to the large positive electric charge on this nucleus. And the yields of the desired products of such reactions, using comparable quantities of target atoms, are a thousand times smaller than the already extremely small yield observed in the mendelevium experiment!

The history of the discovery of element 102 is very complex, and it is for this reason that it does not yet have an accepted name. I will attempt to give a brief description of the complicated series of experiments performed by various groups of investigators.

The first attempt to discover the element was made in 1957 by a team of scientists from Argonne National Laboratory in Chicago, Harwell Atomic Energy Research Establishment in England, and the Nobel Institute for Physics in Sweden. They used the simple recoil technique, introduced in the discovery of element 101, with a cyclotron at the Nobel Institute. The possible nuclear reaction involved is as follows:

$$_{96}Cm^{244} + {}_{6}C^{13} \rightarrow 102^{253} + 4n$$

(Here the atomic number, 102, stands in as the chemical symbol for the unnamed element.) They believed that they succeeded in producing and chemically identifying an isotope of element 102 which had a half-life of 10 minutes and decayed by the emission of alpha particles with the energy of $8 \cdot 5$ Mev. Attempts were made to confirm this result in very careful experiments carried out by both the Berkeley Lawrence Radiation Laboratory group and a Soviet group at the Dubna Laboratory near Moscow, but without success.

In 1958 a group at the University of California Lawrence Radiation Laboratory reported the identification of the isotope of element 102 with the mass number 254, produced through the bombardment of curium-246 with carbon-12 ions accelerated in the then-new Heavy Ion Linear Accelerator (HILAC). The nuclear reaction achieved is as follows:

$$_{96}Cm^{246} + {}_{6}C^{12} \longrightarrow 102^{254} + 4n$$

$$102^{254} \xrightarrow[3\,secs]{\alpha} {}_{100}Fm^{250} \xrightarrow[30\,min]{\alpha}$$

This corresponds to the addition of six protons and two neutrons to the starting nucleus. The new element was detected by the chemical identification of its known daughter, fermium-250, which decays by the emission of 7·4 Mev alpha particles, with a half-life of 30 minutes. The removal of the element 102 isotope from the target material and the separation of the daughter element from the parent element 102 were performed by the use of the new method of double recoil technique, introduced for the first time in this experiment. The experimental arrangement is illustrated in *Figure 19*.

Figure 19.   Schematic drawing illustrating the double recoil technique.

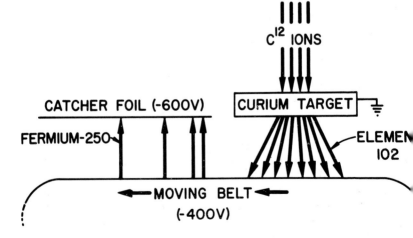

The catcher foil was cut transversely, in the direction of the belt motion, into five equal length sections after a time of bombardment suited to the half-life of the daughter atom. Each section was analyzed simultaneously in the counter and all of the desired measurements could be made for identifying the daughter atoms caught in the catcher foil; thus the half-life of the parent of the recoiling atoms could be determined. It was found that the fermium 250 could be collected on the catcher foil in accordance with the parent half-life, that is, the half-life for the element 102^{254} of three seconds. Changing the belt speed was found to change the distribution of the fermium 250 in the catcher foil in a manner conforming to a three-second parent. As the result of later experiments in which the alpha particles were measured directly, they reported an energy of $8 \cdot 3$ Mev for the alpha particles.

Soviet groups working with the Dubna cyclotron followed this with the production in 1963 of another isotope of element 102, the 8-second 102^{256}, produced according to the following reactions:

$$_{92}U^{238} + _{10}Ne^{22} \rightarrow 102^{256} + 4n$$

$$_{94}Pu^{242} + _{8}O^{18} \rightarrow 102^{256} + 4n$$

$$102^{256} \xrightarrow[8\,secs]{\alpha} _{100}Fm^{252} \xrightarrow[25\,hrs]{\alpha}$$

They also used the Berkeley double recoil technique in order to make chemical identification of the daughter isotope, the 25 hour fermium-252. And more recently, in 1965, the Soviet groups in the same laboratory have apparently produced the same isotope produced by the Berkeley group, 102^{254}, by means of the following reactions, again using the double recoil technique, with chemical identification of the daughter:

$$_{95}Am^{243} + _{7}N^{15} \longrightarrow 102^{254} + 4n$$

$$_{92}U^{238} + _{10}Ne^{22} \longrightarrow 102^{254} + 6n$$

$$102^{254} \xrightarrow[20-50\ secs]{\propto} _{100}Fm^{250} \xrightarrow[30\ mins]{\propto}$$

However, their measurements indicate a longer half-life, some 20 to 50 seconds, lower energy for the alpha particles, $8 \cdot 1$ Mev, and a lower yield of the product.

So, you can see that the situation for element 102 is very complex, and I have perhaps succeeded only in confusing you. This very lack of clarity, however, serves our purpose today by showing us that the production and identification of new elements, one atom at a time, depend on extremely difficult experiments, and that from now on it will be necessary to check each report of a successful discovery in more than one laboratory and by more than one production method.

Lawrencium

With this lesson learned, let us push on further into the trans-uranium region. Those seeking to discover element 103 found themselves facing new difficulties. Isotopes of the undiscovered element were expected to have half-lives too short to make possible any chemical identification experiments. As I mentioned, this had been true of element 102 also. What made the situation doubly difficult, however, was the fact that the isotopes of element 103, which it seemed feasible to synthesize in the first experiments, did not appear to have daughter isotopes suitable for the application of the double recoil method of identification.

Despite these obstacles, a Berkeley group succeeded in the spring of 1961, following three years of preparatory work, in producing an isotope which they identified as having the atomic number 103. Using a modification of the simple recoil method and heavy (boron) ions in the HILAC (Heavy Ion Linear Accelerator), they utilized the following nuclear reactions:

$$\left. \begin{array}{l} _{98}\text{Cf}^{250} \\ _{98}\text{Cf}^{251} \\ _{98}\text{Cf}^{252} \end{array} \right\} + {}_{5}\text{B}^{11} \longrightarrow {}_{103}\text{Lr}^{257} + \left\{ \begin{array}{l} 4n \\ 5n \\ 6n \end{array} \right.$$

$$\left. \begin{array}{l} _{98}\text{Cf}^{250} \\ _{98}\text{Cf}^{251} \\ _{98}\text{Cf}^{252} \end{array} \right\} + {}_{5}\text{B}^{10} \longrightarrow {}_{103}\text{Lr}^{257} + \left\{ \begin{array}{l} 3n \\ 4n \\ 5n \end{array} \right.$$

The alpha particles from the new element 103, lawrencium, were counted directly with a radiation detector. They assigned this radioactivity, which had a measured half-life of about 8 seconds, and alpha particles of energy $8 \cdot 6$ Mev, to the isotope lawrencium-257. Although chemical identification was not possible, this assignment was made on the basis of substantial nuclear evidence. The evidence consisted of the variation of yield of the 8-second activity with energy of the bombarding boron projectiles and the comparative yield or absence of the 8-second activity when californium and other transuranium elements were bombarded with various different heavy ion projectiles. The name lawrencium was suggested in honour of Ernest O. Lawrence, the inventor of the cyclotron and founder of the Lawrence Radiation Laboratory.

More recently, in 1965, a Soviet group applied the double recoil technique to the identification of another isotope of lawrencium. They used the following reaction to produce law-

rencium-256 with a half-life of 45 seconds, which decays to
the daughter fermium-252 in the somewhat complicated way
shown. It was possible to identify the daughter isotope chemically
despite its relatively long half-life of 25 hours with its consequent
low level of radioactivity.

$$_{95}Am^{243} + _{8}O^{18} \longrightarrow _{103}Lr^{256} + 5n$$

$$Fm^{252} \xrightarrow[25\ hrs]{\alpha}$$

Element 104 and beyond

Experiments have continued in the direction of producing and
identifying the next heavier transuranium element, that with the
atomic number 104. Soviet groups of scientists at Dubna have employed the method used by the Berkeley group to discover element
103, augmented by some chemical experiments. They have used
heavy ion bombarding projectiles with the simple recoil technique,
and based their first identification on the relative yields and absence
of yields of the product obtained, with variations in the target
materials and types and energies of projectiles used. By measuring
fission tracks in a special glass with a microscope, they detected
an isotope which decays by spontaneous fission. They suggested
that this isotope, which has a half-life of 0·3 second, and appears
to be produced according to the following reaction might be 104[260].

$$_{94}Pu^{242} + _{10}Ne^{22} \longrightarrow 104^{260} + 4n$$

Element 104 is expected to have chemical properties similar to those of hafnium, as I shall explain further in a few moments, and hence is expected to form a relatively volatile compound with chlorine (a tetrachloride). They feel that their chemical experiments have shown that the chloride compound of the 0·3-second activity is more volatile than the relatively non-volatile actinide chlorides (which are trichlorides). Although this experiment doesn't fulfill the classical test of chemically separating the new element from all previously known elements, it provides valuable evidence for evaluation in connection with the nuclear evidence, i.e., the method of production and decay of the 0·3-second activity. If the very difficult nuclear and chemical experiments can be confirmed they will be cogent evidence for the discovery of element 104.

There are efforts under way at the University of California Lawrence Radiation Laboratory to confirm the Soviet discovery or, alternatively, to produce another isotope of element 104. Scientists there are attempting to utilize reactions such as those shown here.

$$_{98}Cf^{250} + {_6}C^{13} \longrightarrow 104^{260} + 3n$$

$$_{96}Cm^{246} + {_8}O^{18} \longrightarrow 104^{260} + 4n$$

Both the Berkeley and Dubna groups are also attempting to produce elements with atomic numbers higher than 104 by bombarding heavy transuranium targets with heavy ion projectiles. The yields of transuranium isotopes become decreasingly smaller as we go up the scale in atomic number. In most of the cases when all or only part of the projectile enters into a fusion with the target nucleus the intermediate (transition) nucleus splits in half by the fission reaction — less than one in a million of these

intermediate nuclei end up as the sought-after new heavy transuranium element. Thus the yields become smaller and smaller—
even less than one atom per experiment! Strange as it may seem,
this is still not an impossible situation under the experimental
conditions of today's science. A yield of one tenth atom per
experiment, for example, may simply mean that under some
experimental conditions you must conduct ten experiments in
order to produce one atom — or under other continuous experimental arrangements it may mean that you must, in effect,
conduct the bombardment for ten times as long.

There are many possible combinations of target nuclei and
heavy ion projectiles — you might enjoy piecing together a number
of these combinations in this field of atomic or new element
arithmetic. There are, of course, certain subtleties which suggest
that some possibilities may be more profitable than others. Space
does not permit me to explore these with you. A couple of
possible reactions for the production of element 105, not necessarily
very perspicacious or subtle, are shown in the following reactions:

$$_{98}Cf^{252} + _{7}N^{15} \longrightarrow 105^{263} + 4n$$

$$_{95}Am^{243} + _{10}Ne^{22} \longrightarrow 105^{260} + 5n$$

Need for target material

I believe that it will be possible to synthesize and discover a
number of still heavier transuranium elements. However, whether
this is done by bombardment with heavy projectiles, or by another
method that I will describe presently, we will need larger amounts
of target isotopes for the transmutation experiments than are now
available. Fortunately, the transuranium elements all have the
potential for production in much larger quantity than we have
succeeded in producing up to the present time. The known elements
beyond einsteinium have isotopes of such short half-life that it

doesn't seem possible to handle them in weighable quantities in the ordinary sense, although it will apparently be possible to produce at least fermium in sufficient quantities to use it successfully as a target material.

You may recall that I said that the discovery experiment for mendelevium, element 101, was performed with less than one-trillionth of a gram of einsteinium as the target material. Although in the intervening years such "huge" amounts as one-millionth of a gram (a million times more) of einsteinium have become available, we will require even larger quantities in order to insure the success of our quest for still heavier elements. We will need much more californium than the multimicrogram amounts now available, and larger amounts of the other transuranium elements for use as target materials and for other purposes that I will describe later.

Fortunately, we know very well how to produce the transuranium elements in greatly increased quantities, and, therefore, it is only a matter of planning and financing the effort to accomplish this. An effort leading toward this result was started several years ago and is well on the way toward culmination. The method is to irradiate an element such as plutonium with as many neutrons as we can pack into the nucleus in a reasonable time. To do this, we need nuclear reactors with the highest possible concentration — flux —of neutrons. The programme starts by irradiating plutonium, and continues on to irradiate the products of the plutonium irradiation, and then the products of that irradiation, and so on. In this way we will be able to proceed up the scale of mass numbers (and eventually atomic numbers) by adding one neutron after another. A required "high neutron flux" reactor, known as the High Flux Isotope Reactor (HFIR), has been built and is in the early stages of operation at Oak Ridge National Laboratory, where the special facilities required for the chemical isolation of the precious transuranium products of this reactor are also under construction and nearly completed.

In actuality, our AEC programme for the larger scale production of heavy transuranium elements will use the new HFIR in conjunction with existing facilities. The first step is to irradiate large amounts of plutonium — tens of kilograms — with neutrons in the huge plutonium production reactors at our Savannah River Plant.

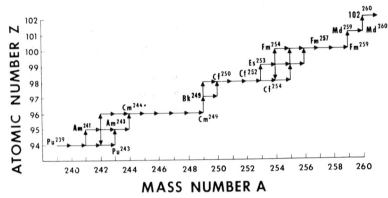

Figure 20. Nuclear reactions for the production of heavy elements by intense slow neutron irradiation. Neutron capture reactions are interspersed with beta-decays. Each neutron capture adds one unit to the mass number (horizontal arrows), and each beta-decay increases the atomic number by one unit leaving the mass number unchanged (vertical arrows).

Several years of this type of neutron irradiation produces intermediate isotopes, such as plutonium-242, americium-243 and curium-244, which are separated and purified. These can then be placed in the HFIR reactor for further neutron irradiation in order to produce the heavier transuranium elements. A special reactor at our Savannah River Plant has also been configured to a very high flux mode of operation (the highest neutron flux ever obtained anywhere) as a further contribution to this effort. Under this programme, it is planned to produce in a few years, for example, more than gram amounts of californium. This is a tremendous quantity which it would take decades to produce in our best previous type of research reactors, and which underscores, therefore, the need for such very high neutron flux reactors. As I indicated, these materials can serve as targets for bombardment with heavy ions to possibly produce still heavier transuranium elements.

So much for the practical aspects of the new production method. Let me consider for a moment the theoretical basis and some theoretical limits. *Figure 20* shows the nuclear reactions by which plutonium is "fattened up" through the successive addition of thermal or slow neutrons. You will notice as the isotope plutonium-

239 is irradiated, the neutrons are captured one after the other and the mass number builds up, going from left to right. Then, as the number of neutrons becomes large enough there is the emission of a beta particle converting a neutron in the nucleus to a proton, thus transforming the isotope into the element one higher on the atomic number scale. That element, in turn, can capture more neutrons and a product again decays by the emission of beta particles until we reach the isotopes high up on the atomic number and mass number scales.

The present world's record for the largest mass number by this method of production is fermium-257, that is, the element with the atomic number 100 and the isotope with mass number 257. This means we have successfully added six protons and twelve neutrons to plutonium-239. Although we hope to exceed this record by this method — that is, the successive addition of neutrons over a period of time — the heights we can hope to reach ultimately by this method are apparently quite limited. The reason for this is that the chain of build-up includes nuclei which decay so quickly (chiefly by undergoing spontaneous fission) that it is very difficult to accumulate them in the quantity required to make the successive capture of neutrons possible — in other words, their quick disappearance effectively blocks the build-up of still heavier nuclei. The isotopes beyond fermium-257 in *Figure 20* represent the predicted course of future additional build-up after these difficulties have been overcome.

Production by explosion

Now I want to tell you about a very fascinating and quite different method for producing new transuranium isotopes, and perhaps even new transuranium elements, under a programme which the U.S. A.E.C.* is pursuing. This method uses the neutrons from underground nuclear explosions, as shown in *Figure 21,* to transmute target materials to heavier and heavier isotopes by means of neutron capture reactions. This brief — of the order of a millionth of a second — but very intense source of neutrons makes it possible to capture successively a very large number of neutrons all in one element, such as uranium. This type of reaction to

---

* United States Atomic Energy Commission.

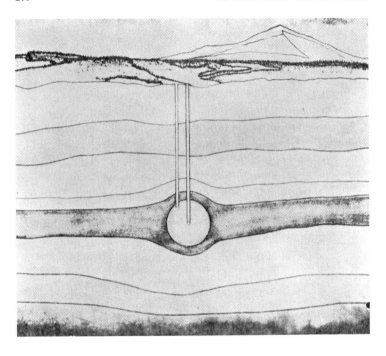

Figure 21.   Underground nuclear explosion to produce new isotopes and new elements.

synthesize heavy elements occurs in some of the stars, and it is truly a thing of wonder that man has succeeded in producing it here on earth. Schemes and devices are being devised for the very rapid recovery of a portion of the exposed sample in order to identify new isotopes and new elements by chemical procedures. Larger samples are recovered after the nuclear explosion by drilling down into the ground and bringing the material to the surface.

A possible sequence of nuclear reactions is illustrated on *Figure 22.* The starting material, uranium-238, might, in less than a millionth of a second, capture successfully as many as thirty-seven neutrons, for example, and produce uranium-275, as shown in the right-hand part of the mass number scale. Then the uranium-

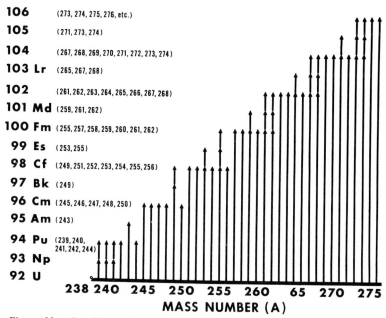

Figure 22. *Possible nuclides that might be produced through use of a nuclear explosion as a source of neutrons to be absorbed in uranium for production of nuclides of higher atomic number than now known. The predicted short half-lives of elements synthesized in this manner may make recovery and identification very difficult.*

275 might undergo fourteen successive electron emissions, converting some of its excess neutrons to protons, and as a result might end up as an isotope of the undiscovered element 106. The net result would be the addition of fourteen protons and twenty-three neutrons to the uranium-238. Of course, any of the transuranium elements, when they become available in quantity, might be used as the target material instead of uranium.

Numerous experiments utilizing underground nuclear explosions in Nevada have been carried on by scientists of the Lawrence Radiation Laboratory at Livermore and the Los Alamos Scientific Laboratory in New Mexico. These scientists are collaborating with scientists at the Argonne National Laboratory in Chicago and at the Lawrence Radiation Laboratory in Berkeley in chemically and physically identifying the products. Interestingly enough, the heaviest isotope produced by this method to date also is fermium-257, matching the world record for atomic number and mass number set by neutron irradiation in high flux reactors which I mentioned earlier.

I might also add that this method of capture of neutrons furnished by nuclear explosives has the advantage that it leads to isotopes which have an excess of neutrons for each of the elements ultimately produced. There is reason to believe that these isotopes will have longer half-lives than those produced by bombardment with heavy ion projectiles. The latter are neutron-deficient and consequently are likely to have relatively short half-lives.

Future prospects

I believe you can see, on the basis of what I have told you so far, that we hold out high hopes for the production of still heavier transuranium elements, that is, elements with atomic number greater than 103 or 104, by either the bombardment of heavy isotopic targets with heavy ion projectiles, or the irradiation of uranium or transuranium elements with the instantaneous high flux of neutrons produced in underground nuclear exposions, or by both methods. The limit of how high we can advance up the atomic number scale will, of course, be set by the yields of these nuclear reactions and by the half-lives for radioactive decay (by alpha particle emission and especially spontaneous fission), both of which are apparently decreasing as we go up the atomic number scale. Both of these trends suggest increasing difficulty in our attempts to reach greater heights on the atomic number scale. And when I note increasing difficulties on top of the almost insuperable difficulties that I have described in the experiments on elements 101, 102, 103 and 104, I am suggesting difficulties almost beyond imagination.

Nevertheless, I will bet on the ingenuity of scientists and the increasing sophistication of their apparatus and equipment and predict that the atomic number barrier will be broken again and again.

One particularly hopeful sign is the theoretical suggestion that our difficulties are in part due to the fact that we have encountered a pocket of instability in the region of elements 102 and 103, leading to abnormally short half-lives. This theory suggests that this region of instability will begin to "heal" around element 105, leading to heavier isotopes with longer half-lives. Even if this is not the case, I believe the scientists' ingenuity will make it possible to synthesize and identify elements with atomic numbers as high as 108 or 110. However, if we find such predicted areas of increased stability, it will be possible to synthesize such elements sooner and much more easily, and the prospects for synthesizing and identifying even heavier elements will be much brighter.

But our cause for optimism goes even beyond these prospects. There is reason to believe that there may be regions of extra stability in the very heavy unexplored transuranium region. These would correspond to the so-called closed nucleon (the collective name for protons and neutrons) shells that exist much lower down in the Periodic Table and which give rise to relatively stable nuclei such as those of tin and lead. A particularly exciting possibility is that isotopes with about 126 protons and 184 neutrons, corresponding to predicted stable nucleon shells — that is, isotopes like the one with the atomic number 126 and the mass number 310—will be sufficiently stable to make discovery and identification possible. Possible reactions for the production of such an isotope are shown in the following sequence:

$$_{90}Th^{232} + {}_{36}Kr^{82} \rightarrow 126^{310} + 4n$$

$$_{72}Hf^{180} + {}_{54}Xe^{132} \rightarrow 126^{310} + 2n$$

$$_{64}Gd^{156} + {}_{62}Sm^{154} \rightarrow 126^{310}$$

There may be another similar region of stability around the element with the atomic number 114.

If we are going to exploit this possibility, it will, of course, be necessary to have available in quantity much heavier ions than are now available. Scientists have already designed accelerators capable of making bombardments with ions as heavy as krypton or xenon, and we even look forward to the day when it will be possible to bombard uranium with uranium ions.

Such heavy ions will open new approaches to the production of new transuranium elements. One process, which we might call "inverse fission", is illustrated by the following reaction:

$$_{52}Te^{130} + _{54}Xe^{136} \longrightarrow 106^{266}$$

The advantage of this method of production lies in the possibility of producing the transuranium isotope with minimum excess energy, thus presumably minimizing its great tendency to split into two parts by the fission reaction, and maximizing its tendency to adhere together as is required for the production of a transuranium isotope. Particularly interesting is the "ultimate" possibility — that of bombarding uranium with uranium — because after the fusion of two such nuclei we might expect extremely interesting products of the very probable fission reaction. For example, the intermediate nucleus with an atomic number like 184 might split asymmetrically to yield a detectable product with an atomic number like 114, as illustrated in the following reaction:

$$_{92}U^{238} + _{92}U^{238} \longrightarrow [184]^{476} \longrightarrow 114^{298} + _{70}Yb^{166} + 12n$$

(Theoretical considerations suggest that the reaction illustrated may not be possible because the nuclear charge of element 184 may be too large to allow it to exist for the required length of time as an intermediate nucleus.) These, of course, are just illustrative examples of what are admittedly imaginative prospects, but the possibility of such reactions and such detectable nuclei certainly

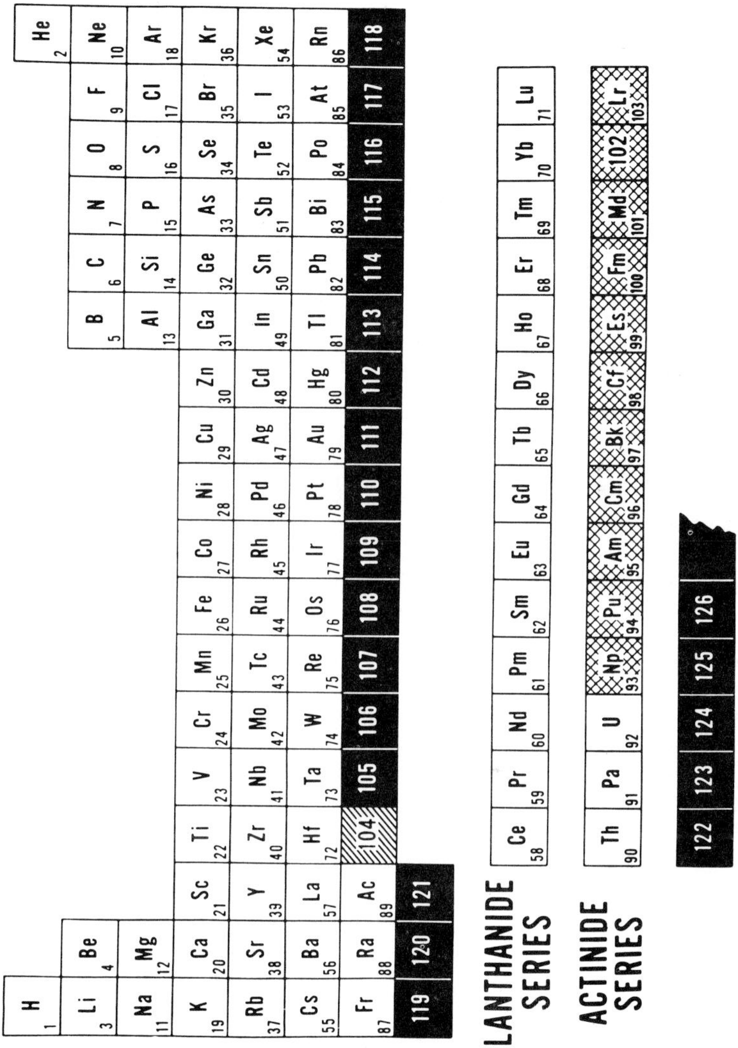

Figure 23. *Periodic Table of the Elements.*

cannot be ruled out on the basis of present knowledge and is even reasonable on the basis of some theoretical considerations.

Predicted chemical properties

In view of these prospects for very heavy transuranium elements, let me show you another very imaginative periodic table in *Figure 23*. Note that I have chosen to fill in elements 119, 120 and 121 under the elements, francium, radium and actinium, with the atomic numbers 87, 88 and 89. After element 121 I have indicated a third rare-earth-like series at that point which I placed at the bottom of the periodic table, below the lanthanide and actinide series, on the assumption that again an inner electron shell is in the process of being filled. (For purposes of simplicity I shall not try to distinguish between the two different kinds of inner electron shells that should begin to be filled in this region.) You will notice that on this basis, element 126 would be chemically analogous to plutonium — whatever that means.

It would, of course, be a chemist's paradise if such heavy elements could eventually be produced and if their half-lives are sufficiently long to make it possible to study their chemical properties by the tracer method. You may be interested to know that it is the nuclear instability that imposes the limit; the extra-nuclear electronic structure is predicted to be stable for elements even heavier than element 126. It may, of course, never be our lot, or that of our children, to study the chemical properties of elements as heavy as element 126. I believe, however, that it will be possible before long to study the chemical properties of a number of transactinide elements, that is, elements beyond element 103, even if our expectations for relatively long half-lives for these elements are not fulfilled. I feel this way because of my faith in the ingenuity of chemists. I believe, for example, that they will find ways to study the chemical properties of very short-lived isotopes using techniques involving migration of gaseous atoms or ions, volatility properties, reactions with surfaces, or gas flow reactions. In particular, it should be possible within the next few years to demonstrate what Mendeleev would call the eka-hafnium, eka-tantalum and eka-tungsten properties of elements 104, 105 and 106.

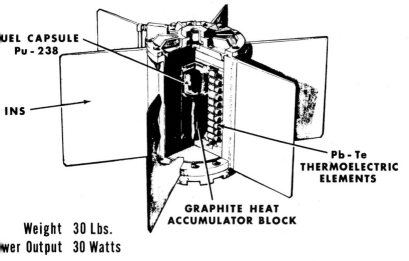

Figure 24. *SNAP-19 Generator. SNAP stands for* **S**ystems for **N**uclear **A**uxiliary **P**ower.

Some practical applications

The prime reason for conducting these intricate, difficult, even exotic experiments on the transuranium elements has, of course, been to increase our understanding of nature through an increase of our understanding of atomic and nuclear structure. As has been the case with so much prior basic research work, however, practical applications of great importance, many of them wholly unexpected, have already appeared and many others are likely to follow. I would like to conclude my remarks with a few comments about some of these applications.

The enormous practical importance of plutonium in the form of the fissionable isotope plutonium-239 is, of course, well known. This material can be used not only as the explosive ingredient for nuclear weapons, but also as a nuclear fuel to generate electricity to serve the world's needs for centuries to come. The future importance of plutonium-239 as a nuclear fuel arises, of course, from the fact that it can be readily produced from the

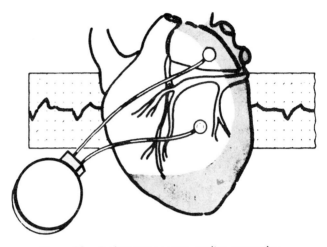

Figure 25. Radioisotope-power cardiac pacemaker.

abundant, but non-fissionable isotope of uranium, uranium-238, thereby unlocking the enormous stores of nuclear energy contained in uranium.

Not so well known are the potential uses of another plutonium isotope, plutonium-238. This isotope, which has a 90-year half-life, and was the first isotope of plutonium to be discovered, may prove to be one of the most valuable assets of mankind. It can be used as a compact source of electricity through the conversion of its heat from radioactive decay by thermoelectric or thermionic devices. Such plutonium-238 fueled power units, one of which is illustrated in *Figure 24,* are very compact and light in weight and hence are admirably suited for long-lived power sources in space and terrestrial applications. It is important to note that they can be handled safely and directly by technicians, since very little external radiation is emitted from power units fueled with plutonium-238.

The first space-orbiting of such a nuclear battery took place on June 29, 1961; it is powering equipment that is still sending signals back to earth more than five years later. Among the many

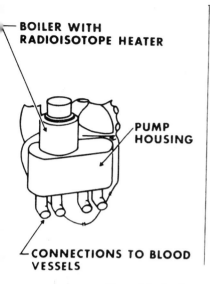

BOILER WITH RADIOISOTOPE HEATER

PUMP HOUSING

CONNECTIONS TO BLOOD VESSELS

POSSIBLE SPECIFICATIONS

WEIGHT – 2–4 POUNDS

DIMENSIONS   6" x 7" x 3"

OUTPUT – 1–3 GALLONS   MINUTE

WEIGHT OF RADIOISOTOPE 60 grams Pu-238

USEFUL LIFE –> 5 YEARS

Figure 26. Implanted mechanical heart.

potential uses of such nuclear batteries in our space programme is the plan to have our astronauts deliver such a power source to the moon and leave it there to power radio transmission equipment for a year or more after their return to earth. There are also many potential uses of plutonium-238 on earth. One is to power pacemakers for heart patients, as illustrated in *Figure 25.* Even more exciting is the idea now being considered of using plutonium-238 to power an entirely artificial heart, shown in *Figure 26,* which can be surgically implanted in the patient. (The isotopes thulium-171 and promethium-147 are other possible power sources for this purpose.)

The projected requirements for plutonium-238 in space nuclear batteries over the next decade or two run into tons of material. If the artificial heart application should materialize, the requirements will be substantially greater than this. Fortunately, plutonium-238 is derived from neptunium-237 which is produced as a by-product in the operation of nuclear reactors, including electricity - producing nuclear power reactors, according to the following reactions:

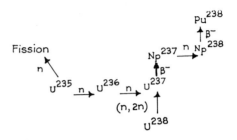

Neutron irradiation of the chemically separated neptunium-237 isotope results in its conversion to plutonium-238.

The isotope americium-241, which has a half-life of 460 years, has a number of important industrial uses due to its 60 Kev gamma ray. It has a wide range of uses in fluid density gauges, in thickness gauges, in aircraft fuel gauges, in distance-sensing devices and a number of other uses. It is produced as a decay daughter of 13-year plutonium-241 which is a constituent of reactor-produced plutonium.

The possible practical applications of other transuranium isotopes are also very interesting. For example, as mentioned earlier, it is possible to produce curium-244, an isotope with an 18-year half-life, by neutron irradiation of plutonium in a nuclear reactor. This isotope, like plutonium-238, can also be used as a fuel for nuclear batteries, and is produced according to the following reactions:

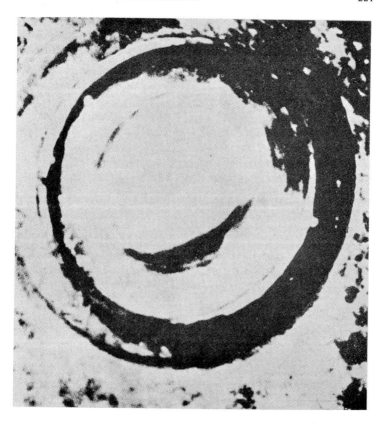

Figure 27. Sample of curium-242 and americium-214 self-heated to nearly 2000°F. by radioactive decay.

The AEC has a program for the production of three kilograms of curium-244, to be used to test its attributes as an isotopic fuel, using one of the Savannah River plutonium production reactors configured to operate in a very high flux neutron mode. While curium-244 would require greater shielding than plutonium-238 in its applications, it has the advantage that it can be more readily produced in very large quantities, should the assessment of its properties turn out favorably.

I have a special interest in the production of curium-244 because of the tremendous by-product production of even heavier transuranium isotopes that would inevitably follow from its production in large amounts. If this material turns out to have the properties required for widespread use as an isotopic power source, one can imagine its future production in ton quantities. This would require the conversion of a number of plutonium production reactors to the manufacture of curium-244. Such quantities of curium-244 are almost beyond comprehension when we recall that our first experience with this isotope, which was as recently as 1950, involved picogram quantities, that is, quantities of the order of a million-millionth of a gram. Thus, we are now talking about an escalation in production of the order of more than a million billionfold.

Isotopic heat sources of the type that I have been describing develop very high temperatures in the process of the conversion of their heat energy into electricity. This is illustrated in *Figure 27,* which shows a 3-gram mixture of curium-242 (and americium-241) oxide powder, still other useful transuranium isotopes, at a self-generated temperature of 1000° Centigrade (nearly 2000° Fahrenheit). This is just illustrative of this type of material. Similar temperatures are developed by the other isotopes that I have discussed, such as curium-244, as the inevitable consequence of assembling multigram quantities. Incidentally, the energy emission rates are: about one hundred and twenty thermal watts per gram of curium-242, about three thermal watts per gram of curium-244, and about one-half thermal watt per gram of plutonium-238, and these emission rates are continuous, diminishing only at the same rate as that of the isotope's radioactive decay.

Alternatively to producing larger quantities of heavier transuranium elements as by-products of the production of curium-244, one could, of course, produce such isotopes as primary objectives in order to meet the possible demand for their potential applications. One such isotope is californium-252, which is produced through successive neutron capture in high flux nuclear reactors, according to the reactions I indicated earlier *(Figure 20).* This isotope, due to its high rate of neutron emission, has potential widespread applications as a point neutron source for radiography or as a portable and reliable source for conducting neutron activation analyses in locations on earth and out in space where conventional neutron generators are not possible. (Neutron activation analysis is a method for the detection of trace quantities of chemical elements by making them radioactive through irradiation with neutrons.) It may also have special useful widespread applications for therapy in a number of medical uses.

Impressive as are the uses already found or being considered for the heavier transuranium elements, I feel certain that even more noteworthy applications will be found. Although the addition to basic knowledge alone would justify this program of fundamental research, there seems little doubt that the practical applications will also in themselves justify a continuing investigation of the transuranium elements.

I predict that the transuranium elements will be a field of fruitful and exciting research for many, many years to come.

Gravitation

and the Universe

by

PROFESSOR H. BONDI

Professor H. Bondi, F.R.S.
Professor of Applied Mathematics, King's College,
University of London

CHAPTER 1

Universal Gravitation

The most evident property of gravitation is that it is so universal. Everything drops, irrespective of the material from which it is made. Even when we see what looks at first sight like an exception, such as a balloon rising in the air, or a cork floating on the water, we know that this motion is due only to the fact that the air or the water, respectively, itself is attracted by the earth. Newton saw that this universality extended much further afield; that not only the apple was attracted by the earth but also the moon. In our kind of environment gravitation is, perhaps, the most ever-present entity in all physics. One would, therefore, think that with more examples of gravitation at work than of any other force, it would be easier to describe gravitation. But this is not quite true. Its very universality leads to certain problems and difficulties in investigating it. The most direct method one uses in science to establish linkages, to establish connections, is to vary the conditions. To give a trivial example, if I want to know whether a particular switch is the switch for a light, then I switch it on and off several times to see whether the light comes on and goes off as I move that switch. If I altered the position of the switch only once—say I switch it on and the light comes on—then I *could* worry whether, perhaps, this was just a coincidence; that, in fact, the light was controlled by quite a different switch which somebody else switched on coincidentally at the same moment as I switched mine. But by repeating the manoeuvre on and off a few times, I can satisfy myself, in the end, that indeed my switch controls the light.

Innumerable experiments in physics can be carried out in just this way, by altering conditions at will and seeing what the consequences are. Indeed, this is of the very essence of the entire concept of experimentation. There is, however, no direct or obvious way in which we can use this method for gravitation. There is no means of switching it off; there is no means of insulating any body against gravitation. It was one of Galileo's great discoveries that all bodies fall equally fast, that gravitation affects every material in the same manner. This is the most fundamental and remarkable property of gravitation, and I shall discuss it at some length before describing the particular obstacles and complexities in our investigations that are due to this property of universal gravitation.

First of all, we recognise the very essence of science in Galileo's statement that all bodies fall equally fast. It is a statement of great simplicity, extreme generality, one that now seems obvious to every boy and girl at school, but is yet in conflict with immediate direct observation and was, in fact, quite different from the situation as it was imagined before his day. It is perhaps the mark of every great scientific discovery that it becomes difficult, if not impossible, to imagine what the world looked like before the discovery was made. In order to see just how great a step forward Galileo took, it is worth while thinking a little about the contrary evidence which convinced people before his day that the order of things was quite different.

It is very easy to make the mistake of believing that people who didn't know what everybody now knows must have been extremely stupid. This is entirely and utterly false; there is not the slightest reason to believe that human intelligence has improved; the only thing that has improved, in a certain sense, is education. Each new generation receives as its "baggage" the cumulative experience of earlier generations, and since the amount of experience is increasing all the time, this means that each generation has a better start than its predecessors.

It is, of course, quite obvious that a leaf falls slowly, that a steel ball falls fast, that a balloon filled with hydrogen doesn't fall at all but will rise. This is the direct evidence of our senses, and Aristotle based himself on this direct evidence in his description which lasted through hundreds and hundreds of years. This view was that the heavier a body, the lower its proper position; the lighter a body, the higher its proper position, and each body tended to move towards its proper level. All this was overthrown by Galileo's remarkably simple statement which yet is contrary to the immediately available evidence. Why should we, as Galileo did (and why are we entitled to), discount the immediate evidence of our senses? The point here is that in physics, as in all science, we strive to understand the *simple* situations but the simple situations are not the common situations. The point is that we live in an extremely complex environment on the surface of the earth. Just how complex this environment is we have really only learned nowadays through space travel and space medicine. The extreme complications of reproducing in other conditions the environment in which alone we can live have driven home to us time and again how peculiar and complex our environment is. This is not surprising. We ourselves, like all life, are exceedingly complex. Life could never have evolved in a simple environment. Whereas the "commonsense" attitude might be: "Let us investigate and account for what goes on near us in our familiar surroundings. If we can't understand what goes on further away, well, that's just too bad!" It has turned out that, in fact, the situation is quite the opposite. It is infinitely easier for us to understand and describe what goes on in circumstances very different from those of our neighbourhood and only gradually, and with a great deal of difficulty, can we appreciate what goes on near us. It was this great step away from the mesmerising influence of our immediate surroundings that Galileo took and by which he advanced science so very much.

The particular circumstance of our environment that affects observations of gravitation is the existence of the air. In an evacuated vessel everything will, indeed, fall at the same speed—the steel ball, the leaf and the hydrogen-filled balloon. This is a simple law of physics readily stated and it can be tested without too much difficulty, though a very detailed investigation of the statement requires more advanced thought. The effect of the air on the motion of bodies through it is, however, a very much more difficult matter. The whole branch of physics known as *aerodynamics* deals with this, and the computation of the air resistance of a leaf is a very complex and difficult matter that we have not yet fully mastered. Thus you see in Galileo's work an example of one of the prime tasks of the scientist. He must see through all this incredible wealth and tangle of information that we have and by instinct, by intelligence, by sheer ability, pick out the few simple questions. Often, it may seem, at least at first sight, that the questions to which a simple answer can be given are not the most interesting questions. Thus, you could readily have said to Galileo three-and-a-half centuries ago, "I am quite uninterested in how bodies fall in a vacuum; the only real thing that intrigues me is how leaves and balloons and steel balls fall here, in my neighborhood". But a man who argued like this would not be a scientist at all though he could, perhaps, be called a philosopher of the more ancient and old-fashioned kind. The scientist must go for results; he must ask the questions to which he *can* give answers, with not too much worry as to whether the questions look to him important or not. In particular, he is not interested whether they could be classified as more or less important to the questions to which he cannot find the answer. We can only hope, in science, that by asking more and more questions to which we *can* get an answer, we will gradually work our way up and along and find, in due course, answers to questions that, even to the "man in the street", look important.

In the case of gravitation it was not difficult to see the application of Galileo's result. It could readily be applied by Newton to the motion of the moon and the planets and their satellites. Thus Newton formulated his theory of gravitation and we have, then, the remarkable situation that it is relatively easy to describe precisely the motion of all the many bodies in the solar system, such as the planets and their satellites, and the comets and all these bodies, but we still find it very hard to calculate how a leaf should fall.

Gravitation, it turned out, had a further property that made experimentation extremely difficult. Gravitation, as Newton discovered, was caused by mass, but it needs a very large mass to produce a noticeable gravitational field. Thus, the gravitational field due to an ordinary size of mass (say 1lb.) is almost unmeasurably small. It needs bodies like the Earth or the sun or the moon to produce large fields; fields of gravitation which can readily be measured. We can neither manufacture bodies of such size, nor affect their motion. It is purely a fortuitous and lucky circumstance that we live in a solar system with so many gravitating objects. Conditions for life on the earth would have been indistinguishably like the existing ones if the solar system had consisted entirely of the sun and the earth, with no other body whatever in it. But how different would the history of science have been! There would have been none of that ancient astronomy and astrology due to the complicated apparent motions of the planets. There would have been no concentration on the motion of these distant bodies. It would have been far more difficult for a Galileo and a Newton on such an earth to break away from a futile investigation of our immediate surroundings in their enormous complexity, to the simple laboratory of the heavens where everything is relatively easy. Perhaps we owe it to the centuries-long sway of astrology that people found the work of Galileo and Newton really interesting. Certainly, without astrology, there would have been no wealth of data accumulated over hundreds of years, and so no Kepler would have produced the laws of planetary motion. The fortunate fact is that, in the motions of the planets and their satellites, we have countless examples of gravitation at work by which the theory of Newton could be tested and cross-checked as, perhaps, no other scientific theory was tested through several centuries.

The basis of all this work is, as I have been saying, Galileo's result that all bodies fall equally fast. How precise is our knowledge of this? With what accuracy do we know that all bodies fall equally fast? Naturally, with the primitive technology of Galileo's day, he could establish this result only with a very limited precision, but nowadays we know that, in fact, his law is correct to an enormous accuracy. The discrepancy between different bodies must be smaller than one part in perhaps a hundred thousand million. We know Galileo's result to be correct to a higher precision than we know with many other physical laws. How can such precision come about? How can it be, when it obviously must be a matter of extreme difficulty to measure the speed of falling bodies with high precision, and when clearly, even in what we call a vacuum, there are enough residual gases left to have some slight influence on the motion of falling bodies? In fact, the measurement is made in an entirely different way, based on Newton's theory of dynamics. This theory again is a marvellous piece of abstracting from local circumstances.

Before Newton, it was thought that an agency or force was required whenever a body was in motion; that the natural state of motion, as it were, was rest, and that an explanation had to be offered whenever a body was found not to be at rest. Once again we can see that this is a very clear and evident deduction from what we see going on in our surroundings, and again it needed a genius to see that our surroundings, with ever-present friction and ever-present air resistance, are highly complex. Galileo and Newton saw their way through this tangle and arrived at the result most clearly stated in Newton's first law of dynamics: *A body on which no forces act moves in a straight line with constant velocity.*

The way I like to look at this law is to think of it as saying, "If you see a body moving in a straight line with constant velocity, do not bother to look for an agency responsible for the motion—you'll be wasting your time." Look for such an agency—look for a force—only when you see a change of velocity in magnitude or direction, an acceleration.

Newton then proceeded to his second law, which related the magnitude of the deviation from the straight line motion with constant velocity, that is, the magnitude and direction of the acceleration, with the agency responsible for it—the force. He found that with the same force different bodies were accelerated differently, but that the difference in acceleration affected only the magnitude of the acceleration and not its direction. Thus when we allow the strength of a compressed spring to accelerate a small ball or a large ball, we will find that it will give less acceleration to the large ball than to the small one. Moreover, if we have two bodies, then the ratio of the magnitudes of acceleration imparted to them by different sets of forces is always the same. There is, accordingly, an intrinsic property of the body which measures, as it were, its resistance to being accelerated. This property of the body Newton called the *inertia* or the mass. In order to be definite we shall call it the *inertial mass* of the body. In the experiments on which Newton's second law is based, one has to be very careful to apply the *same* force to different bodies as in the case of the compressed spring.

How does all this fit in with Galileo's statement that all bodies fall equally fast? Clearly this must mean that they all have the same acceleration. Therefore, what Galileo's statement must imply is that the force of gravitation on a body is proportional to its inertial mass. Let us not jump to this conclusion, but let us look at this by comparison with other forces. When we have a field of force, say an electric field of force, or a magnetic field of force, then how much force this exerts on a particular body depends on certain properties of that body. Thus an electric field will pull a charged body and will not pull an uncharged one, and the magnitude of the force on the body is proportional to its electric charge. Similarly, a magnetic field will affect different bodies differently. A magnet will attract a lump of iron and will not have any effect on a piece of glass. In these cases and in others I could quote, there is, as it were, a property of the body on to which the force hooks. This property we call the electric charge or the magnetic moment, and so on. We can then invent such a property for the gravitational field and say there is a property of the body on to which gravitation hooks just like the electric field hooks on to the electric charge and we shall call this property the *passive gravitational mass* of a body. Therefore, the gravitational force on a body is proportional to its passive gravitational mass.

What Galileo's statement now means (that all bodies fall equally fast) is that the passive gravitational mass, which determines the force on the body, is proportional to the inertial mass which determines its resistance to being accelerated. In other words, Galileo's law is that the ratio of passive gravitational mass to inertial mass is the same for all bodies. It is this formulation that can be tested with such accuracy.

First, I would like to remind you of the fact that when a body follows a circular path with constant speed, then its velocity is changing in direction all the time and you readily see that such a body has an acceleration towards the centre of the circle. When a body follows its circular path, therefore, a force has to be exerted, pulling it towards the centre. This is easily experienced when we swing around a stone in a sling. In this case, the acceleration is determined by the speed of the body and the radius of the circle, and, therefore, the force that has to be exerted is in proportion to the inertial mass of the body, and is directed towards the centre

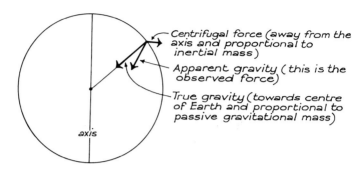

FIG. 1 : THE EOTVÖS EXPERIMENT

of the circle. By Newton's third law, *the equality of action and reaction,* the body is therefore pulling away from the centre with a force called the *centrifugal force,* which is proportional to its inertial mass. Owing to the rotation of the earth, any body at rest on the surface of the earth is describing a circle. Since the rotation is around the axis of the earth, there is then the centrifugal force pulling away from the axis of the earth in a direction at right angles to this axis. As you readily see from the illustration *(Figure 1)* such a force will be vertically upwards on the equator and at some angle to the vertical in any other latitude. The gravitational force on a body, on the other hand, is, as we have been saying, proportional to its passive gravitational mass and points in a direction, roughly speaking, to the centre of the earth. In any intermediate latitude, therefore, these two forces are not in opposite directions, but make an angle with each other which is, roughly speaking, equal to the latitude of the location. What we can in fact measure, what we see as the direction of the plumbline, is the combination of these two forces which will combine according to the well-known parallelogram of forces. Note now, that one force is proportional to the inertial mass, the other to the passive gravitational mass. Therefore, the direction of the combined force will be the same for all bodies if, and only if, the ratio of inertial to passive gravitational mass is the same for all of them. Therefore, Galileo's statement is equivalent to the statement that the direction of the combined force (usually called apparent gravity) is the same for all bodies in one location, irrespective of the composition of the bodies. If then we try to balance two bodies against each other such as we do in an ordinary balance, but in suitably refined and sensitive form, we see that we can achieve this balance in all directions only if apparent gravity is the same for the two bodies. We, therefore, have a very sensitive way of testing whether Galileo's statement is actually correct.

This method was first used by the Hungarian physicist Eotvös in the early years of the century and in recent years has been repeated with modern experimental methods to an even higher degree of accuracy by Dicke at Princeton. Eotvös obtained an accuracy of, perhaps, one part in a hundred million and Dicke improved on this by another factor of towards one thousand. And on this basis we know then, all bodies fall equally fast with an accuracy exceeded by few items of knowledge in all our Physics.

CHAPTER 2

Intrinsic Gravitation

We have stressed earlier how much is gained in our understanding if we free ourselves from the peculiar local environment in which we live. One particular condition of this environment is that we live on a solid earth. It is this and this alone that prevents us from falling freely; from being accelerated towards the centre of the earth.

We should then ask, "What does gravitation look like when one is not supported by the solid earth and when one is falling freely?" The answer to this question has been known for a long time, but has been experienced only recently in orbiting spaceships. Since all bodies fall equally fast, an assembly of bodies will fall together. Viewed from one of those bodies, the others will fall with it. In the past, one had to imagine some situation with a very uncomfortable outcome, like jumping from the Eiffel Tower. You could then say that if you decided to jump off, there was no need to worry about your binoculars or your camera; they would fall with you. In other words, you would be accompanied in your fall by all the items of your property around you; they would not have to be held up by you; they would appear to be in a state of weightlessness. Nowadays, of course, we all now about the state of weightlessness from the manned space programme. In a spaceship there is real weightlessness. The astronaut does not put his pencil down, he just lets it go and it stays where he left it. He can try to catch a drop of soup floating around his cabin.

Thus, we might think that gravitation was one of those things due entirely to the particular set of circumstances here. One might think that if we did not happen to live on the solid earth there would be no such thing as gravitation, that we would all live in orbiting spaceships; we wouldn't know anything about fall-ing down. However, this is an oversimplified view. Owing to the non-uniformity of the earth's gravitational field, when we consider two widely separated points on the surface of the earth then the direction of gravitation clearly differs in the two places. If I look from one spaceship at a distant spaceship then I see this following an accelerated orbit. It is accelerated relative to me. If I jump from the Eiffel Tower and somebody in the antipodes jumps from a similar tower there, then I will certainly notice an acceleration of him relative to me since, after all, the distance between us is rapidly diminishing and the rate of this diminution is itself increasing. Thus, free fall abolishes gravitation but does so only in a purely local region. The moment we go further afield, the moment the inhabitants of a spaceship look out and see what goes on far away, they will notice that there is some effect of gravitation. The moment one states such a sharp distinction between the local and the distant, the question raises itself immediately, "How far away is distant?" These effects, as we have been saying, are due to the non-uniformity of the earth's gravitational field and, clearly, it will be non-uniform even over quite small regions. After all, the earth field is weaker further from the earth and stronger nearer the earth. These effects will then be small but with sufficiently sensitive equipment we can detect them. Let us think of our orbiting spaceship and let us remember that, small though it may be in comparison with the earth, it has a size which is not vanishing. Therefore, part of the spaceship will be nearer the earth than the middle and part of it will be further from the earth than the centre of the spaceship. The spaceship in its orbit will be freely falling. With what kind of acceleration? The earth's attraction varies across the spaceship, being strongest in the part of the spaceship nearest the earth, weakest in the part furthest from the earth. The spaceship will thus fall with some compromise acceleration. This will not be quite as much as the acceleration of gravity on the side of the spaceship nearest the earth and a little too much compared with the acceleration of gravity on the side of the spaceship furthest from the earth. Therefore, if an astronaut releases a pencil near the wall of the spaceship nearest to the earth, that pencil will slowly drift towards that side because, as it were, it is falling just a tiny bit faster than the spaceship as a whole. Similarly, a pencil released near the side of a spaceship furthest from the earth will slowly drift towards that side. In general, loose objects will tend to accumulate on the side of the ship nearest the earth and on the side of the ship furthest from the earth. There will be a tendency, as it were, for the whole spaceship to follow this procedure; there will be a slight strain on the shell trying to elongate the shell along the direction joining it to the centre of the earth, so that the spaceship becomes elongated in this direction, the part nearest to the earth getting a little nearer; the part furthest from the earth getting a little further. Small though this effect is, it can be measured and can even be utilised. Thus there is a little bit of gravitation that is left over even when one is falling freely. This is a part that cannot be abolished in any manner whatsoever and so we call this part *intrinsic gravitation*.

Naturally, this stress and strain is not confined to an artificial object like our spaceship. If we like to think of the earth in its orbit around the sun, then there will be a similar tendency for the part nearest the sun to attempt to get yet nearer, for the part furthest from the sun to get yet further. If there is matter free to move on the surface of the earth, it will move in this manner: thus, the ocean will rise on the side nearest the sun and on the side furthest the sun, producing the tides due to the sun—the solar tides. Their position is more or less fixed by the direction to the sun. The earth rotates, as it were, under these tidal bulges, turning right round its axis once in a day, and, therefore, passing *two* of these bulges in a day, leading to the well-known phenomenon of twice-daily tides. There is, similarly, an interaction between the earth and the moon. It is not quite so easy to realise the geometry here. The earth attracts the moon, and the moon attracts the earth. The earth is much the more massive body and so, by the laws of dynamics, the moon does most of the moving, but not all of it. Both the bodies, to revert for a moment to technical language, revolve about their common centre of mass so that the earth is similarly moving. As in our previous examples, it moves with a compromise acceleration, too small for the side of the earth nearest the moon, too large for the side of the earth furthest from the moon, leading then to the lunar tides which also occur twice a day for just the same reason.

What is the relation in magnitude of the solar tide to the lunar tide? The sun is so vastly bigger a body than the moon that in spite of the fact that the earth is much further from the sun than from the moon, the attraction of the sun upon the earth is yet much greater than the attraction of the moon—about two hundred times as large, to be precise. But we must remember that in our intrinsic gravitation, which is the force which causes the tides, we are not interested in the *total* attraction of the sun or the moon on the earth: that only determines how fast the earth will fall towards the sun and towards the moon. What we are interested in for the tide-raising force is the *difference* in the attraction of the sun on opposite sides of the earth and the difference in the attraction of the moon on opposite sides of the earth. Now the diameter of the earth is a much larger fraction of the distance from the earth to the moon than it is of the distance from the earth to the sun. Thus the difference in the attraction of the sun on the two sides of the earth is a much smaller fraction of the total attraction of the sun than the corresponding difference is of the total attraction of the moon. When we work this out, allowing for the fact that the distance to the sun is almost four hundred times the distance to the moon, then it turns out that the solar tides are only about half the size of the lunar tides. Hence the lunar tides are the bigger ones and we naturally associate the tides with the moon rather than with the sun. But, of course, both tides are of importance. Clearly, when the lunar tides and the solar tides coincide we will get the highest possible tides. These are called the *spring tides*. When they are pulling at different times, then we get lower tides and the lowest tides we can get are called the *neap tides*.

Because the tendency of the tides is to elongate the earth both towards and away from the sun, we get spring tides whenever sun, earth and moon are in line, irrespective of whether the earth is between the moon and sun or the moon between earth and sun. Accordingly, we get spring tides both at new moon and at full moon, and the lowest tides—the neap tides—half-way between— at first quarter and at last quarter.

The oceans are not the only mobile thing on the earth: the atmosphere can move too and even the solid earth is not quite rigid, but only an elastic body. So, indeed, we have tides of the atmosphere and we have tides of the solid earth. Of course, the solid earth is a much tougher object than the oceans, so that the elongation of the earth is not nearly as great as that of the oceans and so we notice the tides of the oceans very well. The tides of the atmosphere can be measured with a barometer and their existence has long been established. Similarly, one can, with delicate instruments, notice the tides of the solid earth.

It will readily be understood that the tides of the ocean are the most complicated ones because the oceans have such extremely complicated shapes, thanks to the curious shapes of the continents —they inhibit free movement of the masses of water. Indeed, the interplay of land and sea gives rise to very complicated phenomena. In many instances the funnelling of the ocean in estuaries and bays leads to a great rise in the tides. Whereas the tidal range in mid-ocean is, according to our calculations, only two or three feet, in suitably shaped bays this can be enormously amplified as the whole mass of water moves up the bay. Thus in the Bay of Fundy in Canada, tides of over forty feet are regularly registered, and the tides round the shores of England are also quite high—twenty feet or so. But there are other parts of the world where the tides are relatively small and not so significant and, of course, this has a great importance for the use of ports by shipping. In enclosed seas and on lakes, there is little inducement for the water to move because it is high tide almost simultaneously at the two ends. Thus even in seas of the size of the Baltic there are virtually no tides, and even in the Great Lakes there are no noticeable tides.

A very intricate dynamic phenomenon is the so-called tidal friction. First imagine a situation with the earth completely covered by ocean. Tidal bulges would then be raised by the sun and the moon as we discussed, and the earth would rotate under these tidal bulges. The motion of water is not free of friction or viscosity and so there would be some rubbing of this spinning wheel, the earth, against the two brake-shoes; the tidal bulges, held fixed in position by sun and moon respectively *(see Figure 2)*. We say fixed in position because in the course of a day the earth turns round its axis but the moon doesn't move far in its motion round the earth, and the earth very little in its way round the sun in this period. Accordingly, we expect some friction which will tend to slow down the rotation of the earth and at the same time will tend

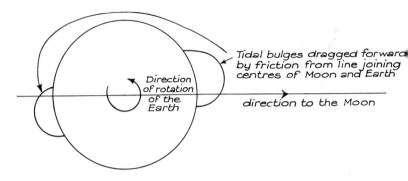

Direction
of rotation
of the
Earth

Tidal bulges dragged forward
by friction from line joining
centres of Moon and Earth

direction to the Moon

FIG. 2 : TIDAL FRICTION

to pull the brake-shoes, the tidal bulges, forward in the sense of the
rotation of the earth. Thus here we have a frictional effect in an
astronomical phenomenon—the rotation of the earth. The consequence of this must be a gradual slowing down of the rotation of
the earth.

There will similarly be friction between the tides of the atmosphere and the rotation of the earth and between the tides of the
solid earth and the rotation of the earth. It turns out that the
friction due to the tides of the solid earth is the most important one.
This friction is of the kind that occurs in the tyres of a motor-car:
as the car moves along, different parts of the rubber of the tyre
are stretched and squashed and strained all the time and, by this
repeated straining and releasing of the rubber, heat is generated.
We all know how hot the tyres get when a car is driven fast. This
getting hot—this conversion of mechanical energy into heat—is,
of course, a characteristic phenomenon of friction. In a perfectly
elastic body there would be no such effect. Real bodies are not
quite perfectly elastic. In stretching and straining, there will be a
loss of mechanical energy. We are also familiar with this from
playing with a rubber ball. When a rubber ball hits the floor,
having been dropped, then it does not rise quite to the height from
which it was dropped because, however nearly perfect the elasticity
of the rubber of the ball, some of the energy is turned into heat.

It is very fortunate for the scientist that it is not the tidal friction
of the oceans that is predominant, for after all, we know from

geology that the shapes of the continents have changed enormously during geological periods. So no doubt tidal friction will have been very different long ago at different periods from what it is now and the cumulative effect over enormous lengths of time of tidal friction would be almost impossible to calculate. On the other hand, the tides of the solid earth have probably encountered much, the same imperfection of elasticity in the past as now, and so we can reasonably calculate backwards in time till, indeed, we discover that the day must have been a little shorter in geological time than it is now. Days are continuing to get longer, though the effect is not large, and the lengthening of the day is a very slow and gradual process.

Just as the moon raises tides on the earth, so the earth will raise tides on the moon. Since the moon is much the smaller body, the effect of the tides raised on the moon, on the motion of the moon, will be much more marked than the effect of the tides raised by the moon on the earth is on the rotation of the earth. Thus, if the moon used to rotate about its axis, never mind at what speed, this rotation will gradually have been slowed down until there was no motion of the moon relative to the tidal bulges raised on the solid moon by the earth. In other words, finally the moon will be rotating so that the tidal bulges do not move relative to the moon; the moon would be forced by tidal friction always to show the same face to the earth, and we know, indeed, that this is the case.

Let us now return to tidal friction on the earth; this also has direct consequences for the motion of the moon. As you may know, it is a consequence of Newton's laws that the angular momentum of a system not acted upon by outside forces must remain constant. If we now consider the system of the earth and the moon, then the angular momentum of this system is composed of the angular momenta due to the rotation of the earth, due to the orbital motion of the moon and the earth and due to the rotation of the moon. This last one is directly linked, as we have now said, to the orbital motion of them both. Now if the angular momentum of the rotation of the earth is diminishing owing to tidal friction, and the total angular momentum of the earth-moon system stays constant, then the angular momentum of the orbital motion of the moon must be increasing. This, it turns out, means that the moon is being driven further and further from the earth. To those of you not familiar with the concept of angular momentum, let me point out that the tidal friction will mean that the tidal bulges on the earth are pulled forward relative to the moon. They are not strictly on the line joining the centre of the earth to the moon but further forward. The effect of this will be to pull the moon itself forward in its orbit (note that the moon revolves round the earth in the same sense as the earth rotates). This forward pull on the moon will strengthen the centrifugal force *vis-à-vis* gravitation. This results, in the end, in the moon's moving further from the earth. So, as a result of tidal friction, the moon is being driven away from the earth.

This raises very interesting questions about the origin of the moon. If the effect of the earth on the moon is to drive the moon further and further away, does it not necessarily follow that the moon was once part of the earth? Although this was believed at one stage, it is extremely difficult to imagine any situation in which a body ejected, by whatever means, from the earth would not either go off to infinity or fall back on the earth. To make an orbiting body from something originating on the earth requires highly complicated manoeuvres, as we know from the launch of spaceships. Such manoeuvres are most unlikely to take place naturally. Yet how can we escape from the conclusion that the moon came from the earth? After all, if it is now receding from the earth, then presumably it used to be rather nearer. Then the tides would have been greater, tidal friction would have been greater, and the rate of recession would have been greater than now. Thus, yet further back in time, it must have been very much nearer to the earth. The only way out of this problem that we can see is this: we remember that had the moon, at any stage, been circling the earth in the direction opposite to the earth's rotation, then the pull of the tidal bulges and the transfer of angular momentum (which is an alternative description of the same problem) would have brought the moon nearer. So if somehow we could imagine that long ago the moon circled the earth in the opposite direction, then the moon might have been gradually brought in from far away where it might have had an independent existence as a member of the solar system. But how can we conceive of the direction of the motion of the moon around the earth to have reversed? Would this not require a catastrophic event? Fortunately, this is not necessary. We should not think of the motion of the moon in just two dimensions; we must remember that we live in a space of three dimensions. The orbit of the moon is more or less circular, but it does not lie in the plane of the equator of the earth. It is a slightly askew orbit inclined at several degrees to the equator of the earth. Tidal friction, it turns out, through a rather complicated interaction, also has the effect of diminishing the inclination of the moon's orbit, for a moon going round the earth in the same direction as the earth rotates, and increasing the inclination for a moon circling in the opposite direction.

We can now imagine a history of the moon where the moon and the earth had an encounter, the moon coming from far away and passing round the earth in the direction opposite to that of the earth's rotation, raising immediately a high tide whose frictional effect made the moon a captive of the earth. The moon then circled the earth in the opposite direction to the earth's rotation; this brought it closer and closer, but increased the inclination of the moon's orbit to the equator of the earth until the moon was in a polar orbit. A slight further move would then have made the moon follow a highly inclined orbit in the direction of the earth's rotation and this would have the effect of driving the moon, which so far had been brought closer and closer, further and further from the earth and diminishing the inclination of its orbit. In this way we could arrive at a lunar orbit such as we see now.

Of course we have only pushed the problem of the origin of the moon back into the great problem of the origin of the solar system, but we need no longer contemplate the difficult, if not impossible, task of getting the moon in some peculiar fashion out of the earth.

CHAPTER 3

Uniform Systems

When Newton formulated his theory of gravitation he had to make an assumption about how gravitation varied with distance and he suggested, as you know, the *inverse-square law* that the attractive force between two bodies is inversely proportional to the square of their distance apart. In order to test this hypothesis he had to calculate the gravitational attraction due to the earth which can be assumed to be a sphere. With some difficulty he established that a spherical body acts externally like a particle at its centre containing all the mass of the body. This is its effect outside the body only. At the same time he worked out that if you have a uniform spherical shell of matter, then there is no gravitational force inside that shell. He used the first result to compare the attraction of the earth on the apple and on the moon. You will be aware of the fact that this result depends very much on how big the earth is, how far we are from its centre. The only way this could be calculated in those days was from measuring the distance around the equator of the earth. When Newton put this figure into his equations, he obtained a wrong result; he was very depressed and put his theory of gravitation into a drawer. Some time later he learned that this early measurement of the length of the equator was incorrect, that a new determination had been made; he became very excited and immediately put the new figure into his formula and obtained the right answer. This led him to announce to the world the theory of gravitation.

Both the result for the solid sphere and for the spherical shell are very particular consequences of the inverse-square law. With any other dependence of force on distance, you would not get these results. Perhaps one can see this most easily with the spherical shell. Consider a particle eccentrically placed inside a spherical shell (*Figure 3*). If we draw a plane through the particle at right angles to the diameter on which the particle is situated, then this will divide the shell into two parts—the part nearer the particle will tend to pull the particle towards that side—the part further from the particle will tend to pull the particle in the opposite direction. By symmetry, the resulting pull must certainly be along the diameter.

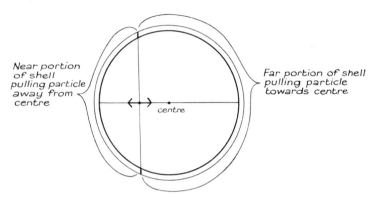

*FIG 3. PARTICLE INSIDE A SPHERICAL SHELL
OF MATTER*

There is more of the shell pulling the particle towards the centre, but all the bits of the shell pulling in that direction are rather further from the particle than the bits of the shell trying to pull the particle away from the centre. This leads to the question of which of them is going to win. If the law of force is almost independent of distance, then clearly the larger portion of the shell will win and the particle will be attracted towards the centre. If the law of force depends very sensitively on distance, then the portion of the shell nearest to the particle will win, and it will be attracted away from the centre. There will be just one type of law of force where the two just balance and no attraction is exerted on the particle. This turns out to be the inverse-square law that Newton uses in his law of gravitation.

Imagine now a large uniform sphere. By *uniform* I mean that the density of matter in the sphere is the same everywhere. Consider then a particle a distance *r* from the centre of the sphere but well inside our big material sphere. If we then draw a sphere concentric with the big sphere, and passing through our particle, then we can readily calculate the gravitational force of our particle. It will be inside a spherical shell. This will exert no force on it at all. And it will be outside a sphere of radius *r* which will act on it just as though all the mass of that sphere was concentrated at its centre. The mass of this sphere is proportional to its volume, since the density is constant, and its volume is proportional to the cube of r. Thus, the gravitational attraction is as though a mass proportional to r^3 were at the centre of the sphere, and so at a distance r from our particle. Thus the attraction on the particle is proportional to r^3 and inversely proportional to r^2 and is, therefore, proportional to r. Thus, if this sphere is moving under the influence of its own gravitational attraction, the acceleration of each particle in the sphere will be towards the centre and proportional to its distance from the centre.

What will be the effect of this acceleration on the composition of the sphere? Can we maintain the uniformity of the sphere with this acceleration? It is, perhaps, a little easier to start this problem from the other end. What kind of internal motion can keep a uniform sphere uniform? We shall use here a very severe condition of uniformity. Not only do we mean thereby that the density stays constant throughout the sphere, but also that the relative motions of neighbouring particles are the same anywhere in the interior of the sphere. One can perhaps make clearer what one means by this kind of uniformity if we imagine "observers" distributed throughout the sphere and fixed to the particles of which the sphere is composed. Then we want to say that by the uniformity of the sphere we understand a situation in which each observer sees the same around him, both as regards distribution of density and as regards distribution of velocity or, indeed, of any other physical parameter. The only cautionary word we must say is about the surface. Clearly, an observer on the surface will see a very different situation from anybody inside. He will see the material of the sphere to one side of him and nothing to the other side. So what we mean by this is merely that we include all those observers whose field of vision does not contain the surface. If we imagine that the sphere is reasonably opaque, so that the field of vision of none of the observers is terribly great, then everybody sufficiently far in the interior will be one of these observers who sees everything the same.

One kind of motion that preserves this strict uniformity is readily imagined. Suppose that we have such a uniform sphere and then we double every distance within this sphere; this clearly will work, because it is equivalent to making our yardstick shrink—looking at the same sphere as before with a yardstick half the size, will yield exactly the same result as doubling all the distances within the sphere. Clearly, shrinking our yardstick cannot upset the uniformity of the sphere; therefore, doubling all the distances cannot upset its uniformity. Instead of doubling, we could have, say, increased all distances by 5% or divided all distances by a factor 10, or whatever you like. Any change in the sphere in which *all* distances are affected in the same way, are multiplied by the same factor—all those leave the uniformity of the sphere unchanged. If we carry out this doubling in a given length of time, then, of course, the sphere will have to have internal motion, and the velocity of any point relative to any other point will be proportional to their distance apart. For since in our period of time every distance has to be doubled, it follows that, if the two points were close together, then doubling the distance doesn't require a high velocity; if they are far apart and the distance has to be doubled then there has to be a high relative velocity.

So here we have a kind of motion in which there is a relation between relative velocity and relative distance of two particles, the one being proportional to the other. And this we can call a velocity-distance relation.

In particular, if we sit at the centre of the sphere, then we see every particle of the sphere moving radially away or towards us, as the case may be, with a velocity proportional to its distance from us; that is, a velocity proportional to r. A somewhat longer mathematical argument shows that this is indeed the only type of motion that transforms a uniform sphere into a uniform sphere.

Now let us return to the problem of the acceleration due to gravitation. The dynamical consideration gave us an acceleration whereas we have now been talking about velocity. It will be clear, however, that if at one instant the velocity of the particles relative to the centre is proportional to r, and for ever thereafter their acceleration is proportional to the distance from the centre, then at all times their velocities will be proportional to their distances from the centre. Thus, if at one instant, the sphere is uniform in the sense that the density is the same everywhere, and that the velocities relative to the centre are proportional to the distances of particles from the centre, then the action of gravitation will automatically maintain this uniformity. We have thus found a remarkable property of the inverse square law not normally considered. With this law we can maintain uniformity.

Are there any other laws of force that maintain uniformity? It will be appreciated that uniformity can be maintained only if the acceleration is proportional to r. With gravitation this works because mass is proportional to r^3, force inversely proportion to r^2, and so the outer shell does not contribute any force inside, which, as I have been saying, is a special property of the inverse square law. Indeed, there seems to be only one other law of force that would have this effect and that is a force that gives everything acceleration proportional to distance and is independent of the mass of the source. If it doesn't depend on the mass of the source, the force would be just as much there in empty space so this kind of force is a kind of property of empty space, perhaps not terribly easily envisaged, but mathematically entirely possible. If such a force exists and does not cause acceleration so high as to be incompatible with observation at the largest distances that the astronomer can see, then this force must be quite minute in any local context within a laboratory, or even within the solar system, and probably even within the galaxy. It would be a force having significance only for the universe as a whole and not in any local sense. Thus a force of this type is generally called a cosmological force.

Let us return to our big sphere. If no external force acts on the whole system (and we exclude such a case) then its centre of mass, that is, its centre, must move without any acceleration. We can therefore say that the observer there situated is an inertial observer. He then looks around at the interior of the sphere and he finds the motion which, as we have been saying, maintains uniformity; he can calculate the gravitational forces appropriate to the particle at any distance from him and he finds that the acceleration is, indeed, just as he calculates. He also realises that he is an inertial observer because he finds that Newton's laws apply in his laboratory. Any other observer in the system is, of course, accelerated; but he is not aware of this because he is simply freely falling. He observes the same pattern of flow around himself as the central observer sees and he notices the same density. When he carries out calculations on the acceleration of another particle relative to him, then he will somehow have to think about what goes on beyond that particle. Imagine now, that he is under the delusion that *he* is at the centre of the sphere; then he will assume that the spherical shells beyond the particle he is investigating will yield no force whatever. He calculates gravitation just as the central observer did and as we did earlier and he finds that everything moves just as he has calculated. Of course, we know he is wrong; since he is eccentrically situated, he is himself accelerated—he is no inertial observer— and outside the particle that he is investigating, the remainder of the sphere, not being centred on him, will form a shell very thin in one place and much thicker in another. Of course, this will introduce an error into his calculation, just as the fact that he himself is accelerated in his free fall will introduce an error in his calculations. As we have seen, the two errors cancel exactly. Thus a non-central observer will not only see the same picture; he will make the same physical deductions as the observer at the centre does and his calculations will do just as well, given that he imagines himself to be at the centre. The only thing that we must be sure about is that none of these observers can actually see the outer surface of the sphere. We just assume the sphere to be sufficiently opaque. It doesn't matter how big this sphere is; all the observers who cannot see its surface will be completely equivalent, both in what they see and in what they calculate. We have a truly uniform system in which all parts sufficiently far from the surface for it not to be seen are wholly equivalent.

Since the outer surface of the sphere is so unimportant for our considerations, we can try and banish it to the very distant regions— to push it away to infinity. Unfortunately, as soon as we do that, our whole sphere has an infinite amount of mass and the gravitational calculations of Newton do not apply to such mass. However, if we use not Newton's theory of gravitation but the modern theory —Einstein's theory—then we can let the boundary go to infinity; we can consider an infinite, uniform system which maintains its uniformity because there is a velocity-distance relation at work. Such a system, as we shall see, makes a tolerably good model of the universe, representing its large-scale features reasonably adequately. How will such a system as our sphere actually move? There is, as I have been saying, an inward acceleration. Suppose that at one moment the velocities are directed outward; then the effect of the inward acceleration will be a tendency to diminish this outward velocity. If the outward velocity was high, then some time later, in spite of the diminution due to the inward acceleration the velocities will still go outward, but rather more slowly. Due to the change in the size of the system, however, the densities have diminished, the gravitational forces have therefore diminished, and the acceleration in the new situation is not as strong as it was before. If the original velocity was high enough, the acceleration, which is constantly getting smaller, just as the velocity is, will then be unable to reverse the direction of motion. The system will go on and on with particles receding from each other all the time, though the velocities of recession themselves will become smaller in the course of time. One can work out that, with sufficiently high initial outward velocities, the ratio of velocity to distance diminishes in time, tending to a postive limit, with acceleration getting weaker and weaker and the system getting emptier and emptier as every particle recedes from every other particle. If the initial velocity was not so high, then the acceleration will be able to reduce the outward velocity to rest at some state of the system and after that the system will be contracting with all particles now having inward velocities. In between the two classes of motions, there is the state in which the system can just but only just expand indefinitely. The acceleration gradually reduces the outward velocities to zero, but they reach zero only after an infinity of time, at which state the system is so tenuous that the accelerations also vanish.

So we have these three modes of motion; first outwards then inwards; first outwards tending to rest in a very diffuse state; first outwards, always remaining outwards. Finally, if the system was originally already moving inwards, with all the velocities directed towards the centre, then the effect of the acceleration would simply be to increase the velocities and go on increasing them.

We get a richer variety of possible motions if we introduce the hypothetical cosmological force about which I talked earlier. If this is an inward force, then it simply adds to the gravitational inward acceleration and does not change the general character of motion. But if it is an outward force, then we could imagine a situation in which this outward force exactly balances the gravitational inward force and we could have a system at rest. However, this state of rest would be highly unstable. If, for some reason, the sphere expanded a little bit, then this would, through the diminution of density, reduce the inward pull of gravitation, but increase, because of increased distances between particles, the outward pull of the cosmological force. The system would start expanding, which would still more increase the disequilibrium between the forces, and the outward motion would become faster and faster. Conversely, if the sphere shrank a little, then the gravitational forces would be increased, the cosmological force would be decreased and the system would collapse.

It will be noted that the sphere can be static (at rest) only if we assume that there is such a purely hypothetical repulsive cosmological force. In all other circumstances the sphere is necessarily in motion and, even with this assumption, the one equilibrium that exists is unstable.

One can readily examine other motions that are possible with this hypothetical force. Consider first the collapse from the unstable equilibrium state. Then if, when the system has nearly completely collapsed, we reverse all the velocities, it should go through the same motions in the opposite order and eventually tend to the equilibrium state. Suppose, however, that instead of just reversing the velocities we make them a little bit larger. Then the system, through the action of gravitation and the cosmological force, will gradually slow down but when it is at the equilibrium density, there will still be a residual outward motion because we made our velocities too high. Therefore it will pass, perhaps very slowly, through this equilibrium state and then go into the state of indefinite expansion that I discussed earlier.

Although we started with a simple model—that of a uniform sphere—we saw that on the basis of Newtonian dynamics, this uniform sphere could remain uniform and all points in it equivalent as long as the observers at these points were far enough from the surface not to be able to see ι. It didn't matter how large this sphere was. If we use, however, the modern theory of gravitation, then there is no surface, there is no limitation and we have a completely uniform system. For a number of reasons, the study of these uniform systems is most important for the subject of cosmology.

CHAPTER 4

Our Universe

It is easy in science to become excited at the prospect of examining some of the deepest questions that exist. It is less easy to confine one's attention, as the scientist must, to those questions to which it is possible to get some form of answer, to those questions where some progress, however slow, however painful, is possible. To think about the universe is attractive to the human mind. To say that one can think about it purposefully, that one can make theories that can be tested by observation and experiment—that is much less easy. We can then examine under what conditions the study of the universe, the subject of cosmology, might show any promise of getting us anywhere and then try and see whether there is any indication that these conditions are satisfied in fact.

Now the simplest and most helpful assumption that one can make is that the universe is in some sense uniform. We know, of course, as an obvious fact, that the universe is not perfectly uniform. After all, one room is very different from another room; some points of space are inside the earth, some are outside, and so on. But the physicist does not necessarily mean by "uniform" something completely and precisely uniform. He may well have in mind something that is only uniform in relation to certain questions. If you want to think about a bag of frozen peas, then certainly this is not uniform. There are peas and there are spaces between the peas and some peas are bigger and some peas are smaller. But for most purposes we would be satisfied to say that the bag is uniform, that if we looked at a region containing, say, ten peas, then in all probability we have seen all that we consider worth seeing of the whole bag. Similarly, when the physicist thinks of a gas, he can say that the gas is uniform, that its density is the same throughout the vessel containing it, but he will not mean perfect uniformity by this because, as we know, the gas consists of molecules. At one instant there are some points of space occupied by molecules and other points not so occupied. There are some regions of the vessel where maybe the density of the gas is a little higher for a moment and others where it is a little lower. But nevertheless, it is a sensible statement to say that the gas is uniform. For many purposes, the degree of examination required to establish this uniformity is quite modest. The great advantage of uniformity from the scientist's point of view is that it saves a lot of labour. If you have a vast system and you can assume that for certain purposes it may be regarded as uniform, then it will be sufficient to examine just a sample of it, so that, having seen it, one can say that one has seen all.

How does one establish uniformity? It is always done only by guess unless indeed you examine the whole system, and then the assumption of uniformity is unnecessary. When you think of your bag of frozen peas, you look at three or four, you say, well, probably it is uniform, but let's look at another four or five samples of three or four peas. If all these samples are the same, then you regard it as no longer worth your while to continue a detailed examination.

So, when we want to establish the uniformity of a large object, we must take, more or less at random, a few samples of the object. If each of those samples is like any other sample, then we regard it as reasonably well established that the object itself is uniform. Of course, there is no proof of uniformity. Uniformity is a scientific hypothesis, like any other, which can be disproved but can't be proved.

The largest of all systems that we can think of is the universe. This may be incredibly complex with each region quite different from any other region. On the other hand, it may be that it shows a certain uniformity. If we want to establish that uniformity is a reasonably good guess, then we have to look at a few samples of the universe around us. If we decide that they are all alike, then it is a plausible hypothesis that the whole universe is uniform, and we can be reasonably happy about this assumption. When we want to examine the universe, we naturally turn to the astronomer and ask him, "Do you notice any uniformity?" And what the astronomer will tell you is, "Well, it depends very much on the size of region I am examining. If I confine my attention to the solar system, then there is certainly no uniformity whatever; the planets all follow their orbits close to the plane of the ecliptic; there are some big and some rather smaller planets, and so on. If I go further out and look at the stars around me, then at first I imagine that I have found some uniformity but, if I look a little further, I notice that the stars are not uniformly arranged around me. The stars form a flat disc-shaped object in which we are situated in a rather excentric position. If we look along the plane of the disc, then we see many more stars than if we look at right angles to the plane of the disc, and this disc, then, gives us the phenomenon of the band of stars across the sky, the Milky Way. This whole stellar system is called our galaxy, and is clearly not uniform."

We may be rather disappointed, now, that the astronomer has gone so far in his investigations and has found no uniformity. But when he takes the next step, then the situation looks distinctly more promising. He sees other galaxies like our own, or perhaps a little different and he sees very many of them. As long as he confines his attention to the nearest thousand or so galaxies, he will feel distinctly uneasy about the suggestion of uniformity because they occur in clusters. In some direction he will see an enormous cluster of galaxies containing very many of them, in another direction he will see only very few such galaxies. But if we encourage him to look even further, to look so far that all over the sky he sees the galaxies in many millions, then he will feel very much happier about the suggestion of uniformity.

In what sense can one say that the astronomer's observations suggest and support the hypothesis of uniformity? The optical astronomer finds it reasonably easy to tell us the directions to the different objects that he sees and when we ask him to plot on the celestial globe the directions to all the galaxies that he finds, then one gets a very uniform distribution over the globe. It is true that the galaxies occur in clusters and before the uniformity becomes really apparent, we must go to very large numbers of galaxies, in their millions. Moreover, even then, he notices a marked non-uniformity. He cannot see any galaxies near to the plane of our own galaxy. This will not surprise him. He knows from his observations of starlight that there are in our galaxies vast clouds of dust that tend to absorb light and so for this reason dust clouds in the plane of the Milky Way account in an entirely plausible manner for the fact that one cannot see any other galaxies within about fifteen to twenty degrees of the plane of our own galaxy. Reasonable as the explanation is, it does not, of course, prove that there are as many galaxies in this obscured belt as elsewhere, but the existence of such an excluded belt in no way contradicts the assumption of uniformity.

The radio astronomer is rather more fortunate in that the radio waves he receives are not absorbed by the material in our galaxy to a significant extent, and indeed, he sees a distribution of sources of his kind of radiation uniformly distributed over the celestial globe. So as far as the angular distribution goes, it is very much in agreement with the assumption of uniformity. The question of the distribution in depth, however, is very much more difficult. The distances concerned are very great. Just let me give you a few figures in terms of the time light takes to travel these distances. Light takes eight minutes to reach us from the sun. In a very few hours light could cross the entire solar system. Between stars, light takes a few years and the nearest star we know is about *four light years* away from us. The disc of our galaxy has a diameter of perhaps seventy or eighty light years. Distances between galaxies are of the order of a million light years. The furthest objects that the astronomer can see are several thousand million light years away from us.

Measuring distances is always a very difficult thing for the astronomer. The only effective method he has for large distances is to assume from the indications from the kind of light received, that two objects are so much of the same type that presumably they send out equal amounts of light. If, then, we receive four times the intensity of light from one of these objects as we receive from the other, then he would argue that the first object was half the distance of the second. When this is applied to galaxies and we assume that galaxies of the same general shape send out much the same amount of light, then one gets some indication of uniformity in depth. One does not get a perfect indication of this kind and that is not anything to be surprised at. After all, because these objects are so far away from us, and light takes so long to reach us from them, we see them as they were long ago. We therefore see, not the present situation but, as it were, as we are looking out into space, we are looking back into history, which thus becomes mixed up with geography. If the universe were different a long time ago from what it is like now, then this would affect our measurements of distance and so, beyond a certain range, we are not really surprised not to get quite an indication of uniformity. After all, we would not necessarily expect uniformity if we see the near regions in the present and the distant regions in the distant past.

So this observation is not, perhaps, a very crucial or very helpful one, but we do get a great deal of help from another quarter. The astronomer can analyse the light he receives from the galaxies. He finds in this light marked features of the spectrum, spectral lines, with which he is familiar from the stars. But the spectral lines he receives from the galaxies are not quite in place. They seem to be shifted, and shifted towards their red end of the spectrum. In physics we know just one reason for a substantial shift as we observe here, and that is a motion of recession. If a source of light is moving away from us then the light that we receive is "redder" than the light that was sent out. One can readily see how this happens. Light, after all, consists of waves of vibrations. If we consider successive peaks of vibration, then if the object has moved away from us between emitting the first and the second, then the light carrying the second peak has a greater distance to traverse than the light from the first peak and there will therefore be extra delay. Thus the rate of arrival will be lower than the rate of departure, the frequency will be lowered and the spectrum will be shifted to the red. The shifts the astronomer sees are large and sometimes quite spectacular. In the biggest shift yet seen, the wavelength of the light arriving is more than three times the wavelength at which the light was sent out. However, such huge shifts are found only in the light of the mysterious quasars. With ordinary galaxies, the red shifts observed are rather smaller than this, ranging up to a wavelength ratio of perhaps 3:2.

For our present purpose, I want to draw attention only to the fact that the amount of red shift is closely correlated with the faintness of the galaxy. The less light we receive from it, the greater the red shift. If now we interpret the red shift as due to a velocity of recession, and the faintness as due to distance, then, indeed, we discover that the velocity is proportional to the distance.

As I pointed out in the last chapter, this is the unique kind of motion that will maintain the uniformity of a uniform system. It is the *only kind* of motion compatible with the assumption of uniformity, so that any measurement of motion is a very severe test of the assumption of permanent uniformity. The universe as we see it passes this test very successfully. I think our strongest reason for thinking the universe to be uniform is the observed velocity-distance relation.

In fact, we can take this argument a little further still. The red shift not only moves the whole spectrum of the galaxy towards the red, it also markedly diminishes the intensity of light we receive. The total intensity is diminished in the square of the ratio of the wavelength sent out and received. Thus if the wavelength we receive is three times what it was when sent out, then we receive only one-ninth of the total energy intensity that we would be receiving if an object of the same brightness were at the same distance at rest. It is therefore readily appreciated that for these objects with large red shifts, the diminution of intensity by the red shift is much more important than the diminution through sheer distance. The further we go the more important this becomes.

When we want to see faint objects, we must use instruments with a large opening so that much of the very low intensity arriving here is caught and centred on one point and this is the aim both of optical and radio telescopes. The cost of these instruments depends very critically on their size. The biggest optical instrument is the 200in. telescope on Mount Palomar in California. The largest radio instrument is the 1000ft. bowl at Arecibo in Puerto Rico belonging to the Cornell-Sydney University Astronomy Centre. If it were not for the red shift then, doubling the diameter of our instruments would double the distance to which we can see, but owing to the red shift, a law of very rapidly diminishing returns has set in. If things go on at great distances further out as we know them to go on further in, then there will soon be little point in increasing the diameters of our instruments unless we increase them very much indeed. We are running, as it were, into a sort of natural barrier—not into a brick wall—but we are coming to a region where it becomes progressively more difficult to make worthwhile observations. Thus, if the region of the universe we can already survey is a fair sample of the regions beyond it, then we can today already examine a very large fraction of what is linked with us in the sense that we can receive from there appreciable intensities. We are not therefore open to the criticism that of the possibly infinite universe we have seen only a negligible portion. Of the universe that is accessible to us at all, we have probably seen a substantial and major portion. This again strengthens the argument in favour of uniformity. If we have established that for a large fraction of the regions relevant to us there is uniformity, then it is not such a wild guess to say that 'for the rest of this accessible region—of this effectively observable region—we have this highly convenient uniformity.

Where do we go from here? What further statements can one meaningfully make about the observable universe? Note that the scientist is interested only in the observable universe. If there is a beyond, it doesn't belong to science and it is senseless to ask scientific questions about it, or, indeed, to examine its existence. We have already seen that the travel-time of light imposes limitations. It means that we see distant regions as they were a long time ago. We have knowledge of our neighbourhood now, of regions a billion light years away as they were a billion years ago, and so on. To interpret our data we must, therefore, supplement our geography of the universe, consisting of the simple word uniformity, by a history of the universe. The simplest way of dealing with this is to assume that location in time is as irrelevant as location in space. It is to assume that the universe on an average is unchanging in time, as well as uniform in space. This does not, and cannot, mean that the individual items of the universe are themselves unchanging in time. On the one hand we know that each star undergoes ageing processes; each star has nuclear reactions going on inside which, in the majority of them, consist of the nuclear fusion of hydrogen into helium, so that as time goes on each such star gets poorer in hydrogen and richer in helium. We have good reason to believe that galaxies themselves age and there is no need to assume that an unchanging universe implies unchanging constituents. After all, we can have a stationary human population in which the individual members are born, grow up, grow old and die, and yet all the average characteristics like the fraction of fair-haired people or the fraction of people under the age of sixteen, remains the same. What such a stationary assembly of ageing individuals requires is a birth-rate and a death-rate. In a stationary universe there is no difficulty whatever about this. Objects simply drift away from us; as they drift further away, they come into regions of higher velocity. That removes them yet faster to more distant regions where the velocity of recession is still higher and so they tend towards invisibility. This is quite enough to give us the required death-rate; all we require is that in any large instrument the number of objects we can see at any given time stays constant. Objects in the course of time will get fainter and fainter until they are invisible. A birth-rate is also clearly required. Through the motion of recession, any given limited region loses material through the boundary. The mean density in an unchanging universe must stay constant and so there must be a replenishment in contradiction to the law of conservation of mass. This, in turn, requires, then, that we examine the significance of the law of conservation of matter. After all, this is not a revealed truth, it is simply an abstraction from a large number of experiments, just like any other scientific rule. However, the experiments are terrestrial experiments and so far based on times very short compared with cosmic ones and on densities very high compared with cosmic ones. A continual rate of creation, which would not have been observed in our laboratory experiments by many orders of magnitude, is yet quite sufficient to keep the universe stationary. I need not go more deeply into this steady-state theory than to say that quite clearly this is the only theory in which we can make statements about what we should see without any clear theory about the evolution of galaxies. Unfortunately, our knowledge of the evolution of galaxies is very rudimentary.

In a steady-state universe this is irrelevant; there is the same mixture of galaxies of all ages present at all times, just as in a stationary human population there is a mixture of humans of all ages at all times, and in the same proportions. Thus one can interpret distant observations and compare them with near ones without knowing how the individuals age or, indeed, what is an old galaxy and what is a young galaxy. Thus, this theory puts the best face on our ignorance and is the theory that is most readily testable. It has a number of successes to its score; in particular, the theory of the origin of the elements and the showing up as erroneous of an interpretation of observations that suggested that distant galaxies radiated light that was "redder" than the light that is radiated by near galaxies. However, the theory has got into very severe trouble through radio astronomical observations that correlate the faintness of sources with their number. The increase of number with faintness is predicted in a perfectly definite way by the theory. The observations of the radio astronomers seem to be in strong disagreement with this. Another difficulty concerns the amount of helium in the universe. We like to think that all matter started as hydrogen. The fusion into helium is, as I have been saying, the chief source of light from the stars. There ought then to be a definite correlation between the amount of helium in the universe and the amount of starlight. Unhappily, it looks as though there was considerably more helium about. If we then have to think of other theories, we can use the models of the uniform sphere that I talked about in my last lecture. To fit in with what we see, we have to take a model with a velocity of recession. To pick out a particular model is not easy. The problem is once again our ignorance of galactic evolution. If only we knew how the amount of light a galaxy sends out varies with its age we would be in a much better position to interpret the observations. If we make the daring guess that over a substantial period of time there was no such change in spite of the evolution of the universe, then it looks as though we were in a decelerating universe. This comes from a difficult interpretation of the difficult measurements relating red shift to faintness, using the greater faintness of some sources as an indication of their greater distance, and therefore that the observations there refer to an earlier stage of the universe. If the system is decelerating, it must have been expanding faster in the past than in the present. If the velocities had stayed the same all the time, then the ratio of distance to velocity tells us the period that must have elapsed since the system was highly condensed and started its outward motion. This period comes out as a mere ten billion years. It seems long enough for practical purposes, but our estimates of the ages of some stellar clusters exceeded this ten billion years by quite a margin. On the other hand, if the universe has been decelerating then this big explosion with which it would have started must be less than ten billion years ago. So again we are in difficult country.

Since early 1963, we have a new help in all this—the quasars—the first of which was located by Hazard from the School of Physics at Sydney. These are objects that look like stars but send out more light than whole galaxies consisting of perhaps a hundred billion stars. We have no clear understanding yet of their significance. Unhappily, it seems as though there were very wide variations in output of radiation of light between them. They are therefore not very good as distance indicators. On the other hand, when we gain an understanding of their structure it will no doubt help us to understand many so far ill-understood features of the universe. We can be reasonably certain that they are young rather than old objects as it is very likely that they don't have enough energy available to go on pouring it out into space at the rate they are doing. Thus, in this field, as in other related fields, wherever we turn there are puzzles and challenges. Fortunately, we are not yet in any danger of exhausting the subject of cosmology of all its challenges.

Radio Astronomy

by

THOMAS GOLD

Professor Thomas Gold, F.R.S.

Professor of Astronomy and Director of the Cornell University Centre for Radiophysics and Space Research, Ithaca, N.Y.; Joint Director of the Cornell-Sydney University Astronomy Centre.

Radio Astronomy

In astronomy one tries to understand things on a scale larger than the earth with its land and oceans and atmosphere, and one tries to understand the place that our earth has in this great and still very mysterious universe.

Most of the knowledge that has been gathered so far has been obtained by looking, looking at the planets and the sun and the stars beyond. Firstly by naked eye, and then with a telescope, and finally with many different instruments attached to the telescope. One investigated the light that came to the earth from these bodies and this light brought with it an enormous amount of information. Not only could one see the position and the apparent brightness of all the multitudes of stars in the sky, but one could also see in detail the colours contained in that light, the spectrum. The light broken up into its component colours could reveal in detail some of the physical circumstances such as sizes, temperatures and surface conditions of many of these bodies. It was possible to deduce the velocities of their motion and in many cases the distances to them. From all this a picture emerged according to which we lived in a galaxy of stars of which our sun is a very ordinary member. It just happens that we are very close to that one and only for that reason it looks so bright. Stars are big balls of gas held together by gravitation, that is, by the fact that all the masses in them mutually attract each other and this always has a tendency to make objects spherical. They are hot, and that is why they shine. The energy that keeps them hot is derived mostly from the nuclear processes which one can deduce must be occurring in their interiors. These stars, some bigger and some smaller than the sun, are exceedingly numerous in our galaxy. There are approximately 10^{11} of them and that is a big number which is quite hard to comprehend. Suppose I go to Bondi Beach with a shovel, and I shovel sand all day about as hard as I can go. How many grains do you suppose I will have moved? Well, if I shovel five tons, then I probably have moved about 10^{11} grains. That is how numerous the stars are in our galaxy, and our own sun is just one of them.

This whole huge cloud of stars has the shape of a pancake, and is rotating slowly. Its diameter is such that it takes light more than 100,000 years to cross it—in astronomical parlance it is more than 100,000 "light years" across. We cannot step outside this structure to look at it and so from inside we get a rather poor view of it. A few of the nearer stars we see as bright dots in the sky and the great multitudes of the further ones that are, of course, concentrated in the plane of this pancake, we see merely as a hazy streak across the sky on a clear night, and we call it "the milky way".

Optical astronomy has also brought us the revelation that this galaxy of ours, enormous though it is, is in turn only one little speck in the next larger assembly of things. The larger scale universe in turn contains millions and millions of such galaxies, with a certain variety of types that basically are the same design, namely agglomerations of stars. The universe of galaxies is known to stretch out over distances of several thousand million light years at least, and again entire galaxies in that assembly are as common as the grains of sand in our last example.

When we look at this largest scale of things we see a new type of phenomenon. We can judge the velocity of motion of an object from a detailed investigation of a light because light suffers the so-called Doppler effect, which is that the apparent frequency of vibration, or the resulting wavelength, is changed by motion much as the sound that we hear from a moving vehicle is increased or decreased in pitch. This effect shows that on this largest scale the universe is in a violent state of motion, and that motion is such that the farther objects are, the faster they seem to be rushing away from us.

Why are they all just rushing away from *us?* Are we in some special position from which everything is being repelled? Is our own galaxy a particular one that is in the centre of everything? How strange that in that huge number we should just be on the centrally placed object!

No such thing is implied by the motion that we observe. A motion of uniform expansion is possible in which each object is moving away from all the others, so that everywhere the system is expanding. If you stand on any one of the objects, all others appear to be rushing away from you. There is no centre and the motion is seen quite the same from everywhere. This is possible only for one particular pattern of motion, namely one in which the velocity of recession of any one object from us gets faster in proportion to the distance it is from us. The "velocity distance law" that has been observed by astronomers is exactly of this kind. We could therefore not think that we have been singled out in any way.

Copernicus first gave us the notion that we were not in the centre of things. He understood that the earth was just one of the planets revolving around the sun. But not only is our earth not in the centre of things, but in turn our sun is not in the centre of things either. Instead it is a perfectly ordinary star among 100,000 million of them. And in turn our galaxy is only a perfectly ordinary galaxy, again in some such enormous number of those. This, then, is the ultimate Copernican point of view—that we are not the masters of the universe, but that we only happen to be in some perfectly ordinary location somewhere within it.

This was the outline of the picture which optical investigations had produced. The picture placed great emphasis of course on the world of stars, since so little else could be seen by optical means. The stars conveniently shine and are very luminous, and can thus be seen a great distance away. But on the other hand, may there not be much other material around which cannot so easily be seen? For a long time astronomers tended to ignore such a possibility.

There had been some hints that tenuous gas existed in spaces between the stars. One could see in the light from certain stars that some light had been absorbed in a way that a tenuous gas between the stars might have done. This was exciting because even if the densities of this gas were very low, the total mass that might be involved in the huge spaces may still be very large. It may then be possible to account for the formation of the stars themselves. A tenuous gas may, under the influence of gravitation, occasionally contract into lumps which, by processes that we understand perfectly well, would form themselves into luminous stars.

From the optical investigations, together with a fairly elaborate theoretical study of the structure of stars, it had also become clear that some stars were very young. The brightest and bluest of them that we can see — that is, the ones with the highest temperatures of their surfaces, cannot continue to shine as they now do for more than a few million years, a very short span in the few *thousand* million years that seems to be the age of the majority of the stars. If, then, we see some stars that have only formed within the last thousandth of the age of our galaxy, must we not expect that the star formation process itself is still going on at the present time? If so, must we not expect that material for forming stars is even now at hand? It would after all be very unlikely that the star formation process just ceased in the last one-thousandths part of the total age of the galaxy.

This was the state of knowledge when the investigations of the sky by radio means began about 20 years ago. It turned out that radio investigations could supply very many additional clues in the story. Radio astronomy became not just a little adjunct to optical astronomy, but an investigation which, together with optical astronomy, could unravel a great deal more of the mysteries than either subject could singly. In particular, radio astronomy filled in much information concerning masses of material that do not happen to be luminous.

Radio waves are of course just the same as light. They are the long wavelength end of the electromagnetic spectrum of radiations. The names that one has given to different parts of this spectrum as we go to shorter wavelengths from radio waves are infra-red light, visible light, x-rays and finally the very shortest wavelengths are called gamma-rays. The difference between all of these is just in the frequency of the vibration, which is in the range of 10 million to ten thousand million cycles per second for the radio band and about 10^{15} cycles per second for visible light. But it must not be thought that the different parts of the spectrum are different in any basic respect. It is not like the case of some other things where there is a continuous range, but where nevertheless all the members of this range are intrinsically different from each other. If I were to take blocks of wood I might make them into any size I like, but a big one will always be different from a little one. However, the

difference between a high frequency and a low frequency electromagnetic wave is not of that kind. There is no absolute criterion
that can distinguish between them. If I looked at the same wave,
but I was myself in a different state of motion, I would observe
it at a different frequency. If I could decide on an absolute
standard of rest, then of course I could define the "real" frequency
of that wave, and if I looked at it from any other state of motion, I
would merely see it as different from what it really is. But since
we now understand that the laws of physics do not single out for
us any particular state of motion, they equally do not allow us
to define a genuine frequency for any given wave. If you are suitably moving, a gamma-ray becomes a radio wave or vice-versa.
Thus, all electromagnetic waves are really the same thing, only
for each particular wave-train one could specify a state of motion
of an observer such that he would see the wave as possessing a
particular frequency.

What then is different about investigating the universe by examining the radio waves?

It turns out that there are many interesting processes going on,
mostly connected with the tenuous gas between the stars, in which
this long wavelength light that we call radio waves are emitted. A
whole new world was opened up for us by the radio investigations
that suddenly gave us indications about the gas masses, their temperatures, velocities, and all kinds of physical circumstances. In
addition, the locations of violent phenomena could be detected, as
it seems that large scale violence almost invariably leads to the
emission of intense radio waves. Some of these violent phenomena
appear to be on a gigantic scale, and although we don't yet understand the situation, we think that we are seeing phenomena there
that will be quite basic to an understanding of the universe.

Now let us get to work and see whether we can understand what
one has to do to investigate the universe by means of radio waves.
With light we already knew what one had to do. One had to look.
Eyes were suitably constructed to take in and interpret information
that was carried by means of light waves. When one wanted other
instruments one fashioned them, really, by close analogy with the
eye. The camera with its lens and photographic plate is not very
different from the eye with its lens and retina. The retina differs

from the photographic plate in being equipped with what we would nowadays call an "on-line data handling equipment". A telescope is really just a very large camera. But what do we have to do to receive the radio waves? What is equivalent to a camera in that case?

It turns out that the equipment looks very different and it is very hard to see the similarity. Big astronomical radio antenna systems don't look at all like an eye, or a camera, or a telescope. They are mostly either huge, saucer-shaped reflectors that can be tipped up and made to face any desired direction *(Figure 1)*, or they are fields full of wires and posts strung out in some complicated way *(Figure 2)*. Nevertheless, the way they function is, in principle, quite similar to an eye or a camera.

What we would really like to do for the investigation by radio waves is, of course, just the same as what we do with light. We would like to get an image of areas of the sky in which the "brightness" in the radio frequency band of different locations can be seen. Just as we have the images of individual stars on our photographic plate, so we would like to construct the appropriate chart giving the radio brightness of every region of sky. However, it turns out that this is a great deal harder to do and requires a lot more instrumentation—and therefore money.

There are two basic reasons why the problem is harder at the longer wavelength. I will first state these reasons quickly and then explain each one in more detail. When the frequency is much lower and the wavelength for that reason much longer, then the dimensions of a telescope capable of defining the things it sees in the sky with a given angular precision gets to be much larger. This immediately means that radio telescopes have to be enormous. Secondly, in optics one has the advantage of the photographic plate which is really like owning a vast number of little receiving elements distributed over a surface. Each grain in the photographic emulsion is a separate receiver and records independently what light falls on it. No such thing exists for radio. A separate receiver and amplifier has to be built for every picture point in our image, and one cannot contemplate building hundreds of thousands of them to compare with an ordinary photographic plate.

Let us discuss first the question of the dimensions of the receiving

Figure 1. The 140-foot radio telescope at Green Bank, West Virginia. It is the world's largest equatorially-mounted radio telescope with a solid surface reflector. (Sky and Telescope, 1966.)

Figure 2. The Mills Cross at the Molonglo Radio Observatory near Canberra, Australia. It is an antenna-system that forms a cross on the ground, each arm being one mile long.

system. To do this we first have to understand how we know what the direction is to a given source of an electromagnetic wave. With light we just say that we see the direction from which the waves appear to come. But how do our eyes, or a camera, or a telescope, really discern that direction? Suppose that I have a very fine-point source of light and I wanted to determine exactly the direction in which it was from me. What would I need to do and what would be the limitation on this precision?

What comes to us is of course a wave, and that means a succession of crests and troughs arrive, and successive crests are separated from each other by the dimension that we call the *wavelength*. If the source is a small point then the waves would spread out such as each crest would, at any instant form a surface of a sphere, just as in the two-dimensional case of waves on a pond, the pattern is one of circles. If we are very far away from the source, then any small bit of this spherical wave is, of course, quite indistinguishable from a plain wave-front. Again if you think of it in two dimensions, if you are far from the stone that was thrown into the pond and you are looking only at a little bit of the circular pattern, it will be just a piece of nearly straight wave-front that will get to you. How would you then judge the direction to the origin of that wave? Well, of course, you will say that the direction has to be the one from which the wave has come and the crest of the wave was, of course, at right angles to the direction in which it propagated. Therefore, you must find the precise direction of the wave-crest at you in order to know the propagation direction.

Now you see at once where the dimension of the receiving system becomes important. If the transverse dimension of the receiving system is long then we need to rotate it through only a small angle before one end would come into the trough of a wave when the other is on the crest. If the dimension is short then, of course, we rotate it by a larger angle before this happens (*Figure 3*). The precision to which we know the direction of the wave-front is, of course, related to this angle. What the instrument can do is to detect from which direction the entire length receives the crest simultaneously and how far off that direction one has to go before a noticeably different situation occurs—that is when the two ends are no longer in the same phase of the wave. You see at once that this

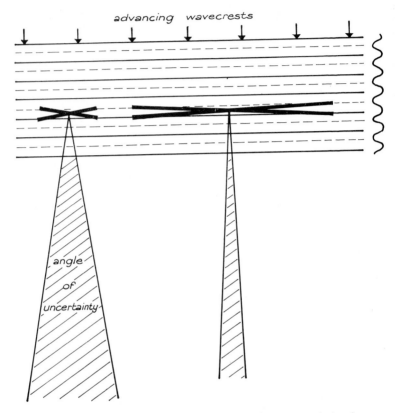

Figure 3. Two different sizes of antennas are shown, each in the two extreme positions relative to the wave-front where its two ends would be "out of phase" with each other. The angular resolution is greater, or the angle of uncertainty is smaller, the longer the transverse dimension of the antenna.

angle of uncertainty then is smaller the shorter the wavelength of the radiation and the longer the transverse dimension of the receiving system. That angle which we call the "angular discrimination" of the instrument is in fact proportional to λ/d where λ is the wavelength and d the transverse dimension. This is true whether the instrument is the eye, in which case the transverse dimension is the aperture of the pupil, or an optical telescope, in which case

Figure 4. The radar-radio telescope at Arecibo, Puerto Rico. The reflector is built in the shape of a section of a sphere in a natural bowl in the hills. Its diameter is 1000 feet and it is made of a wire mesh suspended by a network of steel cables.

the appropriate dimension is the diameter of the reflecting mirror, or whether it is a radio instrument, in which case the relevant dimension is again the diameter of the reflector or the extension of the array of receiving elements on the ground.

The wavelength of visible light is around half a micron, that is 0.5×10^{-4}cms. The wavelengths in the radio band in which we want to look range from 10 metres to 1 cm. Suppose I wanted to do as well at a wavelength of 1 metre in my discrimination of the sky as I can do with a small optical telescope of, say, 4″ aperture (10 cm). λ/d for the telescope would be 0.5×10^{-4}, divided by 10 or 5×10^{-6}. To do the same at the wavelength 1 metre, that is to make λ/d again 5×10^{-6} would now require an instrument of 2×10^5 metres or 200 kilometres (for those who still deal in inconvenient, antiquated units, that is approximately 125 miles). So we see here the reason why radio telescopes are huge—as, for example, our 1000 foot reflector in Arecibo, Puerto Rico (*Figure 4*), or the mile by mile array of Professor Mills, and you realize that even then one cannot obtain as sharp a picture of the radio sky as one can optically by naked eye (*Figure 5*).

The second problem referred to, that arises for the radio and not for the light, is that it is so expensive and cumbersome to have multiple receivers for radio. Instead of getting immediately an image of some limited region as a photographic plate can do, with radio we have to trace out the response of the receiver when pointed in one single direction and build up the picture in little steps in both co-ordinates. An antenna with a single receiving system therefore tends to be very slow.

Some modern antennae are being built with multiple receivers, but even there, one speaks only of some tens of receivers and not of ten million, which might be the number of picture points on a good photographic plate.

What is it that is actually received on radio astronomical antennae? We think of radio signals as usually being in some meaningful pattern because man-made radio signals, of course, usually are. But the radio radiation received from space is just completely incoherent radiation in the same manner as light is. If we detect such incoherent radiation and amplify it electrically we can put the output through a loud speaker and then we hear a noise. It sounds just like a hissing noise and is well known to physicists as the type of noise made by an incoherent signal. This is the reason why the radio radiation from the sky is often referred to as radio *noise*. Of course, what one does is not just listen to the hiss out of the loudspeaker, but one records the average strength of this signal on suitable recording machinery. So with a radio telescope one does not "see" a piece of sky, but one can record the intensity of this radio noise and scan over any particular stretch of sky to build up a picture. One can do this, of course, at different wavelengths and one has been engaged in building up a knowledge of the radio sky for wavelengths that range from ten metres to about 1 cm.

Now that I have told you something about the reason for the large radio instruments you will probably want to know what one really manages to find out with them. I recall very well the historical sequence as this subject of radio astronomy unfolded between the year 1946 and the present. In 1946 we knew already

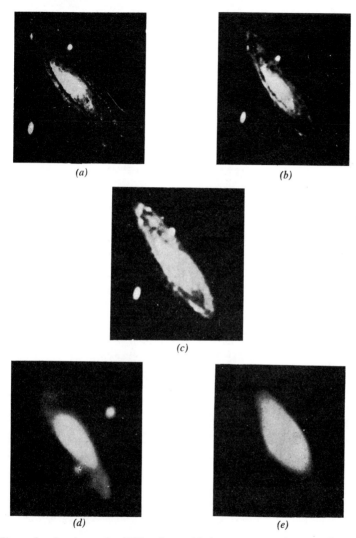

Figure 5. 5a shows the M31 galaxy with its two companions as photo-graphed with an optical telescope, giving a resolution of one second of arc. 5b shows the same galaxy as viewed with a resolution of one minute of arc. 5c shows the same but with a three-minute resolution, while 5d is with a 12-minute resolution. 5e is with a 34-minute resolution.
(Ground-Based Astronomy: A Ten Year Programme, NAS-NRC Report.)

from various investigations, beginning with that of Carl Jansky in the United States, that there was some radio radiation at metre wavelengths that appeared to come preferentially from the direction of the Milky Way in the sky. The Milky Way, as you know, is the streak of diffuse light which is the consequence of all the vast numbers of stars in our own galaxy. Since the galaxy is a flat disk and we are within it we see this concentration of stars as stretching as a band right across the sky. It was from that band that some radio noise appeared to come. Also, it was known as a consequence of war-time radar that the sun contributed to radio noise, and, in fact, there were some episodes during the war when the enemy was credited with very subtle high power jamming systems, which turned out to be outbursts on the sun. After '46 the discoveries came in fast. It was noted first that in addition to a general band of radio noise from our galaxy one could discern particular points in the sky that gave out radio noise. Nothing in particular could be seen at most of these places and so one had not much clue as to the nature of the objects. By the time that some 50 such points had been observed a furious discussion raged as to the correct interpretation. Were these objects very far away, distant other galaxies that for some reason produced radio noise, or were they as close to us as other stars in our own galaxy? I remember a conference in London when this was hotly debated. That was in April, 1951. Some radio astronomers had looked over the data of those 50 sources and had decided that they constituted a rather even distribution over the sky. This, they said, must mean that the objects are not much further apart and further from us than the distances between the stars in our own galaxy. If they were on an average spacing much larger than that of stars, but nevertheless were objects in our own galaxy, then, of course, we should see them heavily concentrated into that band which is our projected view of the galactic plane. If we see no such concentration, then they must be close enough so that a comparatively small number of near objects dominate in our view just as is the case with the visible stars. Of course, in addition there should be the superposition of all the many such objects further away in the galactic plane and we should see them merely as a continuous band of radiation. That, of course, is known to exist anyway, and so to these radio astronomers the interpretation seemed very plausible. They referred to these objects as "radio stars" and considered them to be star-like objects at distances like those between the stars. I can't do better to convey the interest at the time than to give you some abstracts from my paper at that conference and the ensuing discussion. I discussed the origin of cosmic radio noise and the question whether it was near star-like objects or distant galaxies that might be responsible.

"On the basis of the present observations, one is entitled to assume either that all radio noise comes from 'radio stars', or that all of it comes from diffuse gas-clouds in galaxies or that its origin lies partly in the one and partly in the other.

"It is a widely held and very reasonable guess that the radio waves come entirely from objects of roughly stellar dimensions which are scattered throughout galaxies. Ryle and his collaborators have shown that the measurements are compatible with the assumption that these 'radio stars' are between three and ten light years apart within the galaxy, and that the majority of them make up the unresolved galactic radiation, whilst the nearest of them constitute the observed point sources. This statistical test is, however, a rather insensitive one, and the conclusion is by no means compelling.

"Why on this basis, does one not find any identifiable visual object where those very near 'radio stars' are supposed to be?

"The alternative view which one might hold is that radio noise is generated diffusely in the galactic gas. The contribution of our own galaxy would then be merely the unresolved radiation which shows a strong galactic concentration. The point sources would then have to be other galaxies in which similar processes occur at somewhat greater intensities.

"It cannot be ruled out that other galaxies may behave quite differently from our own: for it is known that there are very different types. In particular one might mention those which show light resembling that of novae with greatly broadened emission lines, suggesting that far more violent motions occur there than here. The necessary differences in radio emission may hence exist; the variations between galaxies required for this explanation is certainly much smaller than that which is required between stars for the previous explanation, where some stars would have to emit 10^8 times more than others. It must be added that the only point sources which have been identified are some of the nearer extra-galactic nebulae; it is hence not very far-fetched to consider whether the remaining ones may have a similar origin.

"The fifty point source which are known at present are distributed fairly isotropically over the sky. For the stellar interpretation this implied that they are near, at distances small compared with the galactic thickness. With the possibility of the extra-galactic origin we must hence say that these sources are either very near or very far from us; only then could one understand the absence of a galactic concentration.

"Lastly, I must stress the connection between this problem and cosmic rays. The energy in cosmic rays is so vastly greater, that the radio noise could be a very small by-product of their generation or absorption. If, for example, one supposes cosmic rays to be as intense in the whole galaxy as they are here, then it would suffice if one part in 10^6 of the power which they would dissipate by col-lisions appeared in the form of radio noise. If it were possible to treat this dissipation process theoretically with sufficient precision to discover such small effects, one might be able to show that this alone could account for the galactic noise; or one might even show that cosmic rays cannot be so general, if they would result in more than the observed power of radio waves."

Ryle, a senior radio astronomer and the discoverer of many of the facts under discussion, thought otherwise: "The theoreticians have misunderstood the experimental data. If we are to account for radio stars by extra-galactic bodies we have to postulate the exist-ence of a new type of body whose visible emission is negligible. If we are to account for the observed intensities and diameters of the intense radio stars we must conclude that these bodies have a radio emission at least 10^5 times as great as that from our own galaxy.

"The suggestion that 'radio stars' are situated within the galaxy not only provides an explanation for the observed background radiation from our own galaxy (and the near extra-galactic nebulae) but also requires less formidable requirements of their radio emission."

Here you see the dramatic problem. Either of the two possibilities was quite remarkable. Either there existed objects, practically as common as the stars, that we knew nothing about—a whole new universe was to be discovered; or there existed bodies interspersed among the galaxies which were, however, quite different from ordinary galaxies. They would need to possess at least 100,000 times as much radio radiation as that which was observed from our own galaxy. What could such bodies be?

Now in the intervening years it has become clear that such bodies exist. A very large proportion of the radio sources are indeed outside the galaxy and many of them are quite far away. Radio galaxies exist and other types of objects far outside our galaxy exist that emit powerful radio waves. But the mystery has deepened in the intervening years. The objects are much more remarkable still. We will return to this when we come to discuss the present-day state of knowledge.

The Crab nebula

One object, the so-called Crab nebula, played a very major part in developing an understanding of the origin of radio noise. One strong radio source was observed to lie in the direction of a curious visible nebulosity. Astronomical records kept in China revealed that this object was in the location of a very bright "new" star which flared up in the year 1054. From the description by the Chinese, it seems certain that the object is to be classed as a supernova, which is the most violent form of star explosion which is known. It is clearly an object in our own galaxy and by optical means it has been possible to fix its distance as approximately 4000 light years. It was, of course, quickly realized that there was a wonderful object here for closer investigation, in the hope of finding out what caused the emission of radio noise. A study of the optical object made clear that it was just as hard to explain what caused most of the light that was seen as it was to explain the radio emission. Two Swedish physicists, Alfvén and Herlofson had suggested that the emission of radio waves could be caused by very high energy electrons. Such electrons, when moving through magnetic fields, would emit electromagnetic waves, and from a knowledge of the energy of the electrons and the strength of the magnetic fields one could calculate the frequency spectrum emitted. The process is observed in the laboratory in big electron accelerating machines that are called synchrotrons, and this type of radiation, therefore, has been given the frightful name of "synchrotron radiation". Alvfén and Herlofson suggested it as the cause of the diffuse radio noise from our galaxy. Shklovsky in the U.S.S.R. suggested that this was the cause of optical *and* radio emission from the Crab nebula, which would require remarkably energetic electrons to be present as well as remarkably strong magnetic fields. The critical thing to look for was polarization.

As you probably know, an electromagnetic wave is a wave whose oscillation is transverse to the direction in which it propagates. Such a transverse oscillation can, therefore, define a direction, which is then called the direction of polarization of the wave. Any light wave can be analyzed, for example, into two perpendicular components of polarization and one can see what the intensity is in each of those two components. Most atomic processes that emit light would produce a mixture in which the different directions of polarization would be quite evenly represented. Synchrotron radiation, however, would need to possess a strong polarization related to the direction of the magnetic field in which the electrons were moving. Since such fields were thought to be extensive, one would expect the resulting polarization to be plainly visible. A test was made, first in the U.S.S.R., with a dramatic, positive result. The light from the Crab nebula was polarized.

I was very fortunate when, in 1955, the great astronomer Baade invited me to visit Mt. Palomar and spend two nights with him at the 200 in. telescope there. He had selected a topic for investigation on those two nights which he knew was dear to me and which I had suggested to him some months before, namely the photography in as fine a detail as the 200 in. can show, of the Crab nebula with the light analyzed by a polaroid filter in different directions of polarization. A polaroid filter works by letting through the light that is polarized in one direction only, and on such photographs one would, therefore, be able to see whether different parts of the nebula were indeed highly polarized, but in somewhat different directions so that the overall polarization of all the light was reduced to the 6% that had been observed. This would really clinch the matter and would virtually prove that synchrotron radiation was responsible.

I remember very clearly how after a long observing night we stood in the dark-room to develop the pictures and how thrilled we were when we first held them up against the light and saw the effect. Areas that were bright on one picture disappeared completely on another on which the polaroid had been rotated by 90°. This meant the light was almost 100% polarized. The synchrotron explanation was proved for the Crab nebula. For the first time one could be sure one had detected light from a source in the universe where it was not produced by atomic processes but instead by high energy electrons in magnetic fields.

We spent many hours staring at these pictures which you see here (*Figure 6*). It slowly dawned on us that the pictures not only indicated a very high degree of polarization, but also an interesting, consistent pattern. The filamentary structures which you see appear to be always so polarized that the direction of polarization is at right angles to the length of each filament. That is just what should be the case if the magnetic fields were directed along the filaments—a very reasonable possibility.

From the investigation of the Crab the conviction grew that synchrotron radiation was the main source of radio emission in the universe. It could, of course, occur on smaller or larger scales and indeed one soon discovered another case where optical as well as radio radiation showed polarization. This time it was an object of the dimensions of an entire galaxy. High energy electrons evidently were not so rare. They occurred not only in the remains of supernova explosions—they occurred more diffusely in the whole body of our galaxy and they occurred evidently in some other galaxies in enormously higher concentrations.

Cosmic rays have, of course, been known for a long time and have been another of the great puzzles. Elementary particles, chiefly protons, seem to be coming from outer space with remarkably high energies. Where are the sources for these particles? Where are they accelerated to such high velocities? And is there a similar concentration of them everywhere in our galaxy, in other galaxies also, or even in all of space between the galaxies? Much work and thought has gone into this problem, but without a final solution having appeared. The importance in our present discussion arises from the fact that such a flow of high-energy protons will also

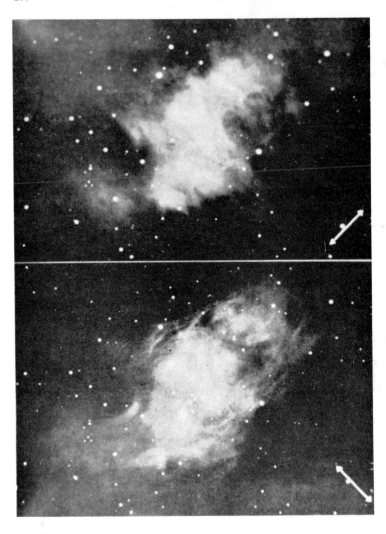

Figures 6a and 6b. Polarization of the Crab nebula. The photographs were taken through Polaroid filters with the 200″ Mt. Palomar telescope. The arrows indicate the direction of the electric field vector recorded.
(Baade, W.B.A.N. *12,* 312, 1956.)

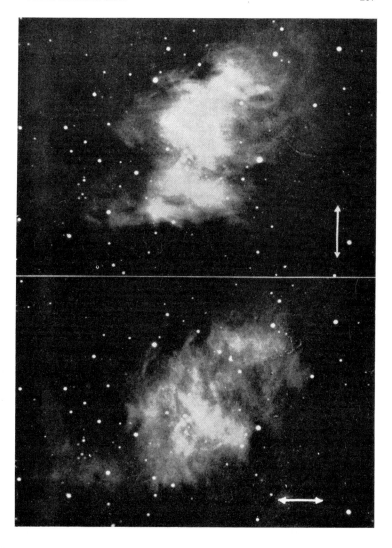

Figure 6b.

produce some high-energy electrons through interactions in the tenuous background gas in the galaxy. The protons themselves would not have any significant radio emission. It is quite another story for the electrons. Electrons are particles that carry the same magnitude of electric charge as the proton, but have a mass that is 1800 times less. For all processes that involve electromagnetic radiation an *acceleration* of a charge is involved. The proton is in general acted on by forces no greater than those that act on an electron, but because of its greater mass suffers a much smaller acceleration. The electron is for this reason almost always the chief contributor in a radiation process. Thus even if only a few per cent. of the high-energy particles are electrons, they would dominate in the radio radiation that is generated. Now it has become clear that in fact electrons produced as secondaries of the cosmic ray flux would be adequate to account for the diffuse radio radiation from our own galaxy, and that it is therefore not necessary to suppose this radiation to be the unresolved contribution of a very large number of small and comparatively closely spaced radio sources, as Ryle had supposed. Cosmic rays and radio noise evidently are manifestations of a high energy world of which we know as yet very little. We will return to this discussion when we come to talk about the recent discoveries of enormously energetic sources of light and radio waves.

The sun as an emitter of radio waves

During World War II when I was working on radar in the British Admiralty, I remember how we became aware of radio waves from the sun. At one time there were reports that the background noise received in sensitive radar receivers had greatly increased and some suspected that the enemy had devised new and very powerful radio jamming methods to diminish the sensitivity of our radar sets. We were relieved to find, however, that it wasn't the enemy but that it was a temporary effect of the sun.

When the war was over and one could devote one's energy and the radio facilities devised during the war to the investigation of nature, one soon discovered that the sun was quite often an emitter of radio noise. Very peculiar and interesting things happen on the surface of the sun. The light and heat output does not change significantly and by naked eye we can't see anything happening at all. Yet to many other instruments the sun is a very variable object. Particular wavelengths in the optical spectrum and the low frequency radio noise are strongly affected. Solar disturbed times show outbursts at these wavelengths, sometimes lasting minutes and sometimes hours. It had been known that solar outbursts represented explosions on the surface of the sun from which gas was ejected into space, and expanded out into the interplanetary volume. Some of this gas interacted with the earth one or two days later producing a measurable disturbance in the earth's magnetic field—a so-called magnetic storm. Now the new information was that these same outbursts were related to big radio disturbances.

The sun, of course, is very hot, about 5000°K on the surface and a certain amount of radio radiation is associated with that. As you know, a hot body sends out electromagnetic waves more and more intensely as you make it hotter, and reaching up to shorter and shorter wavelengths. That is why an object gets red hot or white hot if you heat it enough. Radio waves, which, of course, are just the long wavelength end of the same spectrum, are also affected and with sensitive radio instruments one can detect the temperature of an object in the antenna beam by the amount of these thermal radio waves that it emits. This is no different from detecting the temperature of an object by an optical or an infra-red device that measures the amount of radiation in each of those wavebands—as, for example, the pyrometer that is used in the smelting of metals. So one had fully expected that when one turned a sensitive radio system at the sun one would see the radiation corresponding to the solar surface temperatures. What one saw was quite different, however. At the shortest radio waves one saw more or less the predicted temperatures. But as one looked at longer waves, a host of unpredicted effects appeared. Firstly, the apparent temperature was most of the time very much higher than had been thought. Secondly, at disturbed times on the sun, enormous peaks in intensity occurred which would have corresponded to temperatures far in excess of what could possibly occur in any part of the solar atmosphere. Clearly some other process and not thermal emission was responsible.

A number of investigators in the mid-fifties looked into these peculiar effects in fine detail. The outstanding investigation was

Figure 7. A frequency-time spectrum of "Type III" and "Type II" bursts on the sun. The frequency decreases upwards. The time span represented horizontally is 20 minutes.

(A. Maxwell and A. R. Thompson, Ap.J. *135*, 1962.)

that by Dr. Paul Wild in Sydney, who built himself the apparatus to analyze not only the time variations of the noisiness of the sun in the radio band but also to see in detail how within the radio band the different radio wavelengths were affected during a burst. A most remarkable set of observations was made. It became clear that there were a number of different types of disturbances that the sun could generate, clearly falling into several distinct groups, and that there would be information here for deducing in some detail motions that were taking place in the solar atmosphere (*Figure 7*). Of course, the subject has been studied extensively by now and one understands a great deal of the processes that lead to the emission of these radio waves. The basic energy source appears to be the magnetic fields which, in the hot and electrically conducting gasses of the solar atmosphere, are carried around and deformed. Explosive events can then occur that suddenly destroy the magnetic field in some region and deposit the energy in high-energy particles. These in turn have various ways in which they can lose their energy and make radio waves.

The sun is after all just an ordinary star. If it makes radio noise, then we expect the other stars to do likewise. Would we then not expect to see radio noise come to us from some of these stars and to see the diffuse background of all the multitudes of others? The answer is "No". The solar radio noise, although very intense here, is really terribly weak. We just happen to be so close to the sun. If other stars made no more radio radiation than the sun, they would be quite undetectable by ordinary radio instruments and even the sum total emitted by all the stars in the galaxy would not amount to anything measurable. The radio sources in the sky and the diffuse radio radiation in the sky certainly had to be ascribed to something else.

But even if solar radio astronomy did not provide an explanation for the radio sources it made a fascinating investigation in its own right. A great deal of what we now understand about hot conducting gasses was learned there. The solar surface is the nearest place and the most accessible one to our instrumentation in which phenomena are displayed that depend on motion and magnetic fields in conducting gasses.

Radio observations of the planets

Radio astronomy in the fifties continued to make one great discovery after another. Not only were there mysterious sources in the sky and an unexplained diffuse background . . . not only did the sun produce a variety of outbursts, but even the planets in our solar system had great surprises for us. The planet Venus, as you know, is shielded from our view by the fact that its atmosphere is exceedingly cloudy. It is a planet of rather similar size to the earth and being a little closer to the sun it was suspected of being a little warmer. It might have been a fine candidate for life. Circumstances there might be just as good as on the earth for the development of life, though, of course, not of the same forms. Then, however, came the shock when the radio radiation was measured and found to be that corresponding to a surface at about 300° centigrade. Optically one was able to see only the top of the cloud layer and never through to the surface. In the waveband that we call infra-red, in which one might measure the temperature, one did not expect to see through to the surface either, and at those wavelengths one could therefore only measure the temperature high up in the clouds. That temperature was low and not very different from what it would be in high clouds on the earth. The radio waves on the other hand could penetrate through thick layers of cloud and therefore give an indication of the temperature underneath. If that is indeed where the radio waves come from they would seem to indicate this very high temperature.

This, of course, is very sad. Humanity had hoped to inherit one day not just an extra piece of land, but a whole planet just as big as the earth. There was the possibility of a geological investigation of another planet giving us the chance of finding what is peculiar to the earth and what is more general in the geologic record. Then above all there was the chance of seeing perhaps another independent evolution of life and all the multitudinous forms that it might have taken there. The value of that is not just in seeing more life forms. If we wanted to do that we can still discover them by the thousand if we dredge up bits from the Pacific Ocean or go to the jungles of Brazil. The value would be in seeing whether another evolution of biology occurred by the same general principles. Would it also work through natural selection, through the principle of the survival of the fittest? Would there also be a genetic system that could communicate a certain mixture of the characteristics of two parents to each offspring? All these things are common in terrestrial biology which seems, however, to have developed from a single origin. If we could only investigate a biological system based on a different origin we would understand so much better what is chance and what is necessity in evolution. Here one radio observation seems to rule out all that. At 300° Centigrade we don't expect much of the kind of chemistry that is critical for our type of life. Perhaps some high temperature biology exists and has developed on Venus and perhaps one day we shall discover that and investigate it. But that would not have nearly the same fascination for us as if it had been biology operating in the same conditions as ours. Nor would we learn as much as we would have done from a comparison in comparable circumstances.

At 300° centigrade the chance of exploration by man seems quite remote, and even investigations by means of unmanned instruments are very difficult. So if this temperature deduced by radio investigations is correct, Venus will remain a closed book to us for quite some time. Is there any chance that it is not correct?

There is no question that the radio observations themselves are correct. Possibly there is still a problem with the interpretation. It could be that the radio waves are not produced merely as the heat radiation from the surface, but that they arise in unsuspected fashion in the atmosphere. Electrical storms on the earth produce electrical phenomena and very low frequency radio noise. What was seen on Venus is quite different from that and in the higher register of radio frequencies. But even so we have to admit that no one would have predicted the particular electrical disturbance that the terrestrial atmosphere can make and so perhaps no one has predicted the correct form of a high-frequency disturbance that the very different atmosphere Venus might make.

Let me digress a little and tell you what thoughts we have about the circumstances on Venus. On the earth, various gasses came out of the ground as the body of the earth heated up as the result of the internal radio activity and the internal compression. The most prominent volatile substance to come to the surface was water of which about 300 kgs. per square cm. came up through the surface, averaged over the entire surface, and throughout geologic time. It came up in the form of steam and in the terrestrial circumstances it condensed on the surface. It, of course, formed the oceans. The next most abundant volatile constituent to come up was carbon dioxide, of which 20 or 25 kgs./sq. cm. seemed to have appeared. That would have made an atmosphere on the earth with an atmospheric pressure 25 times as high as that of our present atmosphere and composed of CO_2. Why don't we have such an atmosphere now? The reason is that the carbon dioxide enters into various chemical processes on the earth, most of them facilitated by the existence of various organisms which makes the carbon end up in a solid form such as calcium carbonate, formed in the oceans. The excess oxygen serves to oxidize other rocks and is tied down there. In this way the CO_2 seems to have been kept at a low level in the terrestrial atmosphere despite the fact that in total quantity it was by far the major constituent. Nitrogen which is now our main atmospheric constituent was 25 times less abundant but did not happen to be removed to any great extent. Oxygen, our other atmospheric constituent, would not be present at all were it not for the activity of the green plants and it would disappear almost completely from the atmosphere in a very short fraction of geologic time if the green plants ceased to liberate it. Again, it would be tied down in oxides of various constituents of the rocks.

Now on Venus we believe that carbon dioxide is a major constituent and if the particular processes that have removed it from the atmosphere on the earth were not active there we should not be surprised if the Venutian atmosphere consisted chiefly of carbon dioxide and had an atmospheric pressure 25 times that of ours. Carbon dioxide has, in fact, been detected by spectroscopic means and found to be a major constituent of Venus. That, of course, strengthens our belief that we can think of Venus as an earth-like body but not having the same processes occurring on its surface.

A very deep and dense atmosphere would in general help to make the surface temperature high. It leads usually to the effect that light can get down through it, but the longer wavelengths of the heat radiation from the ground cannot penetrate. The result is that the ground heats up by what is called the "greenhouse effect" until of course the total amount of energy radiated out equals the total amount of sunlight coming in. The more opaque the atmosphere is to the longer wavelengths, heat radiation, the higher this temperature has to be. All this is clearly understood and so, therefore, an elevated temperature on Venus was perhaps not too surprising. The actual amount, however, seemed excessive even for the best reasonable greenhouse effect. One may still wonder whether, even though it probably is rather warm on Venus, it is perhaps not really so hot and some other effect, as yet undiscovered, contributes radio waves that simulate a very high temperature. The planet Venus may yet be the object of the greatest fascination and interest for us.

The planet Mercury also gave a surprise when its heat radio radiation was measured and showed that there was no significant difference between the side that was illuminated by the sun and the side that was not. One had thought that the dark side of Mercury would be extremely cold and this was evidently untrue. When we come to discuss the observations of the rotation rate of that planet the solution of the puzzle will become clear.

The planet Jupiter was the richest field of investigation in planetary radio astronomy. As you know, Jupiter is the largest planet, being some 300 times more massive than the earth. Unlike the inner planets, the outer or major planets as they are called, are made mainly of gaseous substances and it is not at all clear what one should describe there as an atmosphere and what as the body of the planet. Perhaps at some depth, there is a change from a gas to a liquid or a solid phase, but, in any case, of similar substances. Such a change is likely to be quite deep down where the pressure is hundreds of atmospheres. With radio waves we certainly cannot penetrate that kind of a depth, and, therefore, whatever we see comes from higher up in the atmosphere.

Jupiter first surprised us when it was found that bursts of radio noise were emitted by it. It was found that these were mainly at the lower radio frequencies, 20 megahertz or so, and it was also discovered that they occurred in a very peculiar manner. Particular spots on Jupiter seemed responsible, and the radio waves seemed to be directed outwards from them in sharply defined directions. When the rotation of the planet brought particular regions to face us we tended to see these bursts, but not at other times. If the sources were either more widely distributed over the planet or radiated out into a wider pattern we could not have seen such an effect. Most people think nowadays that some kind of atmospheric electrical phenomena takes place on a gigantic scale in particular zones and that this radiation can escape through the ionized outer atmosphere of Jupiter, the ionosphere, only along particular directions.

But that was not the only surprise that Jupiter had for us. The other was that high-frequency radio noise was seen which was steady and corresponded to an intensity far outside that which could be accounted for by any thermal radiation. It was discovered that this high-frequency radiation did not come mainly from the disk of the planet, but it came mainly from regions to each side of it. And the conclusion was drawn that Jupiter has enormous radiation belts as has the earth, but of much greater intensity. The high speed particles in such radiation belts, when moving in a sufficiently strong magnetic field, will generate the observed type of radio noise. The radiation belts on the earth are thought to be produced by an interaction with the sun. Jupiter is a great deal further from the sun, more than five times as far, and it is, therefore, a great puzzle why it should have more intense radiation belts. The other thing that is very puzzling is how it comes to possess such a strong magnetic field as is required for this explanation. The field has to be stronger than the earth's magnetic field by factor of at least 20. What drives around electric currents in the body of Jupiter to generate such strong magnetic fields?

Once more radio astronomy had turned up a new trick. Once

more something quite unexpected has been seen and a deduction could be made that one would never have guessed possible. The presence of a strong magnetic field on Jupiter could be established. This deduction is by now quite certain because various aspects of the radiation that have been observed all fit only with an interpretation involving a strong magnetic field.

The other planets have not as yet shown anything very remarkable. On the other hand, as radio instruments improve, I have little doubt that the subject will continue to advance, and perhaps even more remarkable discoveries will be made.

RADAR ASTRONOMY

I want now to discuss a new subject that has come into prominence in the last four or five years. You all know about the technique of radar, first applied in World War II, where a powerful transmitter sends out a pulse of radio waves and thereafter a sensitive receiver picks up any reflections, any echoes that may come back. If the antenna is beamed into the sky and an aeroplane flies through this beam then, of course, each radio pulse will generate a slight echo when striking the plane, to be detected back at the set. These radio waves travel at the speed of light and, therefore, if the time interval can be measured between the transmission of the pulse and the reception of the echo this fixes precisely the distance to the target.

Wartime radar was concerned with distances to targets of rarely more than 100 miles. But out of this has now developed a technology where we are concerned with distances of more than 100 million miles.

Modern radar sets of such power have been devised that the reflection from at least three planets in the solar system can be detected. Our moon is, of course, a trivially easy warming-up exercise for such radar sets. What can be achieved by these means? What is the good of getting an echo back from a target that you know in any case to be there?

A whole lot of new information has in fact been obtained. When an echo can be received it may be possible to analyze the signal in a great variety of ways. Firstly, the precise distance to the object can now be measured to an extraordinarily high precision because time measurements are the most precise physical measurements we can make. A measurement of time intervals to nine decimal places is commonplace now. The flight time of light to a particular planet and back has been determined with a precision of six decimal places, so far, which in fact is a higher precision than that to which the velocity of light is known. The distances to Mercury, Venus and Mars being measured in this way has greatly increased the precise charting of the positions of these bodies. In these days of space flight this turns out to be very important.

But not only that: the return signal can also be analyzed in many other ways. If the target is a more or less spherical planet then, of course, the echo does not come back all at one moment in time. The first bit of a signal may come back, depending on the relative position of the earth and the planet, after a time of ten to twenty minutes. But the pulse coming back will not be quite as sharp as the pulse that was sent out because of the dimensions of the planet itself. There will be a little interval of time between the arrival of the reflection from the nearest point of the planet—that is, from the middle of the apparent disk— to the time that the signal comes back from the furthest accessible part—that is, parts near the edge of the disk. That time interval for the planet Venus, for example, is about 40 milliseconds (a millisecond is $1/1000$ of a second). One can now see how much power is returned from various parts of the planet. If a planet had an exceedingly rough surface then a lot of power would be scattered back from the further parts which are inclined to the line of sight. If, however, it was very smooth, then almost all the power would come back from the nearest part where the ground is perpendicular to the line of sight *(Figure 8)*. (See p. 298.)

A precise study of the way in which the echo strength depends on the time delay within these 40 milliseconds, therefore, gives one an idea about the roughness of the surface. At each radio wavelength the only roughness that is of significance is on a scale equal to or larger than that wavelength. If, for example, we look at Venus at a wavelength of 70 cms. (430 megahertz) we will discover only a coarse structure on that scale or larger. The roughness of pebbles or sand would have no influence. By looking

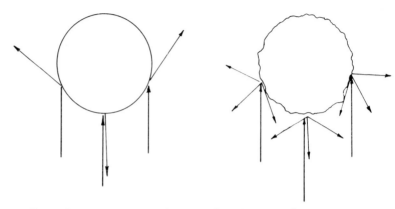

Figure 8. Power is returned toward the radar from the near point on a smooth or a rough planet; but only roughness will cause power to be returned from the further regions.

at the same planet at a number of different radio wavelengths one can, therefore, say something about the manner in which the apparent roughness depends on the examining wavelength. One could see whether a surface had some small scale roughness but to a larger scale was smooth. This is exactly what has happened for the case of the moon. At each wavelength the nearest echoing region gives the biggest signal. At the longer wavelengths it is only a very small fraction of the power that gets returned from the further parts of the moon. At a wavelength of 8 mms. on the other hand there is only a very small decline between the near and the far parts *(Figures 9(a)* and *9(b)).* (See pp. 299, 300.)

For an examination at 8 millimetres the surface looks almost completely rough and scatters just as much back whether the mean inclination is perpendicular to the line of sight or steeply inclined to it. This is just the same as for a rough surface like a white sheet of paper with respect to light. The brightness of a sheet of paper changes very little when you alter its mean inclination to your direction of viewing and of illumination. This is because the paper is very rough on a scale of the optical wavelengths.

So for the case of the moon the information emerged that on a scale of tens of centimetres the surface was rather smooth and

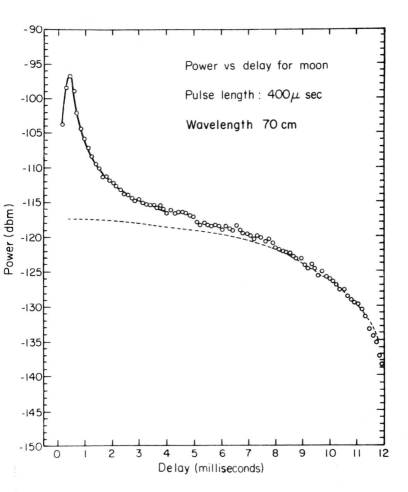

Figure 9a. Plot of the echo power received from different ranges on the moon, at a wavelength of 70 cm., showing the large signal from the nearest part and the sharp drop-off for greater ranges and therefore ground that is more inclined to the radar direction.

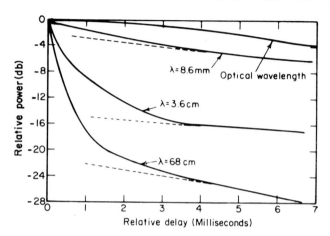

Figure 9b. Echo power (in logarithmic units) plotted against delay time from the nearest echo. At each radio wavelength the power received is given in terms of the power from the nearest echo. The ground is seen to be rough when tested at optical wavelengths or at 8 millimetres, but much smoother for longer wavelengths. (Evans.)

only had gentle undulations in it except for a small fraction of the area. On a scale of one centimetre or shorter, however, the surface was exceedingly rough. You have all seen how as a result of the photography from the three Rangers, from Lunar 9 and from Surveyor I this surface property has been completely confirmed.

The mean power returned in the radio pulse can, of course, also be measured. How does this depend on the object? It turns out this depends also somewhat on the roughness, but not very critically so. It depends greatly, however, on the electrical properties of the surface material. For the case of the moon, for example, it is clear that the average reflection is a lot less intense than it would be if the moon were composed of solid, dense rock. This would be true for all types of rock. Since we think that the moon is made of rock we are forced to suppose that over a depth of many metres from the surface down, the material is not as dense as solid rock. It must be very porous. The estimates are that more than half the space and probably more than three-quarters is voids between rock particles—a very interesting conclusion which again seems substantiated by spacecraft observa-

Figure 10. Photo of the foot of Surveyor 1, showing the indentation it made in its final landing impact. (A deeper indentation was made in the position of the first landing impact from which the vehicle bounced up.)

tions. The foot of Surveyor I sank in a little way and it would certainly not have sunk at all in a non-porous solid rock *(Figure 10)·*

There is another type of analysis of the returned signal that can be made. One can observe its precise frequency and that will not necessarily be precisely the same as that which was transmitted. The reason is that there may be a relative motion between the radar and the target, resulting in what is known as a "Doppler shift." The number of cycles of oscillation that are received per unit time is, of course, equal to that which is transmitted per unit time, plus or minus the change in the number of cycles that are en route at any time. Thus if the target approaches the radar there would be fewer cycles of oscillation on the way later than there

were earlier and, therefore, they will be arriving at a faster rate
—conversely, of course, if the target is going away. The amount
of the effect is admittedly not very large. The proportionate change
in frequency is, of course, just given by the ratio of the velocity
of the target to the velocity of light. Now the velocity of light, in
terms of centimetres per second, is three times 10^{10}. Since one
can measure a frequency to a precision of one part in 10^9 quite
comfortably, one can detect a velocity of the order of 30 centimetres per second. In antiquated units that is one foot a second
or 60 feet a minute, or 3,600 feet (a little more than $\frac{2}{3}$ of a mile)
per hour.

Most astronomical targets, of course, move at much higher
speeds relative to us. The earth goes round in its orbit at approximately 30 kms. per sec. and this is the order of magnitude of
relative velocities between the inner planets. That, of course, is
frightfully easy to detect. But just measuring the velocity of the
targets relative to us is not what we are after. We know that in
any case from the observations of the change in distance after a
certain while. What, however, we can do with the precise observation of the Doppler shift is to observe effects connected with the
rotation of a planet. If, for example, we looked at the radar signal
returning from the planet Venus we would no doubt see in the
returned signal some frequency components that are a little higher
and some a little lower than the mean frequency. That is because
of the rotation of the planet which will make one side approach
us and the other recede from us. It so happened in the case of
Venus that we had no other way of knowing what the rotation
speed was. Now, with the radar we could analyze these frequency
shifts very precisely.

Not only can we observe the frequency shifts in the total
returned signal, we can be even cleverer than that. We can first
cut up the signal according to range, that is to say, we can single
out individual range intervals which, of course, correspond to
rings on the planet, since there each range will correspond to a
circle concentric with a line joining us to the centre of the planet.
Thus we can single out a particular range-ring and then analyze
it for its various frequency components. Now, if the planet is
spinning, there will be some parts that are approaching us and

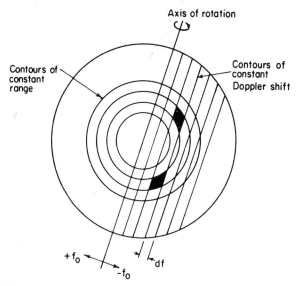

Figure 11. Range-Doppler mapping. Range-rings and Doppler shift strips as seen on the disk of a planet.

some parts that are receding from us. In each range-ring there would thus be frequency components shifted to a higher frequency than the mean and some shifted to a lower frequency (*Figure 11*).

The maximum frequency shift in each range-ring will be sharply limited and the biggest frequency shifts will occur, of course in the farthest range-ring, that is to say, right at the edge of the visible disk of the planet.

Various things can be done with this information. In the first place if we have a planet whose rate of rotation is not known we can discover it from this effect. For both Venus and Mercury this turned out to be important. For Venus the rate of rotation was not known (although one can clearly see the disk of the planet in a telescope) because the ground there is permanently covered densely with clouds and no features can, therefore, be recognized. One had thought it very likely that the planet would be spinning in such a way as to face the sun the same way all the time, in the same manner as the moon faces the earth. One side of the planet would then be always in the sunlight and the other side always in the dark and it would, therefore, spin once around its axis in a period which is its orbital period around the sun. This type of motion had been thought to be the end result of the tides which the sun would cause on the planet. We will return to this point later but let me say here that the radar results were very startling and showed that the planet in fact is spinning such as to take about 248 days to turn around once. The Venutian orbital period is 225 days. The direction of this spin is in the opposite sense to the orbiting motion around the sun. Astronomers call this a retrograde motion. There is here a great puzzle as to what causes this particular motion and how the strong effect of tidal friction did not tie Venus into the synchronous type of motion with the sun. So here we have a result of radar astronomy of absolutely fundamental importance for the discussion of the solar system.

The observations of the spin of the planet Mercury proved to be even more interesting. Mercury as you know is a tiny little planet quite close to the sun and again all the experts had for generations firmly believed that it had settled down to synchronous rotation around the sun. When the radar observations were made with the 1,000 foot radio antenna system in Arecibo, Puerto Rico *(Figure 4, p 277)* it was found that the planet was certainly not in this synchronous rotation state. Instead it was rotating considerably faster, turning around on its axis once in about 58 days instead of once in 88 days, which is the period of its motion around the sun. Here then were the two planets, Venus and Mercury, that are close enough to the sun to have their spin completely dominated by tidal friction. It could be calculated that they both ought to have reached the final state enforced by the tides in a time short compared with the 4 thousand million years which is the estimated age of the solar system. This final state was thought to be synchronous rotation, yet each of these planets, when investigated by radar, was found to be spinning in some different way. What was wrong? Were the new radar measurements wrong? Were the tidal friction orders of magnitude less than had been estimated? Are those planets much younger than the estimated age of the solar system? Had some great event taken place comparatively recently in the history of the solar system that had jerked these bodies to the motion that they now possess? Or was there something wrong in the theory of the tides which had predicted synchronous rotation?

When the radar observation of Mercury was first made I think very few people thought that the solution would come from the last possibility. Most people thought that perhaps the radar technique, which was after all a very new one, was wrong in some way, or perhaps that the spin or orbit of the two planets had suffered some significant perturbation late in the age of the solar system. But the answer, at any rate for Mercury, is quite clearly that the old tidal friction theory was inadequate.

To understand this we have to go a little further into the matter of tidal friction. Let us first discuss a planet on a circular orbit around the sun and possessing a fast spin—more or less the circumstances of the earth. What would be the result of the solar tides? The centre of mass of the earth would be the point moving around the sun on the circular orbit and it would be on this orbit that the outward centrifugal force of the motion was precisely in balance with the inward gravitational force exerted by the sun on the planet. But now the planet is not just a mass point, but a big body and so not all its mass is going around on the path on which the forces just balance. At any one time half the planet is closer to the sun than its centre of mass and half of it is further away. The half that is closer has a greater force of attraction from the sun and a smaller centrifugal force, while the part that is further has a smaller attraction to the sun and a larger centrifugal force. The inner part, therefore, tends to bulge inwards and the outer part to bulge outwards (Figure 12). The planet has a slight tidal deformation which consists of two bulges, one towards and one away from the sun.

If the planet is spinning on its axis then this deformation will move all the time relative to the material. Each piece of material is deformed twice each rotation period. For all materials such deformation will, of course, imply some loss of energy. For most solids something between one tenth and one thousandth of the energy necessary to make a slight deformation is lost and converted into heat. Real solids are not perfectly elastic. With liquids such as the oceans of the earth, an additional source of loss of energy

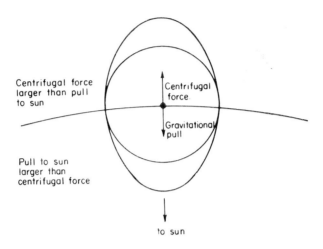

Figure 12.   The two tidal bulges caused by
the imbalance of the centrifugal force due
to the motion around the orbit, and the
gravitational pull to the sun.   (The bulges
are drawn greatly exaggerated.   In reality
for the earth they are only about a foot
high.)

Figure 13.   The tidal torque.   The sun's
pull on the near bulge is larger than on
the far one.   If the bulges are slightly skew
to the planet-sun line there will be a torque
opposing the rotation.

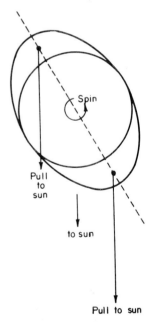

arises from the fact that the deformation causes streaming motion which in turn has friction. So whatever a planet is made of it is clear that if its material is subjected to a cyclical deformation some energy will be dissipated into heat. Where did this energy come from?

The only possible source of supply is from the rotational energy of the spinning planet. Thus if a planet was not spinning relative to the sun but was in synchronous rotation, then the material would no longer be regularly worked but only permanently deformed, and there would no longer be any loss of energy. That was the reason for supposing that tidal drag would finally bring it to this state of rotation.

This discussion did not make clear by what mechanism the rotational energy is made available. In fact, as the planet spins, any slightly non-elastic behaviour of the material will cause the two tidal bulges not to be aligned precisely on the sun-planet line. Instead they will be dragged around a little bit by the spin of the planet. The gravitational force of the sun acting on each of those two bulges will then pull a little bit harder on the nearer one than on the farther one and, therefore, apply a torque in the sense of slowing down the planet's rotation *(Figure 13)*. Now again it is clear that this effect would cease only when a planet's rotation has been brought down to the synchronous one. This tidal drag is greater the closer a planet is to the sun and there seemed little doubt that Mercury and Venus were close enough for the effect to be overpowering in a time much shorter than their assumed ages.

The solution of the puzzle for Mercury came when it was realized that the tidal drag theory had to be modified in an important way for the case that the planet does not go around the sun in a circular orbit. Mercury goes around in an ellipse which goes $1 \cdot 5$ times as far at its furthest point as it is at its nearest. Now the tidal drag is very dependent on this distance, and it is, therefore, much more important which way it pulls in the vicinity of the near approach than for all the rest of the orbit. If you remember Kepler's laws of planetary motion you realize that at near approach the planet moves around the sun in angle at a much higher rate than when it is further away; the tidal drag theory will, therefore, mean that the planet had to settle down to some compromise spin rate, since it could not just be synchronous all the way around the orbit. The tidal effect is, of course, much too small to change the spin rate significantly in any one orbit and, therefore, a compromise spin rate must be reached which will then mean that it is spinning a little too fast when it is far from the sun and a little too slowly when it is close, compared with the instantaneous rate that would make it face the sun the same way. In this compromise rate the near approach will matter far more than the parts of the orbit where it is farther away. The spin rate will, therefore, tend to approximate to the synchronous motion at nearest approach. For Mercury that would come out at about 56 days for one rotation, while it takes Mercury 88 days to go once around its orbit. The right compromise spin rate, which then has to be a period between 56 and 88 days, and much nearer 56, turned out to be in the neighbourhood of 60 days. The observed period was quite close to that, and so when a student of mine, Stan Peale, and I wrote a note explaining this situation we thought we had accounted for the entire story.

Our discussion, of course, was correct, but it turned out not to be the whole story. Colombo published a note shortly after it pointing out that Mercury may be spinning at such a rate that it does precisely one and one half turns each time around the orbit. That would be a period of $58 \cdot 6$ days. In that case, he suggested, there would be a tendency to lock into this period if Mercury possessed any permanent deformation in addition to the bulges raised by the tides. More accurate measurements of the rotation rate seem to confirm a period very close to this one and what evidence can be got from optical observations, though very ambiguous, still indicates that if the period is somewhere near this value then it is probably very close to $58 \cdot 6$. The whole story now seems to be that the tidal drag would have taken Mercury to a spin quite near this value, and that then the small effect of a permanent deformation makes itself felt and it locks in to the precise period which is two-thirds the orbital one.

For Venus the story is not so clear yet. Again it is clearly not spinning at the synchronous rate, but in that case the orbit is too nearly circular to attribute the difference to the same cause as Mercury. The peculiar thing in this case is that it appears to be spinning in such a way that whenever it comes closest to the earth it appears to be facing the earth in the same way. On the other hand all the calculations of the effect that our little earth would make on Venus tend to show that there is no reasonable expectation of it locking in to a rate dominated by the earth.

An added complication for Venus lies in the fact that because of its enormous atmosphere, probably more than 30 atmospheres pressure, the atmospheric tidal effects may be very important. These are modified by the streaming patterns that will no doubt occur in an atmosphere heated on one side, and we do not yet quite understand how the combination of the tidal bulges and the streaming would affect the spin of the planet over long periods of time.

The old and well established subject of celestial mechanics had received quite a jolt. No one had thought that there was much new to be learned in the theory; yet this was the case. The important lesson to be learned out of this is that whenever one has a chance to look at something with better means one should do so, even when it is thought that the subject is completely understood.

Now let us return to the other types of information which radar astronomy can give us. We have said that we can analyze the return signal according to the delay time which corresponds to range, and the Doppler shift in frequency due to a relative rotation between the planet and the point of observation on the earth. For the moon this technique, called "Range-Doppler mapping" has been particularly successful. With our great antenna in Puerto Rico we have a beam which is much narrower than the size of the moon. The fact that in Range-Doppler mapping there would be two areas that would be treated exactly alike *(Figure 11)* both for range and for Doppler shift is no handicap now for we can easily arrange for the beam of this antenna to look in each case only at the one and not the other such region. For the case of the moon and our huge antenna we have such strong signals that we can afford to cut them up into very many intervals in both range and frequency and still recognize them. Consequently we can make very detailed maps. Such maps then represent the variations of radio reflectivity of the different types of ground, and it is very interesting to compare this with the optical appearance of these areas. Much has been learned about the nature of the lunar surface from such

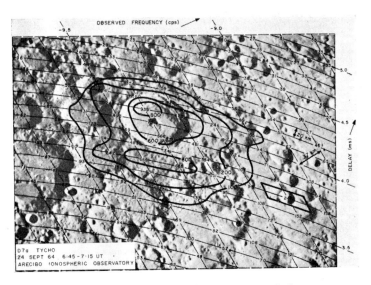

Figure 14. Range-Doppler map of the region around the young crater Tycho, on the moon. The radar reflectivity contours are drawn superimposed on a photograph of the region. The grid of range rings and Doppler strips is shown with figures indicating the reflected power (in arbitrary units).

studies. It has become clear that the regions that look mountainous are indeed rougher also on the scale of the wavelength. The younger looking craters on the moon appeared to be the roughest regions and also the one where the surface material is densest *(Figure 14)*. If big explosions caused by meteoritic impacts made those craters as we think, then indeed a fresh explosion pit ought to be rough and rather solid. Some process must have been at work which gradually aged the older craters, rounded them over, smoothed them, and at the same time, caused the upper layers of material to be fluffed up and become less dense. We think that all this can be achieved through the action of small meteorites that hit the moon all the time.

Venus is rather far away for detailed Range-Doppler mapping even with the Arecibo antenna. On the other hand it is not hopeless, and probably before too many years have gone by we shall have Range-Doppler maps giving a curious geographical description of a planet whose surface we have never seen. We won't quite know what the different areas are but they will be distinguishable from each other from the variations in the radar properties, and the individual areas will no doubt be recognizable each successive rotation of the planet. The planet Mercury is still further away at its nearest approach to the earth, and smaller, and so it is a still more difficult target. Mars can be investigated to some extent by these techniques but a problem arises there because it is spinning at too high a rate. The Doppler shift analysis technique suffers from an inherent confusion in that case.

Radar to the outer planets, Jupiter and Saturn, is still very difficult with present systems. There is no more than an uncertain report of an echo having been obtained from the planet Jupiter. These planets have probably an enormously deep and dense atmosphere which will absorb radar waves before they come to any level at which they would be reflected. Very little radio power would then be returned and it would be very difficult to detect it. Possibly the moons of Jupiter which have solid surfaces will be detected before Jupiter itself.

In the few years in which radar astronomy has existed it has already made very major contributions to our understanding of the solar system. Much more powerful radar systems will be built, much better computing machine technology will be devised for analyzing the results, and I have no doubt that there are many more discoveries to come.

THE GREAT RADIO SOURCES

Now I want to return to the discussion of radio astronomy and the nature of the distant objects that are such powerful emitters of radio waves. We discussed earlier that there were such radio sources in the sky and that their identity and nature was in doubt. In recent years, a huge amount of work has been done in this field and very great discoveries have been made.

Much of the radio emission of the sky comes from small localized spots, the so-called small angle radio sources. It proved very difficult at first to find any reliable way of identifying such radio sources with optically visible objects. Of course there was no guarantee that an optical object existed in that location because, after all, a completely transparent invisible gas could have processes occurring in it that made it emit radio noise. Nevertheless, most astronomers felt that a source of disturbance that created radio noise would probably have some association also with events that produced light. However, there are a great many faint stars in the sky — far too many to be investigated individually. The precision to which the location of a radio source could be pinned down would still leave large numbers of points of light, most of them stars no doubt, in the area in question. The successes came in slowly at first when some larger antenna systems could pinpoint positions better and in some cases optical objects were found which had such unusual properties in the light emission that one readily accepted the identification. Two strange things seen in the same area of sky would surely not be independent of each other. In the first place there was the suggestion that collisions of galaxies were responsible for radio sources. A number of galaxies of very odd shapes were seen to be radio emitters, and in many cases the optical spectrum revealed the existence of very high internal velocities in them. Collision seemed an obvious explanation. In recent times it has become clear that some kind of internal explosion on a galactic scale has occurred in some galaxies and perhaps collisions of galaxies have nothing to do with the matter.

What can be said about the processes that might be responsible for the radio emission? Firstly, if synchrotron radiation, the radiation of electrons spiralling in magnetic fields, is the right explanation for the radio emission then one can deduce something about the quantity of highly energetic electrons that must be there and the strengths of the magnetic fields in which they are moving. When these quantities are evaluated one finds in many cases a very remarkable result. The amount of energy that has to be stored up in one way or another to make that much radio noise is quite enormous. One can debate whether the energy content is a little more in the magnetic fields and less in the high energy particles or vice versa, but the total still always comes out very high. The most energetic event observed before had been the total explosion of individual stars, the so-called supernovae, like the origin of the Crab nebula we discussed earlier. These sources contain as much energy as hundreds of millions of super-novae. Whatever could have been going on to release such huge amounts of energy?

The fact that such large amounts of energy are involved im-mediately implied that a great mass must be involved also. If one were to calculate how much mass is needed to release a given amount of energy on the basis of the most energetic nuclear reactions, for example, one would still find that more than a million times the mass of the sun is needed to build up one of the strong radio sources. Perhaps there are processes in physics that we do not yet know about and perhaps there are circumstances occurring there that we have not yet contemplated; but in any case it seems that a very massive object has to be involved.

This was the state of understanding when the "quasars" were discovered. The technique of pinpointing the position of radio sources in the sky was greatly advanced when my colleague, Hazard, then working at Sydney University, successfully observed occultations of radio sources by the moon. As the motion of the moon takes it across a radio source, the received power drops off very sharply and rises again very sharply as a source gets uncovered. The precise details of the observed change in intensity can be calculated from the theory of diffraction. Even for a point source it will not be a completely sudden effect, but nevertheless it would be an effect that would be much more sensitive to the direction of the incoming waves than even the largest radio antenna. With the aid of this technique radio sources could be pinpointed almost to the full accuracy to which the position of the edge of the moon could be determined optically at any one time. Suddenly radio astronomy had pinpointing accuracy that was as good as that of an optical telescope, though of course only for the band of the sky that was covered by the moon. In a way you might think of the radio antenna and the moon together making up an antenna system of very great size and therefore very high resolution.

Some radio sources, when so pinpointed, were found to have an optical object in that position which did not look like a galaxy at all. Instead it looked just like a star on the photographic plate; that is to say, an object where the light comes from a smaller angular diameter than the telescope could resolve. The images of galaxies are usually recognized on the photographic plate by having definitely a fuzzy outline instead of the sharp spots that represent the image of a star. These objects looked like stars and were regarded as that for some time. Here perhaps were the "radio stars" contemplated long ago.

Then, however, came the startling discoveries, chiefly made by Maarten Schmidt and Allan Sandage at the Mt. Wilson and Palomar Observatories. It was discovered that these objects showed some spectral lines, so that the velocity with which they were approaching or receding from the earth could be measured. In all cases where a definite figure could be obtained it seemed that they were receding at an extremely high speed.

Stars in the galaxy may be moving at speeds up to 100 kilometres a second, or so. Other galaxies may execute a random motion relative to ours that is reckoned in a few hundreds of kilometres per second. The only really large velocities that had ever been observed before had been associated with the apparent expansion of the universe which, as we discussed earlier, makes the distant galaxies rush away from us at speeds proportional to their distance. One had seen galaxies possess as much as four per cent of the speed of light, but the objects one was looking at now came up to 50 per cent. Was one merely looking at objects sufficiently distant so that the expansion speed amounted to that much? If that were the case then of course one could compute the distance. Once knowing the distance one could compute how bright these objects really had to be in order to appear as the observed spot of light on the photographic plate. Again, when that was done, it turned out that the optical intrinsic brightness of these objects was quite enormous. These "quasi stellar radio sources" or "quasars" were certainly very remarkable objects.

Were the large shifts in the spectrum due to something else and not a cosmological expansion and the great distance of these objects? If the spectral shifts were produced in some other way then perhaps the objects were not so far and the observed brightness would then not imply such a large energy output. Spectral shifts can after all be produced by things other than velocity. Some physical effect might be acting there that changes the emission frequencies of the atoms. Very intense gravitation is known to do that and so one might wonder whether the objects were of exceedingly high density and therefore associated with particular intense gravity. Alternatively, one might wonder whether even if a shift was due to velocity it was perhaps a merely locally fast-moving object, not one at rest in the expanding universe at a great distance. Both these points of view have been pursued somewhat and no really good or plausible discussion along these lines has yet come to light. It seems most likely that they are indeed huge, powerful, and very distant objects.

The appearance of the radio emitting region also throws some light on this problem. The galaxies that have been identified as radio sources are most commonly massive so called elliptical galaxies and in very many cases their radio radiation comes not just from the diffuse region surrounding them but quite clearly from two or more centres. Very often the optically visible galaxy was right in the middle between the two radio sources. Apparently the radio emitting gas was normally spewed out in two concentrated blobs in opposite directions, a very strange behaviour and one that is not yet fully understood. Now the interesting thing is that this double shape of the radio sources is just as true for those that have a quasar as the optical object as for those that have a galaxy. This seems to be very suggestive therefore that the quasar phenomenon is occurring in similar circumstances and on the same scale as the radio galaxy phenomenon. Had the quasars been some near object travelling at very high velocities through space it would be very strange for them to result in just the same type of double radio source as distant galaxies do.

In this case we seem to be driven to the conclusion that objects as massive perhaps as entire galaxies can become very much more concentrated and then emit light and high speed gas in enormous amounts. Two possibilities for this are under discussion. Either a super-star is formed, that is to say, that a gas mass millions of times more massive than the sun condenses into a single object and that such objects then develop great surface violence. The second possibility is that a galaxy of ordinary stars contracts so much that some millions of stars in its interior become a very dense star cluster. When these stars start to interact with each other because of their extreme proximity some violence may result. They may interact with each other by agglomerating and forming much bigger stars, which in turn would rapidly become unstable and explode. A succession of exploding stars would then fill such a region. This is the view put forward by Colgate, who then discusses in detail the consequences of the explosions. The other possible interaction is that they simply collide with each other at high speeds and all the light and high energy gas is merely the consequence of such very energetic collisions. We have pursued this possibility and think it an entirely plausible explanation.

The many stars forming a dense cluster and interacting with each other is perhaps made more plausible than the single super star on the grounds that it would tend to bridge the gap between quasars and radio galaxies. The centres of ordinary galaxies appear to have dense clusters in them and, at least in the case of our own galaxy, this is a radio source. Of course this is all on a very small scale compared with a quasar. Many of the intense radio galaxies, however, show also a tendency for dense star systems while there is no evidence whatever that galaxies containing a lot of gas are associated with the phenomenon. If super stars were to form, one might suspect them of doing this preferentially in the spiral galaxies which contain an abundance of gas. Radio galaxies are specifically not spirals. Massive galaxies with dense old star systems or quasars are the objects that make radio radiation and that perhaps suggests that quasars are a development of dense old star systems.

On the star collision theory of quasars these objects would consist of clusters of perhaps a hundred million stars, all concentrated in a very small volume and rushing around at speeds perhaps as high as 10,000 kms/sec. The collisions would shatter the stars completely and produce a great amount of light and x-rays as well as the high energy gas that makes the radio radiation. In this case one would expect to see variations in brightness as different collisions occur and that indeed is seen. One would also expect to see very high internal velocities reflected in the details of the spectrum and this is also the case. Thirdly, one would expect to see the precise velocities vary somewhat as different collision centres become prominent. An unsteady spectrum of just this kind has been observed. I think it very likely therefore that galaxies tend to make star clusters in their interior which, when they are only small, result in weak radio sources like that in our own galaxy, while when they are very big and massive objects they result in the violence observed as a quasar. Possibly the big radio galaxies have all been quasars and generated the radio emitting gas at that stage in their career.

This discussion then brings us again to the question of the cosmic rays. If the radio sources are gigantic emitters of high energy particles like cosmic rays then of course we may speculate that the cosmic rays we observe here are in some way related to the process. There are a number of possibilities.

One possibility would be that the cosmic rays that we observe are just a little bit of high energy gas that was generated in our own galaxy and is filling it, being constrained from too rapid an expansion by the magnetic field in our galaxy. The processes responsible for this gas may of course have been of a similar kind to the processes in quasars and radio galaxies, but on a very much smaller scale. Perhaps the radio source in the centre of our galaxy was responsible—perhaps it was once a tiny little quasar. Perhaps star explosion processes that occur here and there in the galaxy were responsible. On this view the intensity of cosmic rays would be very much less outside our own galaxy, but other galaxies may have a similar intensity inside of them. Just the locations of quasars and radio galaxies would have an enormously greater intensity and much larger regions containing this high-speed gas.

Another point of view is that each quasar or radio galaxy causes the relativistic gas that is spewed out to expand and to fill more and more of space. It could be that eventually all of space, or a large proportion of it is in a region that was once swept over by an expanding bubble of this gas. Our own cosmic rays here may then be the remains of a quasar or radio galaxy that once existed in the vicinity of our galaxy and whose bubble still fills at a low intensity our general region of space. In this case the cosmic rays would have infiltrated into our galaxy from outside. Other regions of space would have more or less cosmic rays in them, depending on when they were last swept over by such a bubble and how intense the gas in this bubble was at that time. Radio astronomy would just show us then those bubbles that are at the present time very intense and still rather localized.

You have seen how in about 15 years radio astronomy has profoundly changed and improved our understanding of the sun, the solar system, the galaxy, and the largest phenomena that seem to occur in the universe. It has done much more than I have been able to go into here and I have left out whole areas just as exciting as some that I have mentioned. The observations of the detailed structure of our own galaxy and some other nearby galaxies through the observation of the radio frequency emission of atomic hydrogen gas is one such area. The observation of the emission of the molecule OH which suggests that an action like that in a laser is taking place in space, is another such area. The whole thing has been a fantastic success story, quite unpredicted by astronomers generally and it has been a wonderful lesson of the way in which science progresses. No one can predict the big developments and no one can steer the path along which discoveries will take us. There is no great general who marshals his forces and attacks according to his plan. Rather it is like guerilla warfare where one attacks in any place where one has gained the upper hand, no matter whether one understands the strategic significance of the onslaught. A new means of investigation, a new technique that becomes available, a new theory or a new thought, all these have to be pursued and the judgment as to their utility has to be postponed until after the results have come in. If astronomical progress had been planned by astronomers 20 years ago, radio astronomy would have been left out. Now it is clearly a subject that takes us to the threshold of a new understanding of the physical world in which we live.

Essays

Historical - Biographical - Humanistic -
Anecdotal

by

JULIUS SUMNER MILLER

Being some Discourse on certain Uncommon Men and Great Ideas
—Revealing briefly the History of their Time, the Strangeness of
their Lives, the Genius of their Minds—Wherein also we hear
abundantly their own Reflections made known to us by their Own
Word and by the Report of others.

"Speech most shews a man: Speak, that I may know thee."
BEN JONSON, *Explorata: Oratio Imago Animi.*

Professor Julius Sumner Miller,
Professor of Physics, El Camino College, California.

Prologos

On those of us invited to lecture in Professor Messel's Summer Science School there falls the mandate to put into writing his own material for "the book". I am singularly honoured by this invitation and I obey with delight the injunction. The reason is clear. The warm reception given to my lectures heretofore has stirred my soul and the writing I have done on another occasion[1] has also been warmly received. So I come to *this* exposition with unbounded pleasure.

The decision on *what to write* was instant though the boundaries were not so quickly defined. I was at once led to these reflections: I shall try in my writing to convey the spirit and the philosophy of science. The view that science is *one thing* and the humanities *another* is much bandied about. *I am not of this mind.* Those who say this mean that men of science have a very different view of the world from that of the humanists. *This is not true.* Of all the divisions of human knowledge and of all the activities of men, science is really the most humanistic. To understand this, however, we must read the lives of those who pursued with incessant struggle this one singular intention and this one noble ambition *which declares what science is:* To Uncover the Orderly Beauty of Nature. With this comes the great satisfaction of *understanding* which must indeed rank as the highest ambition of the human mind. Nature is regulated by universal laws. However great the diversity, however lacking in harmony, the hope always is a coherent doctrine, a consistent array of truths. It is this very search for unity in diversity and for harmony and order that drives the man of science in his labour. Newton put it in that classic and poetic phrase: " . . . and whence arises all that order and beauty which we see in the world?" *This* is the prime mover for the astronomer, for the physicist, for the man of medicine, for the mathematician—to seek out the way of things.

---

[1] *TIME*—H. Messel and S. T. Butler (Sydney 1965).

As Kepler with his strange and tormented genius put it: "To find why things are as they are and not otherwise."

And so it is that science, when properly viewed, in its noblest flights, in its deepest virtues, is indeed one with religion for there ever remains the Sphere of Darkness beyond our reach. It is as with Newton that the Great Ocean of Truth lies all undiscovered.

So, as I say, the decision to write was instant. The study of science at all levels—from the grade school to the highest quarters —from childhood to old age—from the novitiate to the master— all need more history, more biography, more humanism, more anecdote. It is only in this way that science can be seen as a noble activity of the human mind. Without these ingredients it is a lifeless technological monster empty of the human pulse. But the instant decision to write gave me also instant pause and dilemma. History is filled with uncommon men and great ideas. On *whom* shall I write? On *what* shall I write? And any *what* at once involves a *whom* for no event is apart from men. I at once put aside from my mind those on whom I had written before[2]. A new list evolved —a hundred names or so—and the agony of deletion grew abundant.

There is, for example, **Apollonius of Perga,** who attracts me irresistibly. Schooled in Alexandria by Euclid's pupils, he produced 387 propositions on conic sections. Without this work Kepler could not have superseded Ptolemy. "But for this discovery, which was probably regarded as the unprofitable amusement of a speculative brain, the whole course of practical philosophy of the present day, of the science of astronomy, of the theory of projectiles, of the art of navigation, might have run in a different channel; and the greatest discovery that has ever been made in the history of the world, the law of universal gravitation, with its innumerable consequences . . . might never to this hour have been elicited." (James Joseph Sylvester).

For two thousand years Apollonius and Euclid dominated geometry and they had no peer till Jakob Steiner in the 19th century. So here we have a sweep of history with incredible events all resting on the passion of Apollonius. As an aside to these serious things we cannot escape the enchantment of *The Problem of Apollonius:*

---
[2] ibid.

*The right-circular cone of Apollonius. The saw-cuts permit dissection —
separation of the parts — to reveal the conic sections. The other geometrical
solids are those treated by Euclid in his Elements. It is an interesting
exercise to find algebraic expressions for their properties — the volume —
the total surface. E.g., what is the volume of the truncated cone? of the
obliquely-truncated cone?*

Can you name *the sections and* write *the equations of the curves?
The conic sections which result from the "cutting" of a right-circular cone.*

Given three fixed circles, to find a circle that touches them all. The construction is with ruler and compass only! There are eight solutions.

And then too there are the **Letters of Apollonius.** They are possessed of a gripping enchantment.

"Apollonius to Eudemus, greeting. When I was in Pergamum with you, I noticed that you were eager to become acquainted with my Conics; so I send you now my first book with corrections and will forward the rest when I have leisure. These investigations I have arranged in eight books and I will in due course provide the needful emendations."

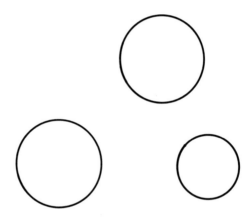

Then there is **Euclid and the Fifth Postulate**—an intellectual gymnastic "sweated out" for 20 centuries by all the mathematical geniuses of every age. D'Alembert was forced to put it aside. Lagrange tackled it but once: "Il faut que j'y songe encore." Laplace abandoned it. Twenty centuries of useless effort convinced many of the geometers that the final settlement of the theory of parallels involved a problem whose solution was impossible. But then Gauss came upon the scene — Carl Friedrich Gauss. For forty years he concealed his thoughts, being certain that he would be mis-understood. "Keep silence," he wrote Taurinus. "Keep silence." It was 1792 that he began his *Meditations,* writing them down "so that it shall not perish with me." In 1832 Gauss received

THE PROBLEM OF APOLLONIUS

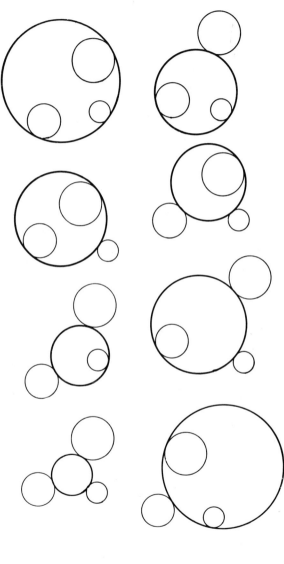

The eight solutions of The Problem of Apollonius. Fix any three circles of any diameter at random in a plane. Now with ruler and compass only find a circle which is at once tangent to all three. The problem is within the competence of first-year students of geometry! What would you say if the 3 circles were not in a plane?

from Wolfgang Bolyai a copy of the work of his son Johann. Johann wrote: "I have made such wonderful discoveries that I am almost overwhelmed. I have created a new universe from nothing." What he had written are the most extraordinary two dozen pages in the history of thought. And in a letter to Bolyai Gauss wrote: "The progress I have made seems rather to compel me to doubt the truth of geometry itself." Now too there came at once upon this scene the geometry of Lobachevski—Nikolai Ivanovich Lobachevski. For forty years he too had laboured and it was only in the year before his death, when he was already blind, that he dictated his final solution. Nor is the drama of this saga ended for now came forth George Friedrich Bernhard Riemann with *space finite yet unbounded*. And *then* came Einstein and Relativity. This tale is heavy with drama and we see once more the great sweep of events bearing out the spirit and hope of science.

Nor can our dialogue with Euclid be complete without exploring the five regular polyhedra which, in his *Book XIII,* he brings to a climax in the stately procession of his logic. These, you will remember, were extolled by Plato and ending with the dodecahedron were made the symbol of the Universe itself. (See diagram opposite and on p. 328.)

Nor can we escape the enchantment of Euclid's **Perfect Numbers**[3] which raised the question: Are there any *odd perfect numbers?* And the question is still unanswered after 2300 years!

And how about the question of *prime pairs*[4]—*prime numbers closely packed?* The proof has not yet been finished! And how about just prime numbers alone? *Euclid started it all.* Gauss' Prime Number Theorem took a century to prove. Fermat thought he had a formula for yielding only the prime numbers[5] but he was mistaken.

Then there is the **Algebra of the Renaissance** which really had its beginning with the Persian poet Omar Khayyam in the 11th

[3] A *perfect number* is one whose factors (divisors) sum to twice the number. Thus 6 is *perfect* since $1 + 2 + 3 + 6 = 12$. So, too, 28 is *perfect*. The next one is 496. What is the next one?

[4] A prime pair closely packed is 11, 13. So is 17, 19. So, too, is 41, 43. But as one proceeds, prime pairs become rarer. But should not the number of prime pairs be infinite?

[5] Fermat's Formula: $Fn = 2^{2^n} + 1$. Thus $F_1 = 5$; $F_2 = 17$; $F_3 = 257$; $F_4 = 65,537$. And $F_5 = 4,294,967,297$. *But is it prime?* Euler factored this in 1732. F_5 is $641 \times 6,700,417$, he said. Is not this fantastic!

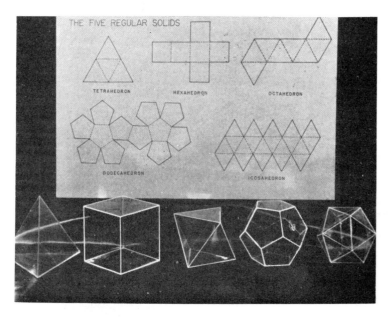

The Five Regular Polyhedra *of Euclid.   Only five are possible!   It is an interesting exercise to construct these out of cardboard, say, and fold them into solid form along the dotted lines.*

Exercise: *Find the volume, the surface, the size and the sum of the face angles.   How many edges are there?   How many vertices?*

century. Then, four centuries later and all at the same time, there came on the scene the most singular team in the whole history of science. They illustrate the Italian Renaissance with incredible perversity and uncommon greatness. Their names: Scipione del Ferro, Niccolo Tartaglia[6], Girolamo Cardano, Ludovico Ferraro, and Rafael Bombelli. Are not these just wonderful names! Their work makes the weirdest chapter in the history of mathematics. It started with the historic equation $x^3 = 15x + 4$. And it was the solution of *this* cubic equation which gave impetus to the strange number $\sqrt{-1}$. But of these "characters" we have named—let us say a word:

Tartaglia had no schooling. He taught himself to read and write. He was too poor to buy paper so he wrote on the tombstones to solve his problems. When Brescia was captured by the French all

---

[6] Niccolo Fontana

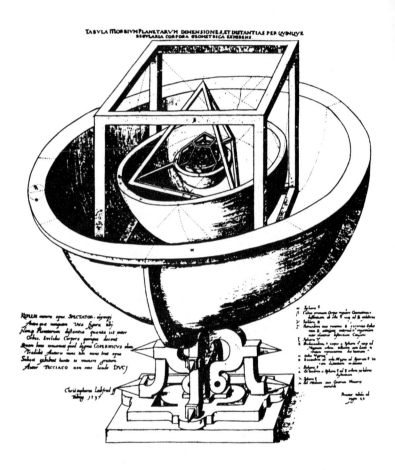

The universe as "constructed" by Kepler.   Note the use of the Five Regular Polyhedra.   The outermost Sphere in the Domain of Saturn.   From Mysterium Cosmographicum 1597.

the inhabitants were massacred in the Cathedral. Niccolo had his skull split and his jaws and palate cut open. His speech thus impaired he was named Niccolo Tartaglia which means "stammerer". He accepted a challenge from del Ferro to solve the most problems out of 30 in 30 days. He—Tartaglia—knowing his opponent could solve a *certain* cubic found the *general solution of all cubics* and did all the problems in two hours!

Niccolo Tartaglia. A woodcut on the cover of his Quesiti et Inventioni — *Venice, 1546.*

Cardan was a maniac, a gambler, a murderer, always in intrigue and scandal. His own sons were wicked—one poisoned his wife and was executed. Cardan, in a fit of rage, cut off the ears of a younger son for some offence. He was astrologer to the Papal Court under Pope Gregory XIII. Having foretold that he should die on a certain day he committed suicide to keep his reputation! He had asked Tartaglia—"How do *you* solve the cubic?" Tartaglia refused to tell him so with deception and threat he *extracted* the solution!

Ferraro was a pleasant little fellow with a cheerful face, of great intellectual power but with the temper of a fiend. He was poisoned by his sister.

So here we have men vain, arrogant, treacherous, vindictive, jealous, crafty, greedy, yet ranking with the greatest mathematical minds of all time.

Of the square-root-of-minus-one ($\sqrt{-1}$) more must be said. This had its origin with the discovery that the *real* number is inadequate for the solution of all the equations of algebra. $x^2 + 1 = 0$ is an example. And the glory of the discovery of the *imaginary* goes to the Italians of the Renaissance. Cardan (1545) was the first *to dare to write* $x = \sqrt{-1}$ and he was led to it by this problem: *Split the number 10 into two parts the product of which is 40*. He showed the solution to be $5 + \sqrt{-15}$ and $5 - \sqrt{-15}$, an impossible expression for his time. But it was the solution of the cubic of the form $x^3 + ax + b = 0$ that gave him no escape. That historic equation $x^3 = 15x + 4$ led Cardan to this illusory solution: $x = \sqrt[3]{2 + \sqrt{-121}} + \sqrt[3]{2 - \sqrt{-121}}$. In a flash of incredible genius Bombelli resolved these two cubic radicals into $2 + \sqrt{-1}$ and $2 - \sqrt{-1}$, the sum of which is 4. Two centuries later Demoivre was able to write

$$(cos\ \theta + i\ sin\ \theta)^n = cos\ n\ \theta + i\ sin\ n\ \theta$$

whereby we can raise a complex number to any integral power or extract any root. And then came Euler with that most exquisite and beautiful identity $e^{\pi i} + 1 = 0$, which shows the amazing mystic kinship of these symbols.

Then there is the life and work of **Robert Hooke**—miserable and sickly all his life—beset with insomnia and fearful dreams— nor well favoured to look upon. No portrait of him exists but he is described as "lean, bent and meanly ugly, with a wide thin

Girolamo Cardano. A woodcut on the cover of his Practica arithmetice —
Milan, 1539.

mouth and a sharp chin." And Samuel Pepys spoke of seeing Mr.
Hooke—"Above all, Mr. Boyle today was at the Meeting, and
above him Mr. Hooke, who is the most, and promises the least, of
any man in the world that ever I saw." But his work was monumental. Strangely enough, all he did he concealed under "anagrams"

fearing the theft of his ideas. The classic one is known to every schoolboy: *ceiiinossssttuv* which, when revealed, reads—*ut tensiosic vis (as the extension so the force)* being the law of the spring. And he said of this: "Now as the theory is very short, so the way of trying it is very easie."

As the Curator of the Royal Society he produced an extraordinary variety of experiments. His great work *Micrographia* ranks him as the founder of microscopic study in biology. It was described by Pepys as "...the most ingenius book that ever I read in my life." Herein he shows the compound eye of the fly, the structure of feathers, a crystal of snow. His figure of the louse is a classic. He was the first to propose *zero* as the freezing point of water. He put forward the first mechanical theory of heat: "Nothing else but a very brisk and vehement agitation of the parts of the body." He was the supreme instrument maker of his time. He reported two experiments showing the formation of craters on the moon: In one he let bullets fall into a mixture of clay and water. In the other he noted the breaking of bubbles in boiling alabaster. The pits he got were exactly like the lunar craters—and we know no better today! His controversy with Newton is classic. They were contumacious adversaries. Newton allowed his *Opticks* to be published only *after* Hooke's death. Maybe Newton in the plenitude of his fame could have shown greater sympathy for Mr. Hooke—"that brave mind and spirit, housed in a suffering body."

And now **Abraham Demoivre** comes to my mind again. He once caught a glimpse of Mr. Newton and thus inspired took up Newton's new *Principia*. To his surprise the book taxed him—though it charmed him, too. And he tore out the pages one by one and carried them loose in his pocket to study them as time allowed. His death was a strange affair indeed. He declared at a certain time in his life that he had to sleep some 10 or 15 minutes longer each day than the preceding one. The day after he had thus reached a total of something over 23 hours he slept 24—and died in his sleep.

This *prolegomenon* is already too long. I have been diverted from its principal and immediate purpose by the enchantment of the men and events which in a flash come to mind and which we could write about. It serves, however, to make clear that our subject although finite is unbounded and that everywhere drama is abundant. So—with deletion followed by deletion—I have brought my mind and my intention to reasonable boundaries. I have chosen to write as the pages forthcoming reveal and I trust that the exposition brings proper honour upon the men and justifies the choice.

Julius Sumner Miller

California, December, 1965.

The Illustrious Bernoullis

The story is told in a certain place[1]: "These are the generations of the sons of Noah, of Shem, Ham and Japheth . . . And Cush begat Nimrod: *he* began to be a mighty one . . . and now nothing will be withholden from them, which they purpose to do."

So it is that we begin the tale of this strange and uncommon family named Bernoulli whose sons were to the number of more than one hundred—all eminent—all superior human beings—not one a failure. Their lives and their work is a "field so spacious that it were easy for a man to lose himself in it; and if I should spend all my pilgrimage in this walk, my time would sooner end than my way."

This illustrious family—originally Dutch Protestant in Antwerp—were driven from Holland by the threat of the Spanish persecutions. The religious freedom they sought they found in Switzerland and they settled in Basel on the Rhine where stands the oldest university in that country.

The beginner of the dynasty which is our principal discourse was **Nicolaus The Senior**—a merchant and a man of great material fortune. The genealogical chart shows the connection to his sons and to the sons of his sons. The confusion which we encounter in their names and their accomplishments is compounded by the interesting fact that Jacob was known also as Jakob, as Jacques, and as James, and Johannes was also called Johann and sometimes John and sometimes Jean. When then we say that something was done—as, say, the finding of a certain isochronous curve—we may simply say "It was one of the Bernoullis!" Nor indeed does it matter much how exact we are for any one of them could do what any of the others could do, for as the Scriptural lesson puts it: "Nothing was withholden from them which they purpose to do."

---

[1] *Genesis: 10.*

THE BERNOULLIS

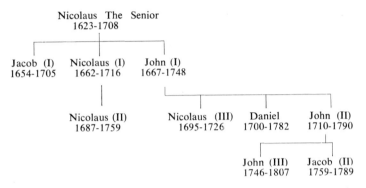

Strangely enough not one of them began his career in mathematics. They started usually in philosophy or in medicine or in theology or in law and then with a sort of explosive violence they blossomed out as mathematicians. It was like a flower which burst forth suddenly into full bloom. It was very likely the way of life in the family that nurtured these events since they were ever in contest—ever in competition—ever in challenge—ever in struggle for superiority—ever in strife and argument. They were to a man most quarrelsome and unamiable. Most of them were violent, abusive, jealous. Their favourite engagement was posing problems for the Academy prizes and for their kin to solve. Nor was their behaviour above reproach or free of invective. None ever showed a weakness, physically or intellectually, and those who lived to 80 years or more retained their powers to the end.

However we view this incredible family—whether it is the power of heredity or the influence of the home and kin—the fact is that their mathematical record is unparalleled. The nearest we have to this in human kind is the Bach family who in eight generations produced some two dozen eminent musicians and several score more of repute. And so we may say that the Bachs were to music what the Bernoullis were to science and mathematics. And their controversies and jealousies were as abundant as their competence and discoveries.

The first of these on our scene is Jacob I—the fifth child in a large family—who mastered the new calculus before he was 16 all

THE ILLUSTRIOUS
BERNOULLIS

Jacob 1. Bernoulli.

Johann Bernoulli.

by himself and who became a strong advocate of Leibniz. In fact, he so championed the differential notation against the fluxion that he influenced its adoption on the Continent. He with his violent younger brother Johannes hated Newton for reasons not altogether clear to us.

His interest was first drawn to mathematics by a certain trivial isoperimetrical problem: *What figure has the greatest area of all figures having perimeters of the same length?* Schoolboys know that this is the circle. Even Pappus knew this in the third century. The problem is to maximize a certain integral. These problems of maxima and minima have enchanting historical complexion. It was a certain Phoenician princess who in an exchange with an African Chieftain took "as much land as she could enclose with an ox-hide." With uncanny talent she had it cut into tiny, tiny strips, tied together at the ends, and on the ground thus got she built Carthage! In Homer's day it was common practice to measure land by how much could be ploughed around by a pair of oxen in a day. The problem: *How shall the ploughing be done to measure the most?* On a more sophisticated scale we might consider how the entropy of a system goes.

But back to Jacob Bernoulli. He made an exhaustive study of the catenary, both the uniform and the parabolic. These are curves taken by uniformly and non-uniformly loaded cables and chains. When then we look at high-voltage transmission lines or at a suspension bridge we ought really to pay this genius a quiet tribute.

In his great treatise *Ars Conjectandi* he established the calculus of probability and extended the reasoning to "civil, moral and economic conditions." The initial stimulus for this work came in fact from Pascal and Fermat who were faced with a gambler's dilemma: how divide the stakes in an unfinished game. This treatise contains the cardinal theorems of probability so useful in insurance, in statistics, in the mathematical study of heredity, in the kinetic theory of gases. Herein is the so-called *Bernoulli's Theorem* or, as it was named by Siméon Poisson, the Law of Large Numbers. "It is this problem," said Bernoulli, "that I have meditated on for twenty years."

At 33 he occupied the Chair of Mathematics at Basel thus beginning a reign of professorships held by Bernoullis for generations.

THE ILLUSTRIOUS
BERNOULLIS

Jean I. Bernoulli.

Daniel Bernoulli (1700-1782).

While tutoring a blind girl in Geneva he designed a method for teaching mathematics to the blind. It was said that this experience mellowed his temper somewhat and demonstrated a human compassion not otherwise discernible.

What can always best bring Jacob's name to mind is his work on the equiangular spiral. This curve is found in a spider's web, in the shells of creatures in the sea, as in the nautilus, in the structure of far-away galactic nebulae, in the sunflower. Indeed, the ordinary daisy shows it well. It is also called the "logarithmic spiral"; its equation is

$$\rho = e^{a\theta}$$
$$\log \rho = c\theta$$

to distinguish it from the Spiral of Archimedes, $\rho = a\theta$ cuts its radii always at right angles. The spiral cuts its radii at a constant angle also—but the angle is not right. Thus we may say that the straight line and the circle are limiting cases of the spiral.

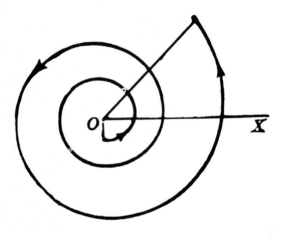

$$\rho = e^{a\theta}, \text{ or}$$
$$\log \rho = a\theta.$$

The Spiral of Bernoulli.

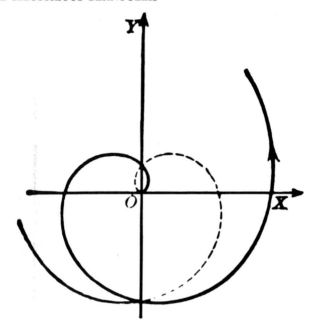

$$\rho = a\theta.$$

The Spiral of Archimedes.

To Bernoulli, in his later years, this curve took on a mystical nature and he envisaged its ever-unfolding loop to be an expression of the growing hope for the Christian people. It brings to our mind the reason for their fleeing Holland. It was, he said, *'spira mirabilis'*. "This marvellous spiral, having such singular and wonderful peculiarity, pleases me so much that I can scarce be satisfied with thinking about it." So taken was he by its beauty—so symbolic was it of his own life and history and faith—that he had the spiral engraved on his tombstone with the words "Eadem mutata resurgo", which is to say, *"Though changed I rise up again in the same way."* We are at once reminded of Archimedes who, being enchanted with the sphere and the cylinder, had the one inscribed in the other and both put atop his tomb.

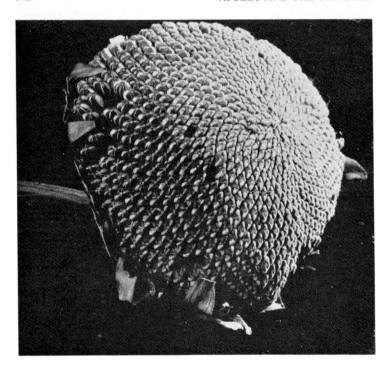

The Spiral of Bernoulli—"spira marabilis"—*in the sunflower*—(L. flos solis)
— *(Helianthus annuus). (See illustration on opposite page also.)*

So—though his father wanted him to be a theologian, his own motto from the beginning was *"Invito patre sidera verso" ("Against my father's will I study the stars")* and this he did.

Now comes Jacob's younger brother John (1)—13 years younger —the tenth in the family—a violent man, mean and unfair, and to all who did not acknowledge his merits in a manner commensurate with his own judgment, he behaved wildly and with turbulent passion. Those who opposed his solutions he attacked savagely. He was indeed a dangerous man. Nor was his honesty the sort to emulate. On a certain isoperimetrical problem his own solution he discovered to be wrong whereupon he substituted another stolen

from his brother Jacob! Later in his years—we shall come upon the matter forthwith—his own son Daniel had the rashness—the unreasonable contempt of danger—to win a French Academy Prize right out from under his father's nose, whereupon the father rewarded him in a very special way: he threw him out of the house! He himself, of course, had planned to win it!

Still in his teens John took a degree in medicine and another in philosophy. As a mathematician he had uncommon versatility and interests abundant. He established the conditions for a geodesic; he wrote on the theory of the tides and on the theory of ship sails. He was the first to note the acceleration of gravity as g and arrived at $v^2 = 2gh$. He explored the beauty of the caustic[2], which is the curve formed by reflection of rays in a concave spherical mirror. You can see this on the surface of milk in a glass—a pretty thing indeed.

He had a passionate zeal for teaching and—*mirabile dictu*—
he tutored Leonhard Euler, who was a fellow-citizen of the Bernoullis. Thus he was for a time Euler's master. *This* pair must
have been something to see! It was, in fact, the influence
of the Bernoullis that brought Euler to his heights[3]. He held the
Chair of Mathematics at Groningen and succeeded his brother at
Basel. He took several Academy of Sciences prizes. One of his
noble expositions was *Lectiones mathematicae de methodo integ-
ralium* and here for the first time is the phrase *calculus integralis,*
which term he suggested to Leibniz.

The highest flight of his career came with the episode on the
path of quickest descent[4]—*linea brachistochrona.* In June, 1696,
he addressed a problem to all the distinguished mathematicians of
Europe. More than this: "To the most ingenious mathematicians
in the whole world." It bore the challenge to solve it.

The problem in its simplest clothing (it is for many a shroud!) is
this: Given two points in a vertical plane but not in a vertical line,
find the path of least time between them. (Imagine a wire from A
above to B below along which a bead slides freely under the action
of gravity alone. We wish the shape of the wire for the quickest
flight). He allowed until Christmas for the solution and in the
event of none he would make known his own. Six months elapsed
and he heard nothing. No solution from anywhere. But a letter
came from Leibniz: "I have cut the knot of that most beautiful
problem. Extend the time until Christmas a year hence so that
the French and Italian mathematicians have no reason to complain
of the shortness of the period." Here came forth the proud arro-
gance of Leibniz, who, we must agree, had title to it. He was the
very last of the universals.

Bernoulli agreed to the extension of the time. The New Year
turned and soon there came to Bernoulli a solution from across the
Channel. It bore no name, but Bernoulli recognized the mind and

---

[2] It is a first-rate exercise for beginners to show the equation to be
$[4(x^2 + y^2) - R^2] = 27 R^4 y^2$ which represents a two-cusped epicycloid.
Under certain conditions the caustic becomes a cardioid.

[3] See *TIME*, page 229 f.

[4] Read about Pierre de Fermat and Pierre Louis Maupertuis on Least Time
and Least Action.

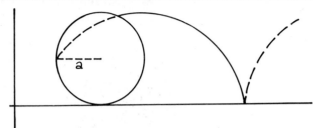

A cycloid is the path described by a point on the circumference of a circle which rolls without slipping on a fixed straight line. The equation of this curve is

$$x = a\,(\theta - \sin\,\theta); \quad y = a\,(1 - \cos\,\theta)$$

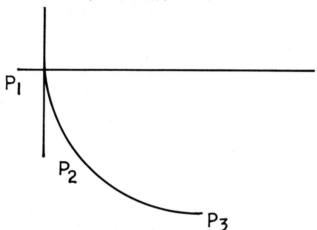

The cycloid, now inverted, becomes the brachistochrone. Moreover, it is also a tautochrone. The time of descent from P_1 to P_3 is the same as the time from P_2 to P_3. *And so it is for all other points.*

This is remarkable!

The proof that this *is* a tautochrone leads to this integral:

$$t = \sqrt{a/g}\int_0^{\theta_0}\sqrt{\frac{1 + \cos\,\theta}{\cos\,\theta - \cos\,\theta_0}}\ d\theta.$$ This leads to $t = \pi\sqrt{a/g}$.

Hence the time of descent on the inverted cycloid to its lowest point is independent of the starting point. It is, therefore, a tautochrone with respect to its lowest point.

A cycloid generator. The light on the circumference of the rolling wheel traces out a cycloidal path. A light at the centre of the rolling wheel clearly traces out a straight line.

Question: *What is the path traced out by the light at R/2 say? This, indeed, is the* general case *of which the cycloid is the limiting case. Show this analytically.*

the writer. It was from Isaac Newton. Said Bernoulli: "Tanquam ex ungue leonem" *("As the lion is known by its claw")*. The problem had come to Newton from France, and that very day he transmitted his solution to the President of The Royal Society. The solution was the cycloid. The properties of this curve are singular and enchanting. When inverted it becomes the path of least time and it has in addition this astonishing character: The time of descent from *all* points on the curve to the lowermost is one and the same. This result is quite incredible. So the curve is also a tautochrone. And it was this last feature that struck Bernoulli as wonderful and admirable.

Now Leibniz heard of Newton's solution reaching Bernoulli in so short a time. He was troubled. Whereupon *he* proposed a problem[5] "For the purpose," he said, "of testing the pulse of the English analysts." There was only *one* English analyst to test!

The Brachistochrone. Three balls released simultaneously from the upper chamber take three paths to the lower in the same plane. The uppermost track is a straight line; the lowermost the arc of a circle; the middle one cycloidal. The ball in the cycloidal route arrives first. Which arrives second? *Be careful!*

The problem reached Newton at his quarters at the end of his day at the Mint and, though fatigued, he reduced it to a fluxion equation before he went to bed. Thus did Leibniz test the pulse of Newton!

And so did John Bernoulli lay the foundations for the variational calculus, a branch of higher analysis of great strength and beauty. He died at 80 unabated in physical and intellectual vigour.

Before ending our account of this generation of Bernoullis there remains to say a few words about Nicolaus The Younger. At 16

---

[5] "To determine the curve which should cut at right angles an infinity of curves of a given nature, but expressible by the same equation."

he took his doctor's degree in philosophy at Basel and four years later his law degree. He was at once Professor of Law at Berne, but soon, like his kin, exploded with his mathematical genius. This brought him to St. Petersburg as Professor of Mathematics at 21, which place he held for some 30 years. So highly regarded was he that the Empress Catherine The Great provided a state funeral for his last journey.

Now John the First begat—in the manner of *Genesis*—three sons—Nicolas (III), Daniel and John (II). Nicolas suffered a long-lasting fever and died at the early age of 31. But he had not been idle. At eight he spoke Latin and French and German and Dutch. He took degrees in both law and philosophy. He was Professor of Mathematics at St. Petersburg for a good part of his life.

John II lived a very full life—all of 80 years—and did significant work in mechanics (the capstan intrigued him), on the propagation of light, and on magnetism.

It was Daniel in this third generation who unquestionably stands as a tower above them all (I trust that the others will forgive my rashness!). He lived a full 82 years and was productive every hour of his life. At 11 he learned most of the mathematics then known, and much of it he got from his brother Nicolas, who was five years older. He and Euler were intimate friends. We can see the consequence of *this*. At 25 he was Professor of Mathematics at St. Petersburg, although he was first an M.D. From the French Academy he won no fewer than ten prizes—one of these in competition with his father who threw him out of the house. Euler, incidentally, won the same number.

Merely to enumerate the work of Daniel would make this discourse encyclopedic. He conceived—he laid the foundations of—the kinetic theory of gases and was thus the forerunner of Joule and Helmholtz and Clausius. "Heat," he said, "may be considered as an increasing internal motion of the particles." He recognised the equivalence of heat and energy and was able to deduce "a law" from the chaos of random motions. He really deduced Boyle's Law.

His *Hydrodynamica* was one of the great flights of his genius and in this we find the principle that later came to be called the

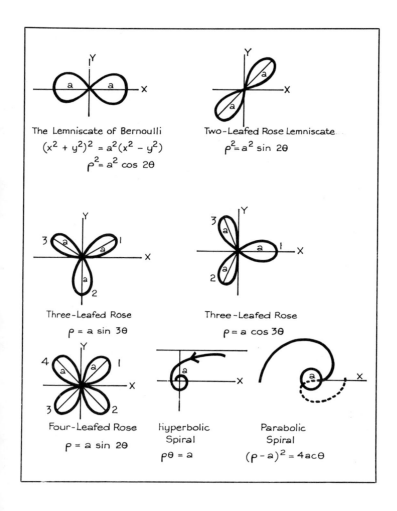

The Lemniscate of Bernoulli
$$(x^2 + y^2)^2 = a^2(x^2 - y^2)$$
$$\rho^2 = a^2 \cos 2\theta$$

Two-Leafed Rose Lemniscate
$$\rho^2 = a^2 \sin 2\theta$$

Three-Leafed Rose
$$\rho = a \sin 3\theta$$

Three-Leafed Rose
$$\rho = a \cos 3\theta$$

Four-Leafed Rose
$$\rho = a \sin 2\theta$$

Hyperbolic Spiral
$$\rho\theta = a$$

Parabolic Spiral
$$(\rho - a)^2 = 4ac\theta$$

The Bernoullis left an array of "pretty things". Here are some of their lemniscates, roses and spirals. (See next page.)

Energy Principle. He was thus at least one hundred years early in his thinking, for it had to wait for the 19th century to establish its universal validity. The title page of his *Hydrodynamica* shows an array of hydraulic machines bearing witness to the phenomenal hydrodynamical knowledge of the time.

His quantitative laws of fluid flow led to the expression which every schoolboy knows:

$$\rho_1 + \rho g h_1 + 1/2 v^2{}_1 = \rho_2 + \rho g h_2 + 1/2 \rho v^2{}_2 = \text{constant.}$$

"Air, like water, is a fluid," he said, and what Daniel did with the fast flow of fluids tells us why an airplane can fly, why a ball can be thrown in a curve, why a fireplace has a good draught, why an atomizer works, why a boomerang does what it does.

In his later years Daniel Bernoulli liked to tell of two little adventures which, he said, gave him more pleasure than all the honours he had gotten. On a journey one time he found himself beside a learned traveller, who asked him his name. "I am Daniel Bernoulli," he replied, answering with some modesty. "And I," said the stranger, "am Isaac Newton." On another occasion he was at dinner with the celebrated mathematician Koenig. Koenig, with some boast, posed a problem which he said had taken him much time to solve and he wondered how Bernoulli would fare with it. On hearing the problem Bernoulli at once spoke out the solution.

Daniel's generation was followed by two sons of his brother John. Johannes III took his doctor's degree in philosophy at 13. At 19 he was the Royal Astronomer at Berlin. Jacob II, who married a granddaughter of Euler, lost his life by drowning at age 30.

Apart from matters practical—mathematics of great usefulness—the Bernoullis left an array of "pretty things". We have, for example, the *lemniscate of Bernoulli,* the *two-leafed rose lemniscate,* the *three-leafed rose,* and many others. When then as schoolboys we plot these curves we should be reminded of the geniuses who left these for our pleasure.

Archimedes

Speak the name of Archimedes and to all—in a flash—boy and girl—pupil and master—fool and sage—schooled and unschooled—there instantly comes to mind the story of his bath and his phrase to move the Earth. But there is more to this—vastly more—for in Archimedes we encounter the greatest intellect of antiquity—the embodiment of the Mind and Spirit of the Greeks—who with his mechanical genius ranks with Leonardo and in mathematics with Newton and Gauss and Einstein.

To Greece we owe the love of science, the love of art, the love of freedom. It was the Greek mind which first combined reason and imagination. With the Greeks came into the world a new spirit and a new interpretation of Nature. It was the Greeks who were first smitten with the passion for Truth and for the love of knowledge for its own sake. It was the privilege of the Greeks to discover the sovereign efficacy of Reason.

"We are all Greeks," said Shelley, "our laws, our literature, our religion, our art, all have their roots in Greece." He could well have added our science and our mathematics. "Except the forces of Nature nothing moves in this world which is not Greek in origin." (Sir Henry Sumner Maine). Poincaré put it all in this noble phrase: "A spirit breathed on Greece and gave birth to poets and thinkers. It is the Greek soul that makes us look ever upward, and this is more precious for the making of a man of science than the reading of many volumes of geometry." The historic fact is that the institutions we cherish are the products of the culture of Greece.

Of the manifold achievements of these Greeks and the names abundant in this era—The Age of Pericles—The Golden Age of Greece (Thales of Miletus—Pythagoras of Samos—Euclid of Megara—Apollonius of Perga—Anaximander of Miletus—Socrates — Plato — Aristotle — Democritus of Abdera — Hippocrates of Cos — Zeno of Athens — Aristarchus of Samos — Plutarch — Phidias — Myron — Praxiteles — Solon — Herodotus — Thucydides — Aeschylus — Sophocles — Euripides — Aristophanes — Pindar — Anaxagoras — Leucippus — Eratosthenes of Alexandria — Hipparchus of Rhodes — the names are legion) we address ourselves to one named Archimedes of Siracusa, "Who," said Einstein, "must rank with Newton." And how did Leibniz (Gottfried Wilhelm Leibniz) put it? "Whoever gets to the bottom of the works of Archimedes will admire the discoveries of the moderns less." We do not come upon such a one again until Newton, nearly twenty centuries later, nor is the work of Archimedes surpassed, if, indeed, equalled, in the 2000 years to our own day.

Strangely enough, we know more of the death of Archimedes than we know of his birth. We are rather sure that he was born in Siracusa on the Island of Sicily about 287 B.C. We know with certainty that he perished in the sack of Syracuse in 212 B.C. Cicero (Marcus Tullius Cicero, the Roman orator) reported[1] in 75 B.C. that after much searching he discovered Archimedes' tomb in Syracuse, "overgrown with a thousand briers," and that he had restored it. But the tomb of Archimedes is now unknown. He was the son of Pheidias the astronomer and he may have been related to Hiero (Hieron II), King of Syracuse, and if not his kin then most certainly his friend. He studied in Egypt, presumably at Alexandria, and maybe with the pupils of Euclid. He knew Conon the mathematician and Eratosthenes—he who measured the Earth—and he had much correspondence with Dositheus. He lived all his life in Syracuse with untiring devotion to his mathematics. And he met his death in the same manner—absorbed in mathematical contemplation.

The regard in which he was held by his contemporaries is evidenced by the titles of affection which were bandied about: "the master"—"the great one"—"the wise one"—"the great geometer." In illustration of his total preoccupation with his thinking mathematics we see him in little stories where he left his meals untouched —where he drew his geometrical figures in the ashes of the fire or in the sand by the sea or indeed in the oil on his body after anointing himself at his bath. His inattention to his dress is classic, as the story of his discovery on the crown reveals. It was here, you remember, that he ran naked through the streets to his home shouting "Eureka, Eureka" ("I have found it"). Modern writers have likened him to Weierstrass, of whom it was said that he could not be trusted with a pencil and the wallpaper in a room!

---

[1] *Tusculanarum Disputationum.*

It would be folly indeed to attempt to give Archimedes a rank among the geniuses of history, but he is regarded as the greatest intellect of antiquity, encompassing a remarkable range of subjects with masterful execution. As for the mathematicians of history, any list of the greatest must contain his name. But who would dare give order to the names Archimedes, Newton, Gauss? It has been said that he and Newton would have understood each other perfectly and that Einstein's Relativity would come at once within his competence. Whitehead names him the founder of mathematical physics. What we must never lose sight of is this: that Archimedes stood alone and *in the beginning*. All his work was original—his discoveries entirely new—his range of subjects encyclopedic. He was no mere compiler. His was complete originality. Even Newton had the shoulders of giants to stand upon! His simplicity and his honesty are disarming and he does not hesitate to say here and again that this problem and that one troubled him for a long time and that he offers the solution only after years of labour. On one occasion he points up an earlier error on a certain proposition and on another, speaking of his friend Conon, declared that, but for his early and untimely death, Conon would have done the solution before him. We are reminded of Einstein's memoriam to Paul Langevin[2]: "It appears to me a foregone conclusion that he would have developed the Special Theory of Relativity had that not been done elsewhere." Thus it is that Archimedes invented things afresh out of his mind with none before him to draw upon. In the case of hydrostatics he invented everything. It is difficult indeed to discover where and to whom he has a debt.

The very best account we have of the episode of the fraudulent goldsmith is that given by Vitruvius[3] in his *De Architectura*. It reads so beautifully, even in translation, that we must hear it all. Moreover, we seldom get the chance to read things in the original nor indeed translations of the same.

---

[2] *Time*—Messel and Butler (Sydney 1965).
[3] Marcus Pollio Vitruvius—Architect. ix, 3. A first-century Roman architect and engineer in the Age of Augustus. His treatise *De Architectura* is the most famous ancient work on building and kindred topics—the only important work on architecture known to the Middle Ages. It was *the* textbook for that period and for the Renaissance.

"Though Archimedes discovered many curious matters that evinced great intelligence, that which I am about to mention is the most extraordinary. Hiero, when he obtained the regal power in Syracuse, having, on the fortunate turn of his affairs, decreed a votive crown of gold to be placed in a certain temple to the immortal gods, commanded it to be made of great value, and assigned for this purpose an appropriate weight of the metal to the manufacturer. The latter, in due time, presented the work to the king, beautifully wrought; and the weight appeared to correspond with that of the gold which had been assigned to it.

But a report having been circulated, that some of the gold had been abstracted, and that the deficiency thus caused had been supplied by silver, Hiero was indignant at the fraud, and unacquainted with the method by which the theft might be detected, requested Archimedes would undertake to give it his attention.

Charged with this commission, he by chance went to a bath, and on jumping into the tub, perceived that, just in the proportion that his body became immersed, in the same proportion the water ran out of the vessel. Whence, catching at the method to be adopted for the solution of the proposition, he immediately followed it up, leapt out of the vessel in joy, and returning home naked, cried out with a loud voice that he had found that of which he was in search, for he continued exclaiming, "I have found it, I have found it!"—

$$\text{"} \epsilon \H{\upsilon} \rho \eta \kappa \alpha, \epsilon \H{\upsilon} \rho \eta \kappa \alpha \text{"}.$$

His attention thus directed to the subject he wrote his work titled *On Floating Bodies*. This is in two books with nineteen propositions, and is the very first application of mathematics to hydrostatics. *Proposition 7* in Book I contains the argument for the solution of the fraudulent crown.

> "*Proposition 7: A solid heavier than a fluid will, if placed in it, descend to the bottom of the fluid, and the solid will, when weighed in the fluid, be lighter than its true weight by the weight of fluid displaced.*"

His procedure then was very likely this: Equal weights of gold and silver weighed in water are no longer equal; each is lighter by the weight of the water displaced.   Since the volume of silver is greater than the volume of gold its weight is more diminished.   If then he weighed the crown against an equal weight of gold and then again in water the gold would weigh more than the crown if the crown had silver in it.   What happened to the goldsmith we are not told!

(The simplicity of this can *now* be recognized by every school-boy.   It is quite like the first part of Newton's First Law: A body at rest wishes to remain at rest.   Are we going to make a case for this?   Does it call for a hearing?   But we must be reminded that it took the genius of an Archimedes *to see it first* and the genius of a Newton to *understand it.*)

Strangely enough, most of the propositions deal with segments of spheres and paraboloids of revolution floating on a fluid: to investigate the positions of rest.   These problems involve geometrical reasoning of great complexity.   We must remember that Archimedes had *none* of our mathematical tools, and accordingly his power of analysis was indeed incredible.

As well known as the episode of the fraudulent crown with Archimedes' shout of "Eureka" is his famous declaration that "Given a place to stand I can move the Earth."   The story is reported by Plutarch in his *Life of Marcellus:*

> "Archimedes, in writing to King Hiero, whose friend and near relation he was, had stated that, given the force, any given weight might be moved, and even boasted, we are told, relying on the strength of demonstration, that if there were another earth, by going into it he could remove this.

> (δός μοι ποῦ στῶ καὶ κινῶ τὴν γῆν) [4]

> Hiero being struck with amazement at this, and entreating him to make good this problem by actual experiment, and show some great weight moved by a small engine, he fixed accordingly upon a ship of burden out of the king's arsenal, which

---

[4] To be read: dos moy poo stow ki kinꟷ tane gain—which is to say: Give me where I may stand and I shall move the Earth.

could not be drawn out of the dock without great labour and many men; and loading her with many passengers and a full freight, sitting himself the while far off, with no great endeavour, but only holding the head of the pulley in his hand and drawing the cord by degrees, he drew the ship in a straight line, as smoothly and evenly as if she had been in the sea. The king, astonished at this, and convinced of the power of the art, prevailed upon Archimedes to make him engines accommodated to all the purposes, offensive and defensive, of a siege. From that day forth Archimedes was to be believed in everything that he might say."

Thus it was that Hiero's ship[5], too large and too heavy to be launched by his men, was pulled out of her slip by Archimedes alone.

It was at this time (about 212 B.C.) that Marcellus, the Roman general and consul (Marcus Claudius Marcellus) set upon Syracuse with unrelenting force. Let us hear the account by Plutarch[6]:

"Marcellus proceeded to attack the city both by land and by sea. The land forces were conducted by Appius; Marcellus, with sixty galleys, each with five rows of oars, furnished with all sorts of arms and missiles, and a huge bridge of planks laid upon eight ships chained together, upon which was carried the engine to cast stones and darts, assaulted the walls, relying upon the abundance and magnificence of his preparations, and on his own previous glory; all which, however, were, it would seem, but trifles for Archimedes and his machines.

These machines he had designed and contrived, not as matters of any importance, but as mere amusements in geometry; in compliance with King Hiero's desire and request, some little time before, that he should reduce to practice some part of his admirable speculations in science and, by accommodating the theoretic truth to sensation and ordinary use, bring it more within the appreciation of people in general."

(Commentary: And so it is in our own day. The **people** must know **what science is and what it is not** — and it is NOT technology.

---

[5] It was built, so Proclus reports, for King Ptolemy and was about to be sent off to him.

[6] The same is reported by Polybius and by Livy.

The spirit and intent and purpose of science is one thing and that of technology quite another!)

"When, therefore, the Romans assaulted the walls in two places at once, fear and consternation stupified the Syracusans, believing that nothing was able to resist that violence and those forces. But when Archimedes began to ply his engines, he at once shot against the land forces all sorts of missile weapons, and immense masses of stone that came down with incredible noise and violence, against which no man could stand; for they knocked down those upon whom they fell, in heaps, breaking all their ranks and files. In the meantime huge poles thrust out from the walls over the ships sank some by the great weights which they let down from on high upon them; others they lifted up into the air by an iron hand or beak like a crane's beak, and, when they had drawn them up by the prow, and set them on end upon the poop, they plunged them to the bottom of the sea; or else the ships, drawn by engines within, and whirled about, were dashed against steep rocks that stood jutting out under the walls, with great destruction of the soldiers that were aboard them.

"A ship was frequently lifted up to a great height in the air (a dreadful thing to behold), and was rolled to and fro, and kept swinging until the mariners were all thrown out, when at length it was dashed against the rocks or let fall . . . So Marcellus, doubtful what counsel to pursue, drew off his ships to a safer distance, and sounded a retreat to his forces on land. By these means Marcellus was compelled to reduce his attack to a mere blockade."

Now Marcellus was much angered by the apparent weakness of his own forces and he derided his men:

"Shall we not make an end of fighting against this geometrical Briareus[7], who, sitting at ease by the sea, plays pitch and toss with our ships to our confusion, and by the multitude of missiles that he hurls at us outdoes the hundred-handed giants of mythology?"

---

[7] Greek mythology; a monster of a hundred hands, Son of Uranus, an ally of Zeus in Homer but an enemy of Zeus elsewhere. As punishment he was buried under Aetna.

But the exhortation fell on deaf ears for the Romans were in such abject terror that

> ". . . if they did but see a piece of rope or wood projecting above the wall, they would cry 'there it is again' and fearing some new attack from Archimedes would turn and run away."

As we know, at length after a tedious siege and blockade lasting three years, Marcellus took the city while the inhabitants were celebrating the Feast of Artemis[8] and were off their guard. It was in these very days that Archimedes was put to death by a soldier and we shall have that account in due course.

Among the miscellaneous ingenious mechanical inventions of Archimedes two invite our interest. One of these, the **Mirror of Archimedes,** he used against the Roman ships in the siege. The story goes that he set them afire, but some scholars reject this story altogether. There can be no objection, however, on the grounds of feasibility, since the French naturalist Buffon (Comte Georges Louis Leclerc Buffon) made one in the manner of Archimedes' and set fire to wood at 150 feet. He even melted lead at over 100 feet. Since he did this in Paris, Archimedes could well have done it in Syracuse in the Sicilian summer[9].

The water-screw, known as **The Archimedean Screw,** is a tube open at both ends and wrapped like a spiral or corkscrew about a cylinder. If the lower end is in water and the cylinder properly inclined, the water climbs up the tube as the cylinder is turned. There is an interesting problem connected with its operation: The inclination of the cylinder must bear the proper relation to the pitch of the screw if the device is to work. It appears that Archimedes invented this while in Egypt to aid in irrigation[10]. It might also be used to pump water from the hold of a ship or out of a mine.

In Cicero's report referred to earlier he speaks of another little mechanical device of Archimedes: a sphere or an array of spheres designed to show the movements of the Sun, the Moon and five planets. This suggests that Archimedes had some occupation with astronomy.

---

[8] Daughter of Zeus, twin sister of Apollo, the greatest of Greek divinities; goddess of the Moon and of the Hunt. Called by the Romans, Diana.

[9] History reports the use of such mirrors in the defence of Constantinople in 514 A.D. And there stands *somewhere* a statue of Archimedes showing him holding such a mirror. It also shows his water-screw.

[10] These are used this very day in Holland. I have seen them.

A statue of Archimedes showing his Burning Mirror and the Archimedean Screw. The inscription bears out the meaning of the mirror. (See next page for Archimedes' Screw.)

Although Archimedes shows a versatile genius it is in the realm of pure mathematics that he reveals the depth and the penetration of his thought and the power of his analysis. As Plutarch says: "It is not possible to find more difficult and troublesome questions or more simple and lucid explanations." His essays were on a multitude of mathematical subjects and in many disconnected monographs and

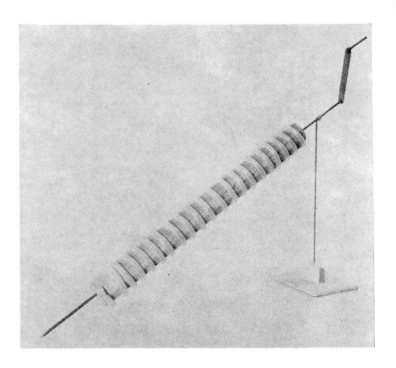

Archimedes' Screw. Water caught up in the lower end "climbs" to the upper end as the cylinder is turned. Can you tell exactly why this happens?

MSS., but scholars have with much labour put these things into a logical sequence preserving the titles given them by Archimedes. We can therefore with some ease meet the requirements of this discourse by setting down in abbreviated form certain of his often incredible results.

Measurement of a Circle: (3 propositions)—

Proposition 3 is absolutely enchanting:

The ratio of the circumference of any circle to its diameter is less than $3\frac{1}{7}$ but greater than $3\frac{10}{71}$.

To arrive at this he inscribes in and circumscribes about a circle regular polygons of 96 sides. He calculates their perimeters with extraordinary geometry and then says that the circumference of the circle lies between them. This is all very fine. It leads him to say that

$$\frac{14688}{4673\frac{1}{2}} < 3\frac{1}{7} \text{ and that } \frac{6336}{2017\frac{1}{4}} > 3\frac{10}{71}$$

This too, is all very fine but out of the clear in all this frightening arithmetic he just tells us that

$$\frac{1351}{780} > \sqrt{3} > \frac{265}{153}$$

without a word of explanation! When the probable steps are reconstructed we discover a fantastic command of inequalities.

So it appears here and many times again that Archimedes is writing for the ablest mathematicians of *his* time and of ours.

Quadrature of the Parabola: (24 propositions)—

"Archimedes to Dositheus greeting. When I heard that Conon, who was my friend in his lifetime, was dead, but that you were acquainted with Conon and withal versed in geometry, while I grieved for the loss not only of a friend but of an admirable mathematician, I set myself the task of communicating to you, as I had intended to send to Conon, a certain geometrical theorem which had not been investigated before but has now been investigated by me, and which I first discovered by means of mechanics and then exhibited by means of geometry . . ."[11].

There are two significant points here: One is *the attack* which Archimedes gives the problem. He calls attention to this: that he encountered the problem *first in mechanics*. So it is the mechanics that gives birth to mathematical argument — a matter of great consequence for the development of both. As late as 1906 a manuscript was found in Constantinople titled *On Mechanical Theorems,* done by Archimedes and addressed to his friend Eratosthenes. The second point is this: that in finding the area of a parabolic segment he is essentially performing an integration by *the method of exhaustion.* Is not this anticipating Newton and Leibniz by twenty centuries?

---

[11] He refers to the efforts to *square the circle* but *no one* had ever tried the parabola.

On Spirals: (28 propositions on Archimedes' Spiral)—

"Archimedes to Dositheus greeting. Of most of the theorems which I sent to Conon, and of which you ask me from time to time to send you the proofs, the demonstrations are already before you in the books brought to you by Heracleides; and some more are also contained in that which I now send you. Do not be surprised at my taking a considerable time before publishing these proofs. This has been owing to my desire to communicate them first to persons engaged in mathematical studies and anxious to investigate them. In fact, how many theorems in geometry which have seemed at first impracticable are in time successfully worked out!

Now Conon died before he had sufficient time to investigate the theorems referred to; otherwise he would have discovered and made manifest all these things, and would have enriched geometry by many other discoveries besides. For I know well that it was no common ability that he brought to bear on mathematics, and that his industry was extraordinary. But, though many years have elapsed since Conon's death, I do not find that any one of the problems has been stirred by a single person. I wish now to put them in review one by one, particularly as it happens that there are two included among them which are impossible of realization and which may serve as a warning how those who claim to discover everything but produce no proofs of the same may be confuted as having actually pretended to discover the impossible."

This spiral, says Archimedes, is another sort of problem having nothing to do with his earlier investigations. He defines his spiral so: "If a straight line of which one extremity remains fixed be made to revolve at a uniform rate in a plane until it returns to the position from which it started, and if, at the same time as the straight line revolves, a point moves at a uniform rate along the straight line, starting from the fixed extremity, the point will describe a spiral in the plane." We say it today this way: "The locus moving with uniform velocity along the radius vector while the radius vector moves about the pole with constant angular velocity." We have hardly improved it!

In these propositions he finds *all* the properties of *his* spiral, including a tangent, which means that he was thinking differential calculus and differential geometry. He finds the area between the curve and two radii and between successive revolutions and herein lies hidden the roots of the summing of series. His method of inquiry — his method of analysis — is in these parts so profound that modern mathematicians have found it easier to invent a new analysis than to follow his!

On the Equilibrium of Planes and Centre of Gravity:

In these two Books of 25 propositions Archimedes lays down the Foundations of Mechanics. His *Law of the Lever* and the notion — the concept — *the idea* — of *Centre of Gravity* are fundamental to the subject. Nothing more is done on mechanics until Stevin in the 16th century, some 19 centuries later.

Outside of astronomy, mechanics is the oldest subject with which the human mind has had concern. Although the lever was most certainly known in primitive days the first formal treatment of its properties was given by Archimedes *and no improvement of this subject has come forth.* It is inescapably true that mechanics has been a difficult subject for the human race.

The principal axioms (postulates?) in *De Aequiponderantibus* are these:

"Equal weights at equal distances are in equilibrium, and equal weights at unequal distances are not in equilibrium but incline towards the weight which is at the greater distance."

"By the centre of gravity of a body we mean the point from which it must be suspended in order to remain parallel with the horizon."

The whole subject of statics rests on these ideas and it needs nothing more. As for dynamics, the Greeks did nothing at all. This chapter was written by Galileo who conceived the idea of acceleration as the criterion of force. And it was Christian Huygens who brought the subject to fruition with his *Horologium Oscillatorium* in 1673. Add to this Huygens' *De Motu Corporum ex Percussione* in 1703 and his theorems on 'centrifugal force' and Newton is ready for his *Principia*.

In closing this part of my exposition I cannot resist the temptation to point up the role which the *Law of the Lever* plays in our everyday affairs — in events simple, humble and plebeian. It is enough to just enumerate the things: The kitchen broom; the can opener (the old-fashioned kind!) — the claw hammer; the scissors; the nut-cracker; grass shears; the screw-driver; the Stillson wrench; striking a match; turning the knob of a door; eating with knife and spoon and fork; writing with a pencil; the human arm; the mechanism of the inner ear; the very act of walking. Thus it is that this Gentleman of Syracuse is ever with us.

On the Sphere and the Cylinder: (60 propositions)—

> "Archimedes to Dositheus greeting. . . . certain theorems not hitherto demonstrated have occurred to me, and I have worked out the proofs of them."

(He tells Dositheus what he has here: the surface and volume of a sphere, of a cylinder, of a cone, of a pyramid.)

> "Now these properties were all along naturally inherent in the figures, yet they were in fact unknown to all the many able geometers who were before my time engaged in the study of geometry, and had not been observèd by any one. Now, however, it will be open to those who possess the requisite ability to examine these discoveries of mine. They ought to have been published while Conon was still alive, for I should conceive that he would best have been able to grasp them and to pronounce upon them the appropriate verdict but as I judge it well to communicate them to those who are conversant with mathematics, I send them to you with the proofs written out, which it will be open to mathematicians to examine, Farewell."

This work Archimedes regarded as his masterpiece — his greatest achievement — his highest flight. Charmed by the relationship of sphere to cylinder he requested that a cylinder circumscribing a sphere within and a proper inscription thereon be put atop his tomb. It was this that Cicero sought out and restored and of this act of duty and piety and compassion Cicero said that he was not as proud of anything else he had done as he was of having paid such honour to Archimedes.

On the character of Archimedes Plutarch writes with charm and feeling and with deep affection:

> "Yet Archimedes possessed so high a spirit, so profound a

Sphere, Cylinder and Cone. They have the same altitude and radius. How do their volumes compare? It is an enchanting exercise to show this with sand and while doing it think on the genius of Archimedes.

The Cylinder circumscribing the Sphere. A classic memento of the genius of Archimedes. The Sphere is circumscribed by the dodecahedron in the work of Hippasus, the geometer. He was a member of the Order *of the* Pythagoreans. *Hippasus discovered this geometry but failing to pay proper tribute to the Master Pythagoras he was drowned at sea!*

soul, and such treasures of scientific knowledge, that though these inventions had now obtained him the renown of more than human sagacity, he yet would not deign to leave behind him any commentary or writing on such subjects; but, repudiating as sordid and ignoble the whole trade of engineering, and every sort of art that lends itself to mere use and profit, he placed his whole affection and ambition in those purer speculations where there can be no reference to the vulgar needs of life."

So now after a tedious siege Marcellus takes the city. As he looked down from the higher places it is said that he wept, commiserating the calamity that hung over it and how dismal and foul the city would be in a few hours when plundered by his soldiers. Some insisted that they should set it afire and level it to the ground but Marcellus would not listen to this. He agreed — since the plunder could not be denied the soldiers — that the money and slaves should be made spoil. But he gave orders at the same time that no free person should be violated nor anyone killed nor should the Syracusans be made slaves.

"Nothing, however, afflicted Marcellus so much as the death of Archimedes; who was then, as fate would have it, intent upon working out some problem by a diagram, and having fixed his mind alike and his eyes upon the subject of his speculation, he never noticed the incursion of the Romans, nor that the city was taken. In this transport of study and contemplation, a soldier, unexpectedly coming up to him, commanded him to follow to Marcellus; which he declining to do before he had worked out his problem to a demonstration, the soldier, enraged, drew his sword and ran him through. Others write, that a Roman soldier, running upon him with a drawn sword, offered to kill him; and that Archimedes, looking back, earnestly besought him to hold his hand a little while, that he might not leave what he was then at work upon inconclusive and imperfect; but the soldier, nothing moved by his entreaty, instantly killed him. Others again relate, that as Archimedes was carrying to Marcellus mathematical instruments, dials, spheres and angles, by which the magnitude of the Sun might be measured to the sight, some soldiers seeing him, and thinking that he

The Death of Archimedes in 212 B.C. A mosaic found in the ruins of Pompeii. It must therefore have been constructed before 70 A.D.

carried gold in a vessel, slew him. Certain it is that his death was very afflicting to Marcellus and that Marcellus ever after regarded the man that killed him as a murderer; and that he sought Archimedes' kindred and honoured them with signal favours."

Thus we have come to our end with Archimedes who in the truest sense was possessed of the divine with his love and delight in mathematics.

Michael Faraday

Of all the men fitting to our purpose in these Essays — of the many having nearly equal claim to our salute and praise — it is Michael Faraday who invites us irresistibly for he characterizes in the noblest way *the very spirit of science.* His early years, his philosophy of life, his way with his work, his manner of speech and his exposition, his character and his warm heart — all these things are heritage to us and they deserve our tribute and our contemplation. If now we add to the virtues of the man the virtues of his labours, this exhortation we cannot escape. It is all this which urges us — indeed, it incites us, to this writing.

His birth was of the humblest sort. His father, James Faraday, was a blacksmith; shoeing horses was his principal business. Michael was the third child born near what is now Waterloo Station in London on September 22, 1791. To this modest beginning he added the diligence of his labour and the strength of his character and thus he came to have the affectionate acclaim of all the world. Throughout his life he felt an uncommon nearness with the Wonders of Nature and was led constantly — when seeing a cloud in the sky or the flame of a candle or a bird on the wing or some such — to exclaim: "Is not that wonderful to see! Is not that something to contemplate!"

The family circumstances were extremely modest. Food was not over-abundant. Eking out a living was a hard but honourable task and the cupboard, we can be sure, had nothing fancy in it. It was said that Michael's allowance was "half a loaf a week." The household was reared in the utmost simplicity and with Christian Principle. These things Michael adhered to throughout his life and as we shall see, he refused the Presidency of The Royal Society — which would also bring him knighthood — saying, when it was offered to him, "I must remain simply Mr. Faraday." Is not this wonderful to think about!

The Faraday family belonged to an uncommon theological order — The Sandemanians they were called. They were Presbyterians to whom the Bible was the absolute guide by which men could live. Faraday was a devout man ever possessed of a solemn and reverent attitude. This phrase embraces well his whole life: "Our whole duty is made up of but three things: that a man live soberly with respect to himself; righteously with respect to his neighbour; and piously with respect to God." (Sharp). This attitude of devotion characterizes men of science generally — they are devout in the highest sense. In his later years and indeed throughout his life Faraday thought that men of science were given to higher moral feeling than other men.

Of his early schooling Faraday had this to say: "It was most ordinary. We were engaged in the principles of reading, writing and arithmetic. My hours out of school were passed at home." These matters — reading, writing and arithmetic (as we know) — Faraday commanded with uncommon respect as his lecturing and his writing later reveal[1].

In his twelfth year Michael got a job as an errand boy and apprentice in a book shop. This was indeed great fortune and it was a turning point in his life. For seven years he lived in a room above the shop and his earnings were sixpence a week! Here in this job Michael could read when the affairs of the shop were quiet and he could take the books to his quarters. And what did he later say of his reading: "It made me think. It was in those books that I found the beginning of my philosophy." We are reminded that our old friend Ben Franklin had a like adventure for Ben was an errand boy and apprentice to a printer and there is a close likeness to the events and the careers of Franklin and Faraday. Young Michael indeed read about Ben Franklin and Ben's work on electricity. He also read the *Encyclopedia Britannica* which had its beginning in 1768. And there came into his hands a book titled *Conversations in Chemistry* which, he said, "Gave me my foundation in that science."[2]

Now while on this job a great event occurred. A customer in the bookshop one day gave Michael some tickets for the lectures given by Sir Humphrey Davy, who was the Chemistry Professor at The Royal Institution. As it was, Michael was already engaged

---

[1] It is inescapably true that the competence and fluency which one has in his later years depends almost entirely on the labour and diligence given these matters *in the early schooling.*

[2] On the virtue of a book we need have no discourse. The connection with a good book has no equal in how it can turn a mind. There is hardly a way of life—especially for the young—which can hold a candle to the wisdom of being in the company of a book.

in doing some experiments which he had read about in some books. As he said of it: "I made such experiments as could be defrayed in their expense by a few pence a week." He could hardly have spent too much of those sixpences he earned! But now a new world was opened up to him. Michael went to hear Professor Davy. It was four lectures he attended. And so stirred was he by the subject that he wrote up the lectures in his own hand—with sketches and drawings and discussions of the science therein.

His interest in science which was already awakened by his abundant reading was now fired afresh by his hearing Professor Davy. He sat entranced—and he got an idea: A job in The Royal Institution—that's what I want—and then I can do science myself on a grander scale. So Michael wrote to the President of The Royal Society. He heard nothing! But Michael was now beset as with a passion and he could not let the matter drop. So now he wrote to Sir Humphrey Davy himself and with this letter he sent Davy the notes he had written up on Davy's lectures. He spoke also of his dissatisfaction with being a tradesman and a merchant and said that trade was "vicious and selfish". On a later occasion Davy pointed out to Faraday that science was a harsh and demanding mistress and that he might do far better as a merchant and bookseller than to be engaged in scientific labour.

Now what ensued is wonderful to think about. Sir Humphrey gets a letter from a blacksmith's son. Professor Davy takes up the matter with the "managers" of The Royal Institution. "I have an inquiry from one Michael Faraday, the son of James Faraday, the blacksmith. He begs a job in the Institution saying he desires to be engaged in scientific occupation. He has sent me his own notes on my lectures." "Engage him to wash bottles," Davy was told. "If he doesn't want this we are rid of him." So Davy engages young Faraday to wash bottles in his laboratory. It was March 1, 1813.

Now very soon Davy found that he had more than a mere bottle-washer. Years later, in fact, Sir Humphrey was asked what he considered his greatest discovery—and he had made many great discoveries in his own right as a chemist of renown— and Davy replied: *"By all means, Michael Faraday."* This we must rank as one of the noblest phrases ever uttered.

So Michael had the job he wanted. He occupied two rooms above the Laboratory and he got 25 shillings a week. It was a fantastic pay. And these rooms he occupied as a young man and then with his wife for over half a century.

On getting the job at The Royal Institution Faraday wrote: "I was formerly a bookseller and binder, but am now turned philosopher[3] . . . . I am constantly employed in observing the *Works of Nature,* and tracing the manner in which she directs the order and arrangement of the world." In this single phrase lies the life and the work and the character of Michael Faraday. It was these *Works of Nature* that so enchanted him and the *Order and Arrangement* is The Great Scheme of Things which was ever in his mind and eye. We shall in due course in this narration meet his own phrase which reveals constantly the stir he felt in his soul when describing a candle flame or the running of a brook or the beauty in a cloud. "Is it not a glorious thing?" he would say. "Can anything be more beautiful?" "Is not this most wonderful?"

Now events took on a faster turn. Sir Humphrey Davy and his wife, Lady Davy, took a journey to Europe—The Continent, it was said. It was October, 1813. Faraday was taken along as Davy's assistant and secretary and valet. Davy was already famous everywhere. Lady Davy, it turned out, was not too pleasant a creature, insistent that Faraday keep his place. She often forbade Michael to eat at the same table with them. The journey, we can well reckon, was hard on young Faraday. But there were compensations. He met the great men of science of that day—Ampére, Gay-Lussac, Cuvier, Volta Alessandro Volta, that great and wonderful Italian—and many others. It was in Milan that he met Volta—hard-by Como where Volta lived[4]. The journey was indeed a most remarkable adventure for Michael—the son of a poor

---

[3] On this word *philosopher:* This applied to investigators in natural science —to physics really. Natural philosophy was the name given to the study of Nature and it was the forerunner of what we now choose to call physics. The best we have of this is Lucretius (Titus Lucretius Carus; 1st century B.C.) whose long poem *De Rerum Natura* (On the Nature of Things) possesses incredible points of view. And the word philosopher brings to mind Chaucer:

> But al be that he was a philosophre
> Yet hadde he but litel gold in cofre."

[4] Here in Como stands *Il Tempio Voltiano,* a magnificent marble structure to ". . . *il grande fisico Alessandro Volta gloria italiana* . . ."

blacksmith—a village boy who might otherwise see little beyond his village boundaries. In fact, he had hardly ever been out of London and at most a dozen miles, and then on foot. They travelled through France and Germany and Italy and Belgium and Holland. In Italy they did electric experiments on the electric eel (*Electrophorus Gymnotus electricus*) and in Florence they burned a real diamond, using an enormous lens to focus the sun's rays. It was all a great and wondrous adventure for a blacksmith's boy. They were on the journey for a year and a half.

In Switzerland he saw the abundant waterfalls and of these he wrote: "Every fall was foaming—the sun was bright—and the rainbows beautiful to see—in the clouds of spray." To a friend at home he wrote: "I have today seen a glow-worm. Be sure and tell my Mother." It was this constant contemplation of Nature which exalted his spirit. In Paris he saw Napoleon in his carriage. In Florence he saw Galileo's first telescope; and he climbed Vesuvius.

In 1821—June 12—Faraday was 29—he married Sarah Barnard. It was *the* great event of his life for their years together were sublime and unclouded and happy. Faraday's letters to his wife—before their marriage and after—are beautiful to read—quite like the letters of the Brownings—Elizabeth Barrett and Robert Browning—which rank high as classics in literature. Years later Faraday wrote of his marriage: "This event contributed more than any other to my earthly happiness and healthful state of mind." And over the years—they were together for forty-six—the union was blessed with increasing depth and strength. The marriage was childless, but Sarah and Michael took unto themselves the pleasant pastime of taking children of the neighborhood on walks in the countryside. On these adventures Faraday would engage them in dialogue and discourse on such wonderful things as *What makes the clouds? What keeps them up in the sky? Why is the sky blue? Why is the sunset red? Why does a brook gurgle?* And always the refrain: "Is not that beautiful to see?" Must not these have been great and wonderful adventures for young minds! And they lived—Mr. and Mrs. Faraday—in the rooms above the Laboratory.

Now it comes 1823. Faraday is elected a Fellow of The Royal Society. The letters F.R.S. brought an honour indeed upon him. This was not without travail, however, for there were some against

it—as is ever the circumstance for men who rise up above their
fellow creatures!   The next year he was made Director of the
Laboratory of The Royal Institution.   In this capacity he gave
himself to lecturing abundantly, and there has come down to us his
elaborate notes on his researches in physics and in chemistry and
especially in electricity.   He recorded every thought and every
contemplation—every experiment—everything he saw and heard and
felt.   And being gifted in human faculties—keen in sight and sensitive with touch and sharpness of mind—he uncovered an incredible array of the workings of Nature.   His *Experimental Researches*
he recorded with unparalleled exactness and care, numbering every
item and observation, and his last entry—his last *Note*—is num-
bered 16,041.   And in these years—the first years—his salary
was £100 a year with quarters, coal and candles.   His private life
with Mrs. Faraday was of the simplest and most humble.   He loved
to visit the zoo and occasionally he took in the theatre to hear the
"Swedish Nightingale," Jenny Lind.

Now at this time the members of The Royal Institution began
the practice of weekly meetings and under Faraday's direction the
Friday Evening Discourses took on renown and repute.[5]   Faraday
became the foremost lecturer in all England, and his delivery was
unequalled in what he said and how he said it.   So attentive was
he to the structure of his lectures—to the way with his experiments
—to the manner of his discourse—that he put down in a small
monograph his *Advice to Lecturers*.   We are led here to sample
a bit of his classic phrase:

> "A lecturer should appear easy and collected, undaunted
> and unconcerned, his thoughts about him and his mind clear
> for the contemplation and description of his subject.   His
> action should be slow, easy and natural . . ."

> "His whole behaviour must evince respect for his audi-
> ence . . ."

> "He should endeavour by all means to obtain facility of
> utterance and the power of clothing his thoughts and ideas in

---

[5] We are reminded of Blaise Pascal.   It was his father's practice to have
weekly meetings at his home "where all the ingenious men in Paris
related their own discoveries or examined those of others".   Pascal joined
in these conversations.   They called these meetings Académie Libre and
they were the forerunner of the Académie des Sciences.

language smooth and harmonious and at the same time simple and easy."

"He should deliver it in a ready and free manner . . . and digress as the circumstances may demand or the localities allow."

"A lecturer should exert his utmost effort to gain completely the mind and attention of his audience, and irresistibly make them join in his ideas to the end of the subject . . . no opportunity should be allowed to the audience in which their minds could wander from the subject."

"A flame should be lighted at the commencement and kept alive with unremitting splendour to the end."

". . . I disapprove of long lectures. One hour is enough for anyone . . ."

"I would by no means have a lecturer glued to the table or screwed to the floor."

"The experiments should approach to simplicity."

" 'Tis well, too, when the lecturer has the ready wit and presence of mind to turn any casual circumstances to an illustration of his subject. Any particular circumstances that have become table-talk for the town, any local advantages or disadvantages, any trivial circumstance that may arise in company, give great force to the illustrations drawn from them, and please the audience highly as they conceive they perfectly understand them."

"Some kind of order should be preserved on the lecture table . . . If the lecture table appears crowded, if the lecturer (hidden by his apparatus) is invisible, if things appear crooked, or aside, or unequal, or if some are out of sight without particular reason, a lecturer is considered (and with reason) as an awkward contriver and a bungler."

"On the orderly arrangement of the material, I would, if possible, imitate a tree in its progression from roots to a trunk, to branches, twigs and leaves . . . the effect precise and determined."

In his own lectures Faraday had a card before him saying *SLOW* and nearing the end of the hour his man Anderson would fetch a card saying *TIME*.

It was at this time—about 1826—that Faraday started the great and wonderful *CHRISTMAS LECTURES FOR CHILDREN*— "Lectures," as he called them, "adapted to a juvenile auditory."[6] They began in the great lecture hall of The Royal Institution. Their purpose: to expose the boys and girls to scientific thinking and experiment. And these have continued down to the present day. Let us look at the Lecture Theatre: It is filled with children—the adults are in the back rows, for, as he said: "I mean to pass away from all those who are seniors amongst us. I claim the privilege of speaking to juveniles as a juvenile myself."

In the front of the Lecture Hall is a long table with apparatus on it—mostly sticks and strings and sealing-wax. And hard by his assistant, Mr. Anderson. It was no less a genius than Helmholtz who said of Faraday: "It was some bits of wood and wire that served him so well for his great discoveries . . . "

Of his assistant Mr. Anderson, who was a retired soldier, Faraday spoke in a warm and reverent way: ". . . He assisted me in all my researches . . . to his care, steadiness, exactitude and faithfulness . . . I am much indebted." And Mr. Anderson, a respectable, truthful, altogether trustworthy man, remained the reverential helper of Faraday for 40 years. His allegiance to Faraday was extraordinary and the tale is told that one day—at the end of the day—Faraday just forgot to tell Mr. Anderson to go home, and the next morning Faraday found him still at work—having been there all the night! Apocryphal or not, tales of this sort possess an uncommon charm.

All told, Faraday gave the Christmas Lectures 19 times—lectures on chemistry—on gravitation—on electricity—on magnetism. So here we can see Mr. Faraday—facing the audience—his face alight with boundless enthusiasm—his skilful hands now doing this—now that—with that experimental sharpness which brought him world renown . . . his lecture masterfully delivered—speaking with a drama and bringing to life the beauty of the thing before him—a burning candle—water in a flask—a chunk of ice—asserting that *all these wondrous things are tied together by The Great Laws of Nature.*

In 1859 the lecture series was entitled *ON THE VARIOUS*

---

[6] It is regrettable that this term juvenile (L. *juvenilis,* young) is now bandied about with another quite unpleasant connotation. Faraday uses it here to mean the young people as distinguished from their seniors.

FORCES OF NATURE AND THEIR RELATIONS TO EACH OTHER. The several lectures, of which there were six, bore these titles: Lecture I: *The Force of Gravitation;* Lecture II: *Gravitation— Cohesion;* Lecture III: *Cohesion—Chemical Affinity;* Lecture IV: *Chemical Affinity—Heat;* Lecture V: *Magnetism—Electricity;* Lecture VI: *The Correlation of the Physical Forces.* Let us hear a few lines taken here and there wherewith we feel the pulse of Mr. Faraday:

"You know very well how the oceans surround the globe giving roundness to it, clothing it like a garment . . ."

"Now, it is not very easy to make these things quite clear at the outset, and I must take care not to leave anything unexplained as I proceed; and, therefore, I must make you clearly understand that all bodies are attracted to the earth, or, to use a more learned term, *gravitate.* You will not mind my using this word; for when I say that this penny-piece gravitates I mean nothing more nor less than that it falls towards the earth, and if not intercepted, it would go on falling, falling, until it arrived at what we call the *centre of gravity* of the earth, which I will explain to you by and by."

"I have here a quantity of shot; each of these falls separately, and each has its own gravitating power, as you perceive when I let them fall loosely on a sheet of paper. If I put them into a bottle, I collect them together as one mass; and philosophers have discovered that there is a certain point in the middle of the whole collection of shots that may be considered as the one point in which all their gravitating power is centred, and that point they call 'the centre of gravity'. It is not at all a bad name, and rather a short one—the centre of gravity."

The lecture abounds with simple things—a piece of paper— water boiling in a flask—a chunk of ice—"very beautiful, although very common—most beautiful things are common . . ." In this lecture Faraday reveals the existence of *certain forces—powers* he calls them—and suggests that there are really not so very many *different powers:* ". . . on the contrary, it is wonderful to think how few are the powers by which all the phenomena of Nature are governed." The time now passing, Mr. Faraday says: "I am sorry to see our time for parting is drawing so near."

Introducing the second lecture he addresses the audience: "Do me the favour to pay me as much attention as you did at our last meeting, and I shall not repent of that which I have proposed to undertake." He proceeds to talk gravitation:

> ". . . and I need not tell you that on the other side of this world the people are standing and moving about with their feet towards our feet . . . and all by means of this power of gravitation . . . and knowing this law, philosophers have discovered most wonderful things."

Now Faraday shows some experiments on cohesion: "Is not this attraction most wonderful?" And now he pours some iron filings over the ends of a horseshoe magnet. A "bridge" is formed across the gap: "See! I could let a mouse run through it . . . " And it is in this lecture that we find him saying: "Light is a thing which is, so to say, attracted by every substance that gravitates (and we do not know anything that does not)."

In Lecture III we meet an important feature of Faraday's *philosophy of experiment.* "How beautifully we get our results when we are right in our proceedings! It is not that Nature is wrong when *we* make a mistake."[7] Here now he inquires into the forces of cohesion:

> "Now, let me gradually lead your minds to a knowledge of the means we possess of making this attraction alter a little in its force; either of increasing, or diminishing, or apparently of destroying it altogether."

Mr. Anderson takes in hand an iron rod. "It has at present a great deal of strength, due to its attraction of cohesion." Anderson heats it red-hot in a fire. "We shall then find that it will become soft . . . and the more it is heated the softer it becomes. Ah! but what does *soft* mean? Why, that the attraction between the particles is so weakened . . ." And now Mr. Faraday bends the iron rod with ever so gentle a force. "And now you know how the smith takes a piece of iron and heats it, in order to render it

---

[7] The phrase is often heard: "The experiment failed." I cannot subscribe to this view. *Experiments do not fail.* Nature does precisely what she *must* do with the provisions you make. If you seek a certain effect then you must make those provisions which Nature requires to *reveal* this effect. If anything is wanting in the conditions you provide Nature will show what she *must* show in *these* circumstances. JSM.

soft for his purpose; he acts upon our principle of lessening the adhesion of the particles, although he is not exactly acquainted with the terms by which we express it." (Here, as we see, Mr. Faraday is turning to a circumstance and illustration familiar to his audience.)

Faraday now goes to a block of ice. "Why is *this* water hard?" . . . "And what happens when we make the ice warm?" He places a red-hot ball of iron on the block of ice. The events which ensue· enchant him. "Is it not a glorious thing . . ." "And so we learn this beautiful law of our philosophy . . ."

In Lecture V he addresses himself to electrostatic forces. The opening sentence: "I wonder whether we shall be too deep today or not." He shows the strange behaviour of rods rubbed with silk and flannel. He balances a lath on a watch-glass. "You see I am searching for the centre of gravity of this lath . . . And I rub this sealing-wax against my coat . . . you can see how strong the attraction is . . . I can even draw it about. And how curious these electrical forces." He bends a strip of paper into a hoop: "See how it rolls along, travelling after the sealing-wax. If I make the hoops smaller we can have them running faster and sometimes they are actually attracted up into the air."

He now holds up two chunks of lodestone and an artificial magnet. "Is it not, then, very curious to find that there is an attractive power at the extremities which is not in the middle—to have thus in one bar two places in which this force of attraction resides?" He makes a magnet out of a steel bar by rubbing it on a larger magnet and then he breaks the bar into three pieces. With deftness of hand he shows their properties: "And so every part of the magnet contains this power of attraction and repulsion. Now, is not this power a most wonderful thing — and very strange the means of taking it from one substance and bringing it to other matter."

"Now I must not embarrass your minds with this subject too much . . . and tomorrow we shall be able to go further into the consideration of these transferable powers."

We come to Lecture VI:

> "We have frequently seen, during the course of these lectures, the powers and forces of matter of which I have written

the names on the board . . . we must now try and comprehend what relations they bear to each other . . . and it will today require all my care, and your care, too, to make this clear to your minds. I shall be obliged to confine myself to one or two instances, because to take in the whole extent of this mutual relation and conversion of forces would surpass the human intellect."

He produces some hydrogen gas by putting some zinc and sulphuric acid together. "The zinc is pulling the water to pieces and setting free the hydrogen gas . . . Every step we are now taking brings us to a knowledge of new phenomena . . . Now is not this most wonderful and beautiful to see? And what a strange thing it is."

He makes connection to a powerful battery and causes a spark between two conducting gold leaves. "And there they go! Burnt up in that brilliant flash—so strong is the force. Now what is this spark? I take these two ends and bring them together, and there I get this glorious spark, like the sunlight in the heavens above us. What is this? . . . We have here a *chemical* power which sends forth the spark; and it is wonderful and beautiful to see . . ."

". . . and you know that it is only of late years, and long since I was born, that the discovery of the relations of these two forces of electricity and chemical affinity to produce magnetism have become known. Philosophers have been suspecting this affinity for a long time, and had long had great hopes of success; for in the pursuit of science we first start with hopes and expectations. These we realize and establish, never again to be lost, and upon them we found new expectations of further discoveries, and so go on pursuing, realizing, establishing and founding new hopes again and again."

In December, 1860, he gave his last Christmas Lectures. They were entitled *THE CHEMICAL HISTORY OF A CANDLE*. Everywhere there abounds such phrases as we have already met: "Is not this wonderful to see?"—"Now look at that—Is not that a very pretty experiment?"—"Now we philosophers—I hope that I may class you and myself together in this adventure." And everywhere there is warm and affectionate reference to his man Anderson.

In the Introduction to the first lecture on "the candle" Faraday spoke as follows:

"I purpose, in return for the honour you do us by coming to see what are our proceedings here, to bring before you, in the course of these lectures, the chemical history of a candle . . . so abundant is the interest that attaches itself to the subject, so wonderful are the varieties of outlet which it offers into the various departments of philosophy. There is not a law under which any part of this universe is governed which does not come into play, and is touched upon in these phenomena. There is no better, there is no more open door by which you can enter into the study of natural philosophy, than by considering the physical phenomena of a candle."

". . . I mean to pass away from all those who are seniors amongst us. I claim the privilege of speaking to juveniles as a juvenile myself."

At the end of the last lecture Faraday had this to say:

". . . all I can say to you at the end of these lectures (for we must come to an end at one time or another) is to express a wish that you may, in your generation, be fit to compare to a candle; that you may, like it, shine as light to those about you; that, in all your actions, you may justify the beauty of the taper by making your deeds honourable and effectual in the discharge of your duty to your fellow-men."

We must now divert ourselves for a moment to a place and to an event across the sea from England. About the year 1800 the Italians Luigi Galvani and Alessandro Volta had laid the foundations for the production of electricity. You will remember that it was Galvani who explored the strange business of animal electricity with his frog and Volta's work gave us the first battery.

Now it is 1820, and here in Denmark is a young teacher named Hans Christian Oersted. He is experimenting in his lecture with a wire and a battery and a compass. And a fantastic thing is observed: When the current-bearing wire is brought near to the compass the compass needle turns. So—a current-bearing wire gives rise to a magnetic field. This great and classic experiment of Oersted started an avalanche of inquiry unparalleled.

Now in due course Faraday heard of this event—that *electricity makes magnetism*. And in his notebook he wrote: *"Make magnetism produce electricity."* The year was 1820. The report of Oersted's work took Faraday tenaciously. For eleven years he laboured on the idea—*make magnetism produce electricity*. In 1831 the discovery was unfolded. In two classic experiments he uncovered the principles of electro-magnetic induction. In one experiment a magnet thrust into a coil of wire produces an electric current in the wire. In the other experiment a current growing or decaying in one coil of wire produces an electric current in another coil near by. And these great experiments were done with the crudest of things and with the utmost simplicity, but they bore the mark of genius and the character of Faraday.

During these labouring years Faraday wrote to a friend: "I am busy just now on electromagnetism. I think I have hold of a good thing, but cannot say for sure. It may be a weed instead of a fish that, after all my labours, I may at last pull up." But what Faraday pulled up was indeed an enormous fish. It changed the world! And it lighted the world!

His note on Oersted was now accomplished. Magnetism can produce electricity. Soon after the discovery Mr. Faraday demonstrated it to the Prime Minister. "Of what *use* is it, Mr. Faraday?" said the Prime Minister. To which Faraday replied: "Mr. Minister, one day you may be able to tax it." And on another occasion a lady put the same question: "Of what *use* is it, Mr. Faraday?" And he replied: "Of what use is a new-born baby, Madam?"

Thus it was that there came to be the means of lighting our homes and toasting our bread and turning the darkness of the night into the light of the day. And it all came from this wonderful man possessed of the gift of genius, but withal possessed, too, of humility and simplicity.

Now just as the work of Volta made possible the discoveries of Oersted so the work of Faraday started another avalanche of investigations. Four decades later James Clerk Maxwell—that great intellectual giant who liked to play with spinning-tops—thought about electromagnetic *waves—and this discovery was all in his head*. Just as Faraday was a great experimentalist—who inherited from his father a love of tools and workmanship and who possessed in abundance a great manual dexterity and skill—indeed, all who judged him had the same judgment—that Michael Faraday was the greatest experimental philosopher the world had ever seen —so, too, Maxwell was a great theoretician. All his work was in his head. Out of his electromagnetic *waves* came the work of Heinrich Hertz and thus came to be radio and television. And the end is not yet.

Faraday's name and fame were now heard around the world. It was, as they said, "noised abroad". Occasion to make money fell to him repeatedly—by engaging in commercial work. Indeed, in the one year, 1831, he got £1000 as a consultant, but could well have gotten £5000 if he wanted to sacrifice his research. And so he had to decide—make money—gather wealth—or serve science and mankind. His decision we can already guess—and so putting aside the chance at wealth he remained essentially the son of a blacksmith and the worker in the bookshop. And he died a poor man.

The labour of intense experimental work and endless concentration took its toll. Faraday tired. He was in his later years a sick man, and his letters to his friends bear out the strain he was under. His last years were not happy ones. On one occasion he took a restful journey to Switzerland—with his wife. There he had a chance to see the work of the Swiss nail makers—where— like blacksmiths—they heat the iron and shape it into a nail. And he wrote in his *Journal:* "Nailmaking goes on here . . . it is a neat and pretty operation to observe. I love a smith's shop and all things relating to smithery. My father was a smith." Is not this wonderful to read!

Of Faraday's love of labour—of his lofty character—of the beauty of his life—of the quiet he possessed in his soul—much has been written. In his later years he went on occasion to visit the very same shop where, as he said: "That was my working place . . . I bound books in that little shop." And in the Library of The Royal Institution he would often pause and say to a visitor— referring to Professor Davy—"He was a great man. It was on this very spot that he first spoke to me."

Honour came upon him in full measure. He was offered knighthood but he refused it. Remember the simplicity of his life. Twice he was offered the Presidency of The Royal Society but he steadfastly refused it too. His answer to it: "I must remain plain Michael Faraday." And he spoke ever constantly in this refrain: "The sweetest reward of my work is the sympathy and good will which flows to me from all quarters of the earth." Of all his great and wonderful characteristics the most prominent, we may agree, must be his sense of order and his humble heart.

His last lecture was in 1860—he was 70 years old—but he was not up to it in health. Before he reached the end of the lecture he was forced to his chair. The audience gave him a standing ovation. It was his last appearance. His last years he spent in a house provided by Queen Victoria—referred to as a "house with grace and favour". In 1867 he passed away—sitting in his study. His grave can be seen in Highgate Cemetery in London—marked by a simple stone in keeping with the simplicity of the man. He wished only his relatives and closest friends to attend his funeral—with no mourning. Mrs. Faraday outlived him by 12 years.

His successor in The Royal Institution—Tyndall by name—having known Faraday for some years—spoke of the appointment in this way: ". . . His friendship was precious to me beyond all expression . . . and it is for this that I now chiefly prize this place. You might not credit me were I to tell you how lightly I value the honour of being Faraday's successor compared with the honour of having been Faraday's friend. His friendship was energy and inspiration."

Of Faraday's many utterances this stands nobly among them:
"The philosopher should be a man willing to listen to every suggestion, but determined to judge for himself. He should not be biased by appearance; have no favourite hypothesis; be of no school; and in doctrine have no master. He should not be a respecter of persons but of things. Truth should be his primary object. If to these qualities he added industry he may indeed go and hope to walk within the veil of the Temple of Nature."

And so we come to the end of our discourse on Michael Faraday with the phrase, as Tyndall put it: *That Just and Faithful Knight of God.*

Michael Faraday. In his right hand a bar magnet — a proper symbol of his explorations into these strange forces of nature.

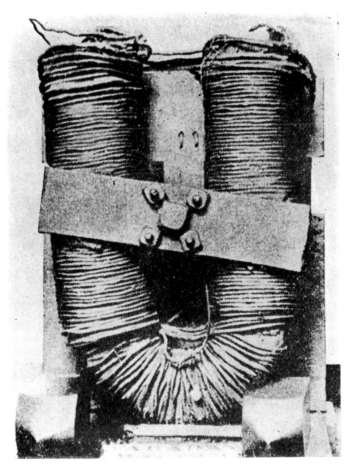

Faraday's "Great" Electromagnet. Note the utter simplicity. The core was the link of an anchor chain cut in two. The winding rough wire insulated by hand and wound by hand. Herein lay a great idea.

EPILOGOS TO MICHAEL FARADAY
BY MICHAEL FARADAY

"And now, let us give place, as juveniles, to the respect we owe to our elders; and for a time let me address myself to those of our seniors who have honoured me with their presence during these lectures. I wish to claim this moment for the purpose of tendering our thanks to them, and my thanks to you all, for the way in which you have borne the inconvenience that I at first subjected you to. I hope that the insight which you have here gained into some of the laws by which the universe is governed, may be the occasion of some amongst you turning your attention to these subjects; for what study is there more fitted to the mind of man than that of the physical sciences? And what is there more capable of giving him an insight into the actions of those laws, a knowledge of which gives interest to the most trifling phenomenon of nature, and makes the observing student find

> "tongues in trees, books in the running brooks,
> Sermons in stones, and good in everything"?

Quick Quiz
On Men And Ideas

BY

JULIUS SUMNER MILLER

When contemplating in the Large View the Great Sweep of Men and Events which make up The Story of Science, we are led irresistibly to give some reflection to these One by One—to the Man—to the Event—to his Utterances. When now we Weave These together making Whole Cloth from the Fragments—Searching out the Unity in the Apparent Diversity—there emerges a Pretty Fair Picture of the Wonderful Story of Man's Intellectual Effort to Understand Nature. It is as René Descartes put it:

> "We must believe that all the sciences are so interconnected that it is much easier to study them all together than to isolate one from all the others. Therefore, if anyone wishes to search out the truth of things in earnest, he should not select any one special science; for all the sciences are conjoined with each other and interdependent."

Now what then do we have here? We give you a thing—an event—an idea. You supply the name. Thus in this exercise you bring together Uncommon Men and Great Ideas. You will, we are sure, find it an exciting intellectual gymnastic.

> "I can tell thee where that saying was born."
>
> SHAKESPEARE, *TWELFTH NIGHT,* ACT I, SC. V, L. 10.

Quick Quiz on Men and Ideas

(Answers may be found on pp. 417 and ff.)

1. Gave us the Law of the Lever with the phrase that he could move the earth. (Greek)

2. A mathematician of antiquity famous for the "square on the hypotenuse" theorem. The "badge" of his order was a pentagram. The motto of the Brotherhood:
   > "A figure and a step forward:
   > Not a figure and a coin."

   He was a Greek.

3. A 1st century B.C. "natural philosopher"—author of *De Rerum Natura*. (Roman)

4. Of all antiquity, the greatest single collector of facts. A Greek.

5. One of the famous Triumvirate of Antiquity—wrote *The Republic*. (Greek)

6. "Let no one presume to enter here unless he has a taste for geometry and the mathematics." (Greek)

7. "Just as the downward movement of a mass of gold or lead, or of any other body endowed with weight, is quicker in proportion to its size." (Greek)

8. Tradition has it that he set on fire the ships of the Romans besieging Syracuse. (Greek)

9. The early title given to physical science.

10. The episode of Hieron's crown wherein we hear the cry "Eureka! Eureka!" (Greek)

11. The School of Thought whose rallying cry was "Natura abhorret vacuum".

12. Another of the famous Triumvirate—wrote *The Politics*. A Greek.

13. The first recorded observer of electrification by friction. Also predicted an eclipse. (Greek)

14. The earliest reputed author of the atomistic doctrine. His ideas exceedingly modern. (Greek)

15. "Moreover, it is possible that some things are held together linked and interwoven as though by rings and hooks." (Roman)

16. The "Father of Medicine"—"I swear by Apollo . . ." (Greek)

17. His theorem is the 47th proposition in Euclid. (Greek)

18. Proved that the lengths of strings which gave a note, its fifth and its octave were in the ratio 6:4:3. (Greek)

19. Set forth the notion of "centre of gravity"—his *Treatise De Aequiponderantibus*. (Greek)

20. The classical paradox of *"Achilles and the Tortoise"*. (Greek)

21. *Three* classical problems which perplexed the Greeks.

22. The third of the famous Triumvirate—teacher of Plato—his death described by Plato in the *Crito* and the *Phaedo*. A "good" man—a Greek.

23. Philip of Macedon summoned him to teach his son Alexander. And what was the name of Alexander's horse? (Greek)

24. The name given to *The School* whose members *walked and talked*—Aristotle was its head.

25. His last utterance: "Crito, I owe a chicken to Asclepius; will you remember to pay the debt?" (Greek)

26. The first logical presentation of geometry—called *The Elements*. (Greek)

27. The *Great Geometer of Perga* who wrote 387 propositions on the cone. (Greek)

28. Set forth the famous *Fifth Postulate* which agonized mathematicians for 20 centuries. (Greek)

29. A German mathematician—first to throw light on the *Fifth Postulate*. His motto: "Thou, Nature, art my goddess; to thy laws my services are bound."

30. A Hungarian mathematician who also "solved" it. "Out of nothing I have created a strange new universe."

31. A Russian mathematician who also "solved" it. He called his solution *Imaginary Geometry*. He did not live to see his work accorded any recognition.

32. A French mathematician who tried it but put it aside with the phrase: "Il faut que j'y songe encore."

33. A 3rd century Greek who made the first measurement of the Earth at Alexandria.

34. The great astronomer of Samos known as *The Copernicus of Antiquity*—thought the sun and stars fixed and immovable.

35. The great astronomer of Rhodes who discovered the procession of the equinoxes and made a star catalogue of 1000 stars which remained the standard for 16 centuries.

36. Author of *The Almagest*—*the* authority on astronomy until Copernicus. (Greek-Egyptian)

37. Known principally for his art (e.g., Mona Lisa), but some 5000 pages of his notes make clear that he anticipated much science, especially mechanics. (Italian)

38. The so-called *Father of Experimental Science*—born the day Michelangelo died and died the year of Newton's birth. Stood the Inquisition in 1633. (Italian)

39. His *first* name was Galileo.

40. Author of *De Revolutionibus Orbium Coelestium* (1543)— took the printed pages in his hands on the very day of his death. Gave the book "four times nine years of labour." (Polish)

41. A Dutchman (Bruges)—the first to take up mechanics after Archimedes. Proposed a "thought experiment" about an endless chain on an inclined plane—"Wonder en is gheen wonder".

42. Experimentally deduced the laws of freely falling bodies and of pendula timed with his pulse. (Italian)

43. A Danish "scanner of the heavens" whose observatory was *Uraniborg—Castle of the Heavens*. Thirty years of gathering data. Lost part of his nose in a duel. Arrogant—irritable—narrow-minded—revengeful. Possessed of remorseless attention to detail.

44. Author of *Dialogues on the Two Great Systems of the World*. Characters: Sagredo—Salviati—Simplicio. (Italian)

45. Immanuel Kant said of him: "When —— rolled a ball down an inclined plane a new light burst upon all investigators of nature." (Italian)

46. Formulated accurate statements on the motions of the planets. Poverty—ill-health—adversity. A fanatical patience—a volcanic imagination—22 years in the study. ". . . I contemplate its beauty with incredible and ravishing delight." (German)

47. *"Exercitatio Anatomica de Motu Cordis et Sanguinibus in Animalibus"*—the greatest name in English medicine—"This means the blood circulates . . . and so on incessantly while life lasts."

48. *"Discours de la Méthode pour bien conduire sa raison et chercher la vérité dans les sciences."* Invented analytic geometry. "I have often wished that I were equal to some others in promptitude of thought, or in clearness and distinctness of imagination . . ." (French)

49. Invented the first mechanical air pump in 1650. Having a great pleasure in astonishing the people had "a team of eight horses on each side . . . whereupon a loud report resulted." (German)

50. Invented the barometer —"I assert that the force holding up the quicksilver is external and comes from without." First name *Evangelista*. (Italian)

51. His father's Académie Libre—meetings at his home—the forerunner of the French Academy of Sciences. Known for his *Hydrostatic Paradox*. Achieved sevenfold immortality: as a mathematician—a physicist—an inventor—chief creator of his nation's great prose—a theologian—a philosopher—a fanatic. (French)

52. Gave us an understanding of "Liquids which issue with violence from an opening in a vessel . . ." A pupil of Galileo at Florence. (Italian)

53. Author of *Traité de l'Equilibre des Liqueurs*. (French)

54. An Italian philosopher burned at the stake for endorsing Copernicus. In the Piazza dei Fiori in Rome stands a monument to this infamy.

55. Author of *Traité de la Lumière*—the highest flight of his genius—got the idea by watching the water waves in the canals at home. (Dutch)

56. Gave us the idea of "moment of inertia"; invented the pendulum clock; author of *Horologium Oscillatorium*. (Dutch)

57. "There are little animals in this rain water. They swim! They play around! They are a thousand times smaller than any creatures we can see with our eyes alone . . . Look! See what I have discovered!" (Dutch)

58. Determined the speed of light by observations on the moons of Jupiter. Opposed by Descartes who thought the propagation of light instantaneous . . . but Huygens and Newton supported him. One of the first members of the French Academy along with Descartes, Pascal, Fermat, Huygens. (Danish)

59. Gave us the expression $e^{ix} = \cos x + i \sin x$, which in turn yields that beautiful equation $e^{\pi i} + 1 = 0$. At 28 lost his right eye: *"J'aurai moins de distractions."* Arago said of him: "He calculated without effort, just as men breathe and as eagles sustain themselves in the air." Proved the existence of God to the French atheist Denis Diderot. (German)

60. A famous Yankee known for a certain experiment with a kite.

61. Born on Christmas Day, 1642. On his tomb in Westminster it says—among other things—"Let men rejoice that so great a glory of the human race has appeared." (English)

62. The famous teacher of #61. When he was a little boy his father had occasion to say: "If it should please the good Lord to take one of his children, he could best spare Isaac." Gave up his professorship at Trinity so that his student could have it! (English)

63. The *German* credited with the invention of the calculus but who himself made the classic error of saying that
$$\frac{d}{dx}(uv) = \frac{du}{dx} \text{ times } \frac{dv}{dx} \text{ !!}$$
Took issue with Descartes on the problem of mv and mv^2. (German)

64. First to observe the moons of Jupiter with a telescope. (Italian).

65. The English credit him with the invention of the calculus.

66. The random motion of particles (molecules?) observed by a *Scottish* botanist.

67. Responsible for the binomial naming of living things (genus and species) which brought order out of chaos. In his early years in abject poverty—wore the cast-off clothes of others —mended his worn-out shoes with paper—frequently went hungry. His thirst for knowledge was unquenchable. Was denied the privilege of lecturing at the University because he had no doctor's degree! (Swedish)

68. Wrote a letter to Hooke saying: "If I have seen farther than you and Descartes it is by standing upon ye shoulders of giants." (English)

69. The Law of the Spring: *"ut tensio sic vis"*. A contumacious adversary with Newton. (English)

70. When discovering the nature of white light he said of it: "The oddest, if not the most considerable detection which hath hitherto been made in the operations of Nature." (English)

71. The French mathematician who setted the dispute over mv and mv^2 raging between Descartes and Leibniz.

72. First to "weigh" the earth with a torsion balance. (English)

73. Established a system of mechanics based on three laws characterized principally by their utmost simplicity. (English)

74. Wrote *"A Defense of the Doctrine Touching the Springe of the Aire."* (English)

75. His pendulum is evidence of the earth's rotation. (French)

76. An *Italian* astronomer who first observed what he thought were "canals" on Mars. The matter is not yet settled!

77. Author of the famous *"Principia"*. (English)

78. A principle which is used—which plays a role—in atomizers —in why airplanes can fly and why baseballs can curve and boomerangs "boomerang". A family of Swiss uncommon in the history of the world—some hundred of them—all superior human beings—many a genius.

79. A *Swedish* astronomer responsible for a certain thermo-metric scale, but he had $0°$ as the boiling point and $100°$ the freezing!

80. A *German* physicist responsible for a thermometric scale with 180 divisions between certain fixed points. His first ther-mometer contained alcohol.

81. A *French* mathematician whose masterpiece *Mécanique Analytique* was described by Hamilton as a "scientific poem". His first reaction to a quéstion: *"Je ne sais pas"*. He was Professor of Mathematics at Turin at 16. Talleyrand said to his father: "Your son has done honour to all mankind by his genius."

82. The variation in the volume of a gas with change in tem-perature. The "strange number" $\frac{1}{273}$ appears! (French).

83. An inverse-square law for electric charges and magnetic "poles". His torsion balance a masterpiece of experimental skill. (French)

84. He made some wonderful observations on the strange behaviour of a frog's leg: *"De Viribus Electricitatis in Motu Musculari Commentarius"*—"Whereupon I was inflamed with an incredible zeal and eagerness." (Italian)

85. The son of a blacksmith who in 1831 discovered electromagnetic induction. "Nothing is too wonderful to be true."

86. A Dane who first observed the magnetic field about a current-bearing conductor in 1820. This led ⁼85 to write: "Make magnetism produce electricity."

87. A *Frenchman* who gave an interpretation to the work of ⁼86 and whose "rule of thumb" for currents and magnetic fields is useful. Stood by the scaffold when his father was executed. Suffered domestic misfortune and for his epitaph wrote: *Tandem Felix.*

88. An *American* whose work was simultaneous with ⁼85.

89. The *law* whereby E-M induction is in such a direction as to oppose the motion which produces it. Evidence that nothing can be got for nothing! (Russian)

90. A high-frequency coil bears his name. An eccentric with a germ phobia and a passionate interest in caring for crippled pigeons. A proponent of alternating current. A Yugoslav.

91. Proposed in the 16th century that the earth behaves like a huge magnet. *De Magnete.* (English)

92. The "Father of Modern Chemistry"—a *Frenchman*. *"La chimie est une science francaise . . . elle fut constituée par —d'immortelle mémoire."* He lost his head by the guillotine.

93. An *Italian* who denounced the "frog leg experiments" of his countryman. His full name Alessandro Guiseppe Antonio Anastasio ——. Napoleon would not accept his resignation at Pavia: "You may give but one lecture a year."

94. Author of *Mécanique Celeste* who gave a copy of it to Napoleon who raised the matter concerning the Creator. Proposed also a Nebular Hypothesis. (French)

95. The relation between voltage, resistance and current in a circuit. (German)

96. First detected electric *waves*. Saw the *physical structure* in Maxwell's mathematics (equations). (German)

97. An *English* physicist interested in psychical phenomena. First denounced Relativity!

98. A *German* often referred to as *The Prince of Mathematicians*. Name originally Johann Friederich Carl —— but he signed it Carl Friedrich ——. Moritz Cantor said of his work: ". . . nowhere and never has a single error been detected." At age 12 he was already looking askance at the foundations of Euclidean Geometry!

99. A *Hungarian* who brought forth a solution to the Fifth Postulate—his work the most extraordinary two dozen pages in the history of thought.

100. His collected works bear the title: *Experimental Researches on Electricity* (1838) in which appear 16,041 observations! (English)

101. The invention of the stethoscope (1819)—"The first instrument consisted of a roll of paper." (French)

102. The greatest man of science *Ireland* has produced. By 13 he bragged that he had mastered one language for each year he had lived. When he entered Trinity some declared that a second Newton had arrived! $i^2 = j^2 = k^2 = ijk = -1$

103. An *Englishman* who caused an intellectual and religious upheaval with his views of *"The Descent of Man."*

104. The founder of modern bacteriology, the father of the germ theory of disease, benefactor of mankind — the greatest name in *French* science. "The wine in Orleans—the silkworms in Alais—the sheep are dying of anthrax."

105. The relation between the properties of the elements and their atomic weights—Dmitri Ivanovitch ——.
"Just as the pendulum returns again . . . so do the properties of the elements . . . " (Russian)

106. Rediscovered Boyle's Law a quarter-century later—and independently—and known in France by this name—"appareil de ——". (French)

107. Deviations from Boyle's Law which follow
$$(p + \frac{a}{v^2})(v - b) = RT.$$ Nobel Prize 1910. (Dutch)

108. Responsible for the equation $E = kT^4$ based on *theoretical* argument. (Austrian)

109. Responsible for the equation $E = kT^4$ based on *experiment*. (Austrian)

110. The behaviour of a gas (at constant temperature) under varying pressure. (English)

111. *"On a New Kind of Rays,"* November 8, 1895. "For brevity's sake I shall use the expression 'rays' and to distinguish them from others of this name I shall call them 'X-rays'." (German)

112. Announced the relation between mechanical work and heat. When giving the paper at the Oxford Meeting he was urged to be brief . . . discussion was not invited. If Kelvin had not been there *no one would have heard it!* Said Kelvin: ". . . he had a great idea to unfold." (English)

113. A famous *German* physician who acquired eminence in physics—especially in sound and light. Invented the ophthalmoscope.

114. The *first* attempt to measure the speed of light. His conclusion: instantaneous. (Italian)

115. A *French* physicist who replaced the Italian's lantern shutter with a rotating toothed disk in measuring the speed of light. Armand Hippolyte Louis ——.

116. An *American* physicist who replaced the toothed wheel by a rotating mirror for measuring the speed of light. Nobel Prize 1907.

117. The medium postulated for light propagation—possessing the strangest properties—extreme tenuity—infinite rigidity and elasticity—absolute continuity—permeating all space! Called the luminiferous ———.

118. A famous *German* poet who joined issue with Newton on the nature of light (colour).

119. A Greek of Alexandria in the 3rd century whose "engine" invokes one of the most fundamental and immutable principles of Nature—momentum.

120. Wrote a classic book titled *Electrons + and* —". American Nobel Prize 1923.

121. The first *American* to win the Nobel Prize in 1907.

122. "We have attempted to isolate this substance in pitchblende, and the experiment has confirmed our expectations . . . We propose to call it *polonium* after the name of the native country of one of us." (Polish)

123. The equation was originally in this form: $\frac{1}{2}\,mv^2 = hf$. This genius showed it must be $\frac{1}{2}\,mv^2 = hf - W$. For *this* he won the Nobel Prize in 1921, although it is generally thought that he got it for something else for which he is indeed better known. (Jewish)

124. Known for the famous "oil-drop" experiment. American. Nobel Prize 1923.

125. Until Linus Pauling the only person to receive the Nobel Prize *twice*. (Polish)

126. That genius of the Renaissance who said: "Man with his large wings by beating against the air will be able to dominate it and lift himself above it." (Italian)

127. An *American* physicist who won the Nobel Prize in 1946 for his work on high pressures.

128. A *New Zealander* whose experiments led to the conclusion that the atom contained a hard, massive core—the nucleus. Nobel Prize 1908. "We wrought better than we thought."

129. Discovered the electron. Nobel Prize 1906. (English)

130. A *Danish* physicist who advanced an acceptable atom-picture to account for spectral lines. Nobel Prize 1922.

131. An *English* physician of the late 18th century who did a famous light-interference experiment in 1801.

132. A *Scottish* physicist whose chief objection to the undulatory theory of light was that he could not think the Creator guilty of so clumsy a contrivance as the filling of space with the *ether* in order to produce light.

133. A 19th century *Scot* who set forth in twenty equations the connection between electromagnetic waves and light. He liked to play with spinning tops!

134. "In the year 1665 I procured me a triangular glass prism . . . At first it was a pretty divertisement . . ." (English)

135. A *Dutch* mathematician of the 17th century whose Law of Refraction bears his name. He died at the early age of 35.

136. A 10th century *Arab* astronomer known for his investigations in geometrical optics.

137. A German who discovered a cheap process for converting nitrogen from the air into ammonia in which form it may be used to make fertilizers and explosives.

138. Defeated Darius—built Alexandria and the greatest library of the ancient world — cut the so-called Gordian Knot — at Gordium — of which an oracle had said that he who untied it would be the lord of all Asia. His temper was his greatest enemy. (Macedonian)

139. A 10th century *Arabian* physician whose Canon—a textbook in medicine—is still used in Mohammedan countries.

140. A *Belgian* — founder of modern anatomy — wrote: *De Humani Corporis Fabrica* in the same year as Copernicus published his theory. Called a "madman" for on dark nights he stole the bodies of hanged criminals.

141. A *French* surgeon: *"I Dressed him, God healed him."*

142. A *French* King who founded the Académie des Sciences in 1666—known for the phrase: "L'etat c'est moi."

143. Independently of a certain English clergyman (and two years earlier) discovered "Fire-Air"—oxygen. Possessed of ceaseless energy and a passionate desire for Truth. (Swedish)

144. A clear distinction between the atom and the molecule is the essence of his hypothesis. Full name: Lorenzo Romano Amedeo Carlo di Quaregna e di Cerreto——— . (Italian)

145. A *Swedish* baron—originator of chemical symbols—known for half a century as the "czar of chemistry".

146. Demonstrated the existence of the bright spot at the centre of the shadow in diffraction by a circular obstacle. A most powerful argument in favour of the wave theory. (French)

147. A *Frenchman* who laid the foundations of thermodynamics with: "Réflexions sur la puissance motrice du feu . . ." He died at 36.

148. A *Norwegian* mathematician who died at age 27 but who left mathematicians enough to keep them busy for 500 years! At 19 proved the impossibility of the general solution of the quintic. Gauss tossed this aside with disgust, saying: "Here is another of those monstrosities." Thereafter he hated Gauss and said the Germans thought too much of him.

149. A *French* teacher of the blind—blind himself from age 3—perfected a system of writing for the blind. (The blind were in these days avoided and regarded as victims of divine wrath.)

150. From an analysis of the perturbations of Uranus (based on Newton's gravitation) he predicted mathematically the discovery of Neptune *and* its precise position in the sky. (French)

151. An *Englishman* who made the very same prediction and independently and simultaneously. But no one listened to him because he was too young!

152. The first use of a surgical anaesthetic. "I inhaled the ether from a towel . . . I did not feel the slightest pain. (American)

153. A young *Austrian* physician who sacrificed his career and eventually his reason (sanity) for preaching the doctrine that the obstetrician must come to his patients aseptically clean.

154. A *German* botanist who brought forth the cell theory.

155. His colleague in these classic discoveries. (German)

156. A mathematically-minded abbot who with his garden peas and years of painstaking labour set forth the laws of heredity in a figure-ridden paper of 20,000 words—which was at once lost and forgotten!

157. A monumental work on insects—*"The Life of the Spider"*— *"The Life of the Fly"*—*Souvenirs entomologiques* requiring 28 years of writing. (French)

158 A *Belgian* chemist whose process bears his name—making soda from common salt. *The Carnegie of Belgium.*

159. A *German* bacteriologist who announced a method of preventive inoculation. Discovered the bacillus of tuberculosis in 1882. Nobel Prize 1905.

160. A *Hungarian* whose torsion balance could detect variations in g to one part in 10^8. Fantastic!

161. Say *this* name and you think of dogs and saliva! Of incomparable memory—boundless energy—immeasurable enthusiasm—his laboratory a tumultuous beehive of activity even when he was 80! Nobel Prize in 1904 for *"Work on the Digestive Glands"*—Nobel Prize 1904. (Russian)

162. Nobel Prize in 1903 (with others) for "The special services rendered by him in the discovery of spontaneous radioactivity." (French)

163. A *Dutchman* at Leiden—Nobel Prize 1913—"For his investigations into the properties of matter at low temperatures which led, amongst other things, to the production of liquid helium."

164. A *Dutchman* who observed that the general laws of Nature are covariant with respect to certain —— transformations. He *predicted* that monochromatic light should be split by a magnetic field. Nobel Prize 1902.

165. This split of monochromatic light in a magnetic field was explained by this *Dutchman* and with #164 won the Nobel Prize in 1902.

166. Descartes in 1650 knew all there was of mathematics; Newton in 1700 was the one man living who knew it all; Gauss in 1800 knew it all. In 1900 no one could really grasp the *whole* subject but —— did! A *Frenchman* with feeble eyesight and fearful temper.

167. A *French* astronomer who popularized the subject with such titles as: *"The Plurality of Inhabited Worlds"*—*"Celestial Marvels"*—*"The Land of the Heavens"*—*"The End of the World."*

168. A *German* physicist whose concept was in direct contradiction with Newton's classical mechanics and doctrine: "Natura non saltus facit"—"Nature does not provide discontinuities." Nobel Prize in 1918 for the conception of *quanta*.

169. A *Frenchman* who married the daughter of a famous pair—
     one French, one Polish—who with his wife took the Nobel
     Prize in 1935 in Chemistry.

170. "It seemed to me that if the radiation could be increased,
     developed, and controlled it would be possible to signal
     across space for considerable distances." (Italian)

171. Gave the first modern theory of the rainbow. (French)

172. Referred to the "stuff" in a discharge tube as "matter in a
     fourth state or condition which is as far removed from the
     state of a gas as a gas is from a liquid." Nobel Prize 1906.
     (English)

173. The *maiden* name of the Polish woman physicist (chemist)
     who married a French physicist.

174. The upper-atmosphere layers (which reflect radio waves
     and thus allow their propagation *around* the earth) bear
     their names. One American—one English.

175. Invented the incandescent lamp. (American)

176. Noticed in the spectrum of a candle flame two bright lines
     coinciding with the two dark lines D of the solar spectrum.
     (German)

177. "The most important fundamental laws and facts of physical
     science have all been discovered, and these are now so
     firmly established that the possibility of their ever being
     supplanted in consequence of new discoveries is exceedingly
     remote . . . Our future discoveries must be looked for in
     the sixth place of decimals." *This* by an *American* physicist
     —Nobel Prize 1907!

178. A *German* physicist whose banker remarked: "What do I care for gold in the sun if I cannot fetch it down here."—On the occasion of a certain discovery.

179. On January 5, 6 and 7, 1896, newspapers in all parts of the world gave prominent notice to a "sensational scientific discovery . . . of a new kind of light which is able to penetrate wood, human flesh and most opaque objects." (German)

180. The *Swedish* student of spectra for whom the unit of wavelength (in light) is named.

181. A *German* who extended a Dane's idea of *circular* electron orbits to elliptical orbits.

182. An *English* Nobel Prize winner in 1933 for a new wave-mechanical idea.

183. *English* father and son—joint Nobel Prize winners in 1915.

184. The *Dean of Russian Physicists*—worked with Rutherford.

185. A *Frenchman* who ascribed wave character to electrons.

186. A *German* who established the wave nature of X-rays by passing them through crystals—Nobel Prize 1914.

187. A *Scot* whose cloud chamber bears his name. Nobel 1927.

188. An *Englishman* whose "real" name was John William Strutt. Nobel Prize 1904 for *Studies in Gases*. Amazing versatility —catholic interest—a pioneer in every subject—a scientific genius.

189. In 1896 Zeeman discovered the effect of a *magnetic* field on light. A *German* Nobel Prize winner in 1919 for the splitting of spectral lines in an *electric* field.

190. A certain optical effect (a beam of light passed through a pure liquid or vapour has some of the scattered wave-lengths changed)—an effect analogous to the Compton Effect for X-rays—bears the name of a *Hindu*. Nobel Prize 1930.

191. A *German* Nobel Prize winner in 1933 essentially for a very special equation bearing his name.

192. A *German* Nobel Prize winner in 1932 for the creation of Quantum Mechanics.

193. Discovered the neutron. Nobel Prize 1935. (English)

194. An *Austrian* who discovered cosmic rays. Nobel Prize 1936.

195. An *American* chemist. Nobel Prize in 1934 for heavy hydrogen.

196. Two *Englishmen*—originators of high-voltage devices for atom-smashing.

197. A modern *Italian* genius whose name is linked with the A-bomb. Suggested having a particle accelerator *around the earth* using the earth's magnetic field. It was said of him that he knew *all* of physics in this 20th century! Nobel Prize 1938 for Slow Neutron Reactions.

198. An *American* farm-boy—inventor of the cyclotron. Nobel Prize 1939. If you can't make the path long enough in a straight line then bend it into a circle!

199. An *American* Nobel Prize winner in 1936 for discovery of the positron.

200. A *German* Nobel Prize winner in 1945 for postulating certain exclusion limits on the number of electrons in each shell. When listening to a lecture he would appear to be asleep but at the close of the lecture he would "awaken" with a fury and say: "I have heard your lecture. Half of what you say I already knew—the other half is wrong."

201. A *Japanese* Nobel Prize winner in 1949 for the theoretical prediction of mesons.

202. *English* physicist and physician of the 18th (19th) century who was the first to use the term *energy* to denote mv^2. Despite all scientific opposition he maintained that "radiant light consists of undulations of the luminiferous ether." His most notable researches were in Egyptian hieroglyphics.

203. A *French* physicist first to suggest the conception of *work* as *the product of force and distance* which was then introduced into physics by Poncelot. He also applied the term *energy* to $\dfrac{mv^2}{2}$ for the first time.

204. An *American* inventor. When asked: "What is Ohm's Law?" he replied: "I do not know, Sir. Ohm's Law contains essentially the whole of electrical engineering and I am not familiar with the whole of that subject."

205. An *American* Tory in the service of both Britain and Bavaria. Founded the Royal Institution. Wrote *"An Experiment in Boring Cannon"* Married Lavoisier's widow. Made Minister of War and Count of The Holy Roman Empire. Invented the casserole and the coffee percolator.

206. The first human being to ascend in a hot-air balloon. *(French).* Ten days later Jacques Alexandre César Charles (discoverer of the gas law) went aloft in a balloon inflated with hydrogen gas.

207. An *American* physician first to prove that the disease yellow fever was transmitted by a mosquito (*Stegomyia fasciata*—now *Aedes aegypti*).

208. A *Swedish* chemist—while unloading cans of nitroglycerine the stuff leaked into the sand—the mixture hardened—he was thus led to the invention of dynamite.

209. An *American* inventor of the telegraph. *"What hath God wrought?"*

210. The *originator* of *The Energy Principle.* *German.* Not understood—hated—ridiculed—tortured in mind and spirit. In 1850 after a sleepless night he attempted suicide—suffering on account of a new and profound idea! Took to hiding in the forest and it was said that he had gone mad and was in an insane asylum!

211. A 16th century *Flemish* geographer. His work an epic in cartography. In his projection the meridians are straight vertical lines—the parallels of latitude horizontal lines perpendicular to the meridians.

212. A *Russian* biologist who with Ehrlich won the Nobel Prize in 1908 for work in immunology. Succeeded Pasteur in Paris. Of the opinion that life could be prolonged to age 150 or more and that senility could be retarded by taking sour milk!

213. An *American* whose phase rule laid the foundations of physical chemistry—*"On the Equilibrium of Heterogeneous Substances"*.

214. A *German* philosopher —*"Kritik der reinen Vernunft"*—(Critique of Pure Reason)—1781—a tiny man physically—only 5 feet tall—incredible schedule in his daily affairs. His neighbours could set their clocks by him! Dunces, he said, cannot be helped by my lectures; geniuses can help themselves!

215. He gave a lecture at The Royal Institution on his Gas Distribution Law. On leaving the lecture he got entangled in the people. "Ho, ——, cannot you get out? If any man can find his way through a crowd it should be you." Who was speaking of whom? (Both English)

216. Jean-Baptiste Joseph —— —son of a tailor—orphaned at 8—at 12 a genius—wayward—petulant. Taught his professors' classes when they were ill. *"Théorie analytique de la Chaleur."* (French.) ($y = a_0 + a_1 \cos x + a_2 \cos 2x + \ldots$).

217. Prepared an arsenical compound "salvarsan"—"606"—for the treatment of syphilis. A *German* bacteriologist.

218. A Czech bishop with a new theory of education—that words and objects must go together—hence the first picture book for the teaching of children.

219. In 1850 stated the Second Law of Thermodynamics. Introduced the quantity *entropy*. Sixth son of 18 children. (German)

220. Of his work with vibrating plates Napoleon said: "—— makes sounds visible." (German)

221. An American born of slaves who spent his lifetime with the chemistry of peanuts.

222. An *American* naturalist and plant breeder who originated 618 new varieties of flowers, fruits, grains, grasses, lumber and shade trees, forage plants, nuts and vegetables! And with no formal schooling!

223. An *English* engineer who revolutionized the making of iron and steel by blowing a blast of air through the iron while in fusion.

224. An American in a Boston attic on March 10, 1876: "*Mr. Watson, please come here. I want you.*"

225. A *German* bacteriologist who discovered animal immunity against tetanus by injecting into it the blood serum of another animal infected with tetanus. A bold adventure! Nobel Prize in 1901 for diphtheria serum.

226. A *Norwegian* who located the North Magnetic Pole in 1905. Discovered the South Pole in 1911.

227. A *Frenchman* who discovered a method for preserving food by enclosing it in hermetically sealed tins. "*Art de conserver les substances animals et végétales.*"

228. In 1887 proposed the theory that aqueous solution of acids, bases and salts dissociated, to a greater or less extent, into positively and negatively charged particles or *ions*. His views were scoffed at. His professors told him that he would never be heard of and they passed him in his examination to "get rid of him". He was the *only one* of his class to be heard of! Nobel Prize 1903. (*Swedish*)

229. An 18th century *Austrian* physician, noting that the inn-keepers tapped their beer kegs to learn the contents, invented diagnosis by *"percussion"*. Thus we have percussion and auscultation, the latter uncovered by a young French physician.

230. A 19th century English mathematician who invented a system of non-communicative algebra and created symbolic logic.

231. A great *French* naturalist — author of the encyclopedic *Natural History of Animals*—ventured the remark—which he later withdrew—that—had it not been for the express statements of the Bible, one might be tempted to seek a common origin for the horse and the ass, the man and the monkey.

232. A *German* mathematician of the late 19th century who laid the foundations of infinite classes and transfinite numbers. His ideas engaged the most bitter controversies.

233. An *Italian* mathematician in the 16th century—contemporary of Tartaglia — a gambler — a murderer — mad on astrology—foretold that he should die on a certain day and to keep his reputation committed suicide! The solution of the cubic and negative and complex roots.

234. An *Englishman* who, when asked: "What was your greatest discovery?", replied, "Michael Faraday."

235. The greatest *Greek* writer on algebra (3rd century)—introduced algebraic symbols—solved indeterminate equations where the number of unknowns is greater than the number of equations.

236. A *Frenchman* of the 17th century known for a famous *Last Theorem:* If n is a natural number greater than 2 there cannot be three natural numbers x, y *and* z, such that $x^n + y^n = z^n$. His marginal note said he had proved it! It has been proved for certain values of n (from 3 to 616) but no one has been able to prove it for *all* values of n. The question is still open.

237. A Frenchman who named the constituents of water *hydrogen* and *oxygen*—"the father of modern chemistry"—sent to the guillotine since "The Republic has no need of savants."

238. The beautiful figures which result from the addition of periodic motions bear his name. (*French*)

239. A *Frenchman* knowing that the actual path of light is an extremum (Hero of Alexandria discovered that reflected light travels by the path which makes the total distance traversed a minimum) gave it a theological argument: "Here then is this principle, so wise, so worthy of the Supreme Being: Whenever any change takes place in Nature, the amount of action expended in this change is always the smallest possible."

The Answers

1. Archimedes 287-212 B.C.
2. Pythagoras 530 B.C.?
3. Lucretius (Titus Lucretius Carus) 96-55 B.C.
4. Aristotle 384-322 B.C.
5. Plato 427-347 B.C.
6. Plato
7. Aristotle
8. Archimedes
9. Natural Philosophy
10. Archimedes
11. Scholasticism
12. Aristotle
13. Thales 640-546 B.C.
14. Democritus 460-370 B.C.
15. Lucretius
16. Hippocrates 460-377 B.C.
17. Pythagoras
18. Pythagoras
19. Archimedes
20. Zeno 4th century B.C.
21. Duplication of the cube; squaring the circle; trisection of an angle
22. Socrates 470-399 B.C.
23. Aristotle
24. Peripatetic
25. Socrates
26. Euclid 300 B.C.
27. Apollonius 3rd century B.C.
28. Euclid
29. Carl Friedrich Gauss 1777-1855
30. Johann Bolyai (János) 1802-1860
31. Nikolai Ivanovitch Lobachevski 1793-1856
32. Joseph Louis Lagrange 1736-1813
33. Eratosthenes 3rd century B.C.
34. Aristarchus 3rd century B.C.
35. Hipparchus c. 130 B.C.
36. Ptolemy (Claudius Ptolemaeus) 2nd century
37. Leonardo da Vinci 1452-1519
38. Galileo Galilei 1564-1642
39. Galilei
40. Nicolaus Copernicus 1473-1543
41. Simon Stevin (Stevinus) 1548-1620

42. Galileo
43. Tycho Brahe 1546-1601
44. Galileo
45. Galileo
46. Johannes Kepler 1571-1630
47. William Harvey 1578-1657
48. René Descartes (Cartesius Renatus) 1596-1650
49. Otto von Guericke 1602-1686
50. Evangelista Torricelli 1608-1647
51. Blaise Pascal 1623-1662
52. Torricelli
53. Pascal
54. Giordano Bruno 1548-1600
55. Christiaan Huygens 1629-1695
56. Huygens
57. Anton van Leewenhoek 1632-1723
58. Olaus (Ole) Roemer 1644-1710
59. Leonard Euler (Leonnardus Eulerus) 1703-1783
60. Ben Franklin 1706-1790
61. Isaac Newton 1642-1727
62. Isaac Barrow 1630-1677
63. Gottfried Wilhelm Leibniz 1646-1716
64. Galileo
65. Newton
66. Robert Brown 1773-1858
67. Carl Linnaeus (Carl von Linné) 1707-1778
68. Newton
69. Robert Hooke 1635-1703
70. Newton
71. Jean le Rond d'Alembert 1717-1783
72. Henry Cavendish 1731-1810
73. Newton
74. Robert Boyle 1627-1691
75. Jean Bernard Léon Foucault 1819-1868
76. Giovanni Virginio Schiaparelli 1835-1910
77. Newton
78. Daniel Bernoulli 1700-1782
79. Anders Celsius 1701-1744
80. Gabriel Daniel Fahrenheit 1686-1736

81. Joseph Louis Lagrange 1736-1813
82. Jacques Alexandre César Charles 1746-1823
83. Charles Augustin Coulomb 1736-1806
84. Luigi Galvani 1737-1798
85. Michael Faraday 1791-1867
86. Hans Christian Oersted 1777-1851
87. André Marie Ampère 1775-1836
88. Joseph Henry 1797-1878
89. Heinrich Friedrich Emil Lenz 1804-1865 (German? Russian? Estonian?)
90. Nikola Tesla 1857-1943
91. William Gilbert 1540-1603
92. Antoine Laurent Lavoisier 1743-1794
93. Volta 1745-1827
94. Pierre Simon, Marquis de Laplace 1749-1827
95. Georg Simon Ohm 1787-1854
96. Gustav Hertz 1887-
97. Oliver Joseph Lodge 1851-1940
98. Gauss 1777-1855
99. Bolyai
100. Faraday
101. René Théophile Hyacinthe Laënnec 1781-1826
102. William Rowan Hamilton 1805-1865
103. Charles Robert Darwin 1809-1882
104. Louis Pasteur 1822-1895
105. Dmitri Ivanovitch Mendelejev 1834-1907
106. Edme Mariotte 1620-1684
107. Johannes Diderik van der Waals 1837-1923
108. Ludwig Boltzmann 1844-1906
109. Josef Stefan 1835-1893
110. Robert Boyle 1627-1691
111. Wilhelm Konrad von Roentgen 1845-1923
112. James Prescott Joule 1818-1889
113. Hermann Ludwig Ferdinand von Helmholtz 1826-1894
114. Galileo
115. Fizeau 1819-1896
116. Albert Abraham Michelson 1852-1931

117. "Ether"
118. Johann Wolfgang von Goethe 1749-1832
119. Hero (Heron)
120. Robert Andrews Millikan 1868-1953
121. Michelson
122. Marie Curie *born* Sklodowska 1867-1934
123. Albert Einstein 1879-1955
124. Millikan
125. Marie Curie
126. Leonardo da Vinci
127. Percy Williams Bridgman 1882-1961
128. Ernest Rutherford 1871-1937
129. Joseph John Thomson 1856-1940
130. Niels Bohr 1885-1963
131. Thomas Young 1773-1829
132. David Brewster 1781-1868
133. James Clerk Maxwell 1831-1879
134. Isaac Newton
135. Willebrord Snellius (Snell van Royen) 1591-1626
136. Alhazen 965?-1039
137. Fritz Haber 1868-1934
138. Alexander the Great 356-323 B.C.
139. Avicenna (Ibn Sina) 980-1037
140. Andreas Vesalius 1514-1564
141. Ambroise Paré 1517-1590
142. Louis XIV Le Grand 1638-1715
143. Karl Wilhelm Scheele 1742-1786
144. Avogadro 1776-1856
145. Jöns Jakob Berzelius 1779-1848
146. Dominique Francois Jean Arago 1786-1853
147. Nicolas Léonard Sadi Carnot 1796-1832
148. Niels Henrik Abel 1802-1829
149. Louis Braille 1809-1852
150. Urbain Jean Joseph Leverrier 1811-1877
151. John Couch Adams 1819-1892
152. Dr. Crawford Williamson Long 1815-1878
153. Ignaz Philipp Semmelweis 1818-1865
154. Matthias Jakob Schleiden 1804-1881

155. Theodor Schwann 1810-1882
156. Gregor Johann Mendel 1822-1884
157. Jean Henri Fabre 1823-1915
158. Ernest Solvay 1838-1922
159. Robert Koch 1843-1910
160. Baron Roland von Eötvös 1848-1919
161. Ivan Petrovich Pavlov 1849-1936
162. Antoine Henri Becquerel 1852-1908
163. Heike Kamerlingh Onnes 1853-1926
164. Hendrik Antoon Lorentz 1853-1928
165. Pieter Zeeman 1865-1943
166. Jules Henri Poincaré 1854-1912
167. Nicolas Camille Flammarion 1842-1925
168. Max Karl Ernst Ludwig Planck 1858-1947
169. Frédéric Joliot 1900-1958
170. Marquis Guglielmo Marconi 1874-1937
171. René Descartes
172. Joseph John Thomson
173. Marie Sklodowska
174. Arthur Edwin Kennelly 1861-1939. Oliver Heaviside 1850-1925
175. Thomas Alva Edison 1847-1931
176. Joseph von Fraunhofer 1787-1826
177. Albert Abraham Michelson
178. Joseph von Fraunhofer
179. Wilhelm Konrad Roentgen
180. Anders Jonas Angström 1814-1874
181. Arnold Sommerfeld 1868-
182. Paul Adrian Maurice Dirac 1902-
183. William Henry Bragg 1862-1942
    William Lawrence Bragg 1890-
184. Peter Kapitza
185. Louis-Victor de Broglie 1892-
186. Max von Loue 1879-1960
187. Charles Thomson Rees Wilson 1869-1959
188. Lord Rayleigh 1842-1919
189. Johannes Stark 1874-1957
190. Chandrasekhara Venkata Raman 1888-

191. Erwin Schrödinger 1887-
192. Werner Heisenberg 1901-
193. James Chadwick 1891-
194. Victor Franz Hess 1883-
195. Harold Clayton Urey 1893-
196. Sir J. D. Cockcroft 1897-
    E. T. S. Walton 1903-
197. Enrico Fermi 1901-1954
198. Ernest Orlando Lawrence 1901-1958
199. Carl David Anderson 1905-
200. Wolfgang Pauli 1900-
201. Hideki Yukawa 1907-
202. Thomas Young 1773-1829
203. G. G. Coriolis
204. Thomas Alva Edison
205. Benjamin Thompson — Count Rumford 1753-1814
206. Jean Francois Pilâtre de Rozier 1756-1785
207. Walter Reed 1851-1902
208. Alfred Bernhard Nobel 1833-1896
209. Samuel Finley Breese Morse 1791-1872
210. Julius Robert Mayer 1814-1878
211. Gerardus Mercator (Gerhard Kramer; Kremer?) 1512-1594
212. Ilya (Élie) Metchnikoff (Mechnikov) 1845-1916
213. Josiah Willard Gibbs 1839-1903
214. Immanuel Kant 1724-1804
215. Michael Faraday (1791-1867) was speaking of James Clerk Maxwell (1831-1879)
216. Fourier 1768-1830
217. Paul Ehrlich 1854-1915
218. John Amos Comenius (Komensky) 1592-1670
219. Rudolf Julius Emanuel Clausius 1822-1886
220. Ernst Florens Friedrich Chladni 1756-1827
221. George Washington Carver 1864-1943
222. Luther Burbank 1849-1926
223. Sir Henry Bessemer 1813-1898
224. Alexander Graham Bell 1847-1922
225. Emil von Behring 1854-1917
226. Roald Amundsen 1872-1928
227. Francois Nicolas Appert 1749-1841
228. Svante August Arrhenius 1859-1927